W9-BZT-726

I ♥ LOVE READING BOOKS

THEME 5
Home Sweet Home

Strum and Hum

DECODABLE WORDS

Target Skill: **triple clusters**

scraps	strum
splits	strums

Previously Taught Skills

Dad	hums	logs	pit
hum	Jen	Mom	

SKILLS APPLIED IN WORDS IN STORY: *m, s, c, t,* short *a;* consonant *n;* consonant *p;* short *i;* consonant *r;* consonant *h;* consonant *g;* short *o;* consonant *d;* consonant *l;* short *e;* short *u;* consonant *j;* /z/ spelled *s*

HIGH-FREQUENCY WORDS

a	go
and	in
finds	the

HOUGHTON MIFFLIN   BOSTON

Strum and Hum

HIGH-FREQUENCY WORDS TAUGHT TO DATE

Grade 1

a	funny	one	would
all	girl	other	write
also	go	paper	you
and	green	people	your
animal	grow	picture	
are	have	play	
away	he	pull	
bird	hear	read	
blue	here	right	
brown	hold	room	
call	hurt	said	
car	I	see	
children	in	shall	
cold	is	she	
color	jump	sing	
come	know	small	
do	learn	some	
does	light	the	
down	like	their	
eat	live	these	
every	long	they	
fall	look	three	
family	love	to	
father	many	today	
find	me	too	
first	more	two	
five	mother	upon	
flower	my	walk	
for	never	we	
four	not	what	
friend	of	where	
full	on	who	
	once	why	

Decoding skills taught to date: m, s, c, t, short a; consonant n; consonant f; consonant p; short i; consonant b; consonant r; consonant h; consonant g; short o; consonant d; consonant w; consonant l; consonant x; short e; consonant y; consonant k; consonant v; short u; /kw/ spelled qu; consonant j; consonant z; /z/ spelled s; consonants -ck; /l/ spelled -ll; /f/ spelled -ff; /s/ spelled -ss; /t/ spelled -ed; /d/ spelled -ed; verb ending -ing; r clusters; l clusters; s clusters; silent k in kn; silent w in wr; silent g in gn; triple clusters; digraph sh; digraph th; digraph wh; digraph ch; digraph -tch

REVIEW
BOOK 37

Strum and Hum

Mom strums and hums.

Strum, hum. Strum, hum.

Dad splits logs.

Jen finds scraps.

The scraps and logs
go in a pit.

Ship Shop

DECODABLE WORDS

Target Skill: digraph *sh*

fish	Shell	shop	shuts
fresh	ship	shut	

Previously Taught Skills

at	has	snacks
chips	sells	sticks

SKILLS APPLIED IN WORDS IN STORY: *m, s, c, t,* short *a;* consonant *n;* consonant *f;* consonant *p;* short *i;* consonant *r;* consonant *h;* short *o;* consonant *l;* short *e;* short *u;* /z/ spelled *s;* consonants *-ck;* /l/ spelled *-ll;* *r* clusters; *s* clusters; digraph *ch*

HIGH–FREQUENCY WORDS

a	the
four	

HOUGHTON MIFFLIN   BOSTON

Ship Shop

SHIP
SHOP
SNACKS

FRESH
FISH
STICKS

Grade 1

a	full	of	walk
all	funny	on	we
also	girl	once	what
and	go	one	where
animal	green	other	who
are	grow	over	why
away	have	own	world
bird	he	paper	would
blue	hear	people	write
brown	here	picture	you
call	hold	play	your
car	house	pull	
children	how	read	
cold	hurt	right	
color	I	room	
come	in	said	
could	is	see	
do	jump	shall	
does	know	she	
down	learn	sing	
eat	light	small	
every	like	so	
fall	live	some	
family	long	the	
father	look	their	
find	love	these	
first	many	they	
five	me	three	
flower	more	to	
for	mother	today	
four	my	too	
friend	never	two	
	not	upon	

Decoding skills taught to date: *m, s, c, t,* short *a;* consonant *n;* consonant *f;* consonant *p;* short *i;* consonant *b;* consonant *r;* consonant *h;* consonant *g;* short *o;* consonant *d;* consonant *w;* consonant *l;* consonant *x;* short *e;* consonant *y;* consonant *k;* consonant *v;* short *u;* /kw/ spelled *qu;* consonant *j;* consonant *z;* /z/ spelled *s;* consonants *-ck;* /l/ spelled *-ll;* /f/ spelled *-ff;* /s/ spelled *-ss;* /t/ spelled *-ed;* /d/ spelled *-ed;* verb ending *-ing;* *r* clusters; *l* clusters; *s* clusters; silent *k* in *kn;* silent *w* in *wr;* silent *g* in *gn;* triple clusters; digraph *sh;* digraph *th;* digraph *wh;* digraph *ch;* digraph *-tch;* long *a* (CVC*e*); /s/ spelled *c;* /j/ spelled *g;* consonants *-nd;* consonants *-ng;* consonants *-nk*

Shell shuts the ship shop at four.

4

Ship Shop

Shell has a ship shop.

1

Shell sells snacks.

2

Shell sells fresh fish sticks.

3

Roth Sloth and His Cloth Cat

DECODABLE WORDS

Target Skill: **digraph *th***

bath	path	Sloth	with
cloth	Roth	thud	

Previously Taught Skills

cat	his	naps	take
gets	must	slips	

SKILLS APPLIED IN WORDS IN STORY: *m, s, c, t,* short *a*; consonant *n*; consonant *p*; short *i*; consonant *b*; consonant *r*; consonant *h*; consonant *g*; short *o*; consonant *d*; consonant *w*; consonant *l*; short *e*; consonant *k*; short *u*; /z/ spelled *s*; *l* clusters; *s* clusters; long *a* (CVCe); consonants *-nd*

HIGH–FREQUENCY WORDS

a	is	the
and	on	

HOUGHTON MIFFLIN   BOSTON

Roth Sloth and His Cloth Cat

HIGH-FREQUENCY WORDS TAUGHT TO DATE

Grade 1

a	full	of	walk
all	funny	on	we
also	girl	once	what
and	go	one	where
animal	green	other	who
are	grow	over	why
away	have	own	world
bird	he	paper	would
blue	hear	people	write
brown	here	picture	you
call	hold	play	your
car	house	pull	
children	how	read	
cold	hurt	right	
color	I	room	
come	in	said	
could	is	see	
do	jump	shall	
does	know	she	
down	learn	sing	
eat	light	small	
every	like	so	
fall	live	some	
family	long	the	
father	look	their	
find	love	these	
first	many	they	
five	me	three	
flower	more	to	
for	mother	today	
four	my	too	
friend	never	two	
	not	upon	

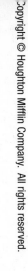

Decoding skills taught to date: *m, s, c, t,* short *a;* consonant *n;* consonant *f;* consonant *p;* short *i;* consonant *b;* consonant *r;* consonant *h;* consonant *g;* short *o;* consonant *d;* consonant *w;* consonant *l;* consonant *x;* short *e;* consonant *y;* consonant *k;* consonant *v;* short *u;* /kw/ spelled *qu;* consonant *j;* consonant *z;* /z/ spelled *s;* consonants *-ck;* /l/ spelled *-ll;* /f/ spelled *-ff;* /s/ spelled *-ss;* /t/ spelled *-ed;* /d/ spelled *-ed;* verb ending *-ing;* *r* clusters; *l* clusters; *s* clusters; silent *k* in *kn;* silent *w* in *wr;* silent *g* in *gn;* triple clusters; digraph *sh;* digraph *th;* digraph *wh;* digraph *ch;* digraph *-tch;* long *a* (CVC*e*); /s/ spelled *c;* /j/ spelled *g;* consonants *-nd;* consonants *-ng;* consonants *-nk*

Roth Sloth gets his cloth cat.
His cloth cat must take a bath!

Roth Sloth and His Cloth Cat

Roth Sloth naps with
his cloth cat.

His cloth cat slips.

Thud! His cloth cat is on the path.

When, When, When?

DECODABLE WORDS

Target Skill: **digraph *wh***

when
whiff

Previously Taught Skills

am	can	gets	it	will
asked	Dad	got	Pam	
cake	get	Gramp	that	

SKILLS APPLIED IN WORDS IN STORY: *m, s, c, t,* short *a*; consonant *n*; consonant *f*; consonant *p*; short *i*; consonant *r*; consonant *g*; short *o*; consonant *d*; consonant *w*; consonant *l*; short *e*; consonant *k*; /z/ spelled *s*; /l/ spelled *-ll*; /f/ spelled *-ff*; /t/ spelled *-ed*; *r* clusters; *s* clusters; digraph *th*; long *a* (CVCe)

HIGH–FREQUENCY WORDS

a	I	said	what
eat	is	she	
here	of	we	

HOUGHTON MIFFLIN   BOSTON

When, When, When?

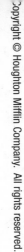

Grade 1

a	full	of	walk
all	funny	on	we
also	girl	once	what
and	go	one	where
animal	green	other	who
are	grow	over	why
away	have	own	world
bird	he	paper	would
blue	hear	people	write
brown	here	picture	you
call	hold	play	your
car	house	pull	
children	how	read	
cold	hurt	right	
color	I	room	
come	in	said	
could	is	see	
do	jump	shall	
does	know	she	
down	learn	sing	
eat	light	small	
every	like	so	
fall	live	some	
family	long	the	
father	look	their	
find	love	these	
first	many	they	
five	me	three	
flower	more	to	
for	mother	today	
four	my	too	
friend	never	two	
	not	upon	

Decoding skills taught to date: *m, s, c, t,* short *a;* consonant *n;* consonant *f;* consonant *p;* short *i;* consonant *b;* consonant *r;* consonant *h;* consonant *g;* short *o;* consonant *d;* consonant *w;* consonant *l;* consonant *x;* short *e;* consonant *y;* consonant *k;* consonant *v;* short *u;* /kw/ spelled *qu;* consonant *j;* consonant *z;* /z/ spelled *s;* consonants *-ck;* /l/ spelled *-ll;* /f/ spelled *-ff;* /s/ spelled *-ss;* /t/ spelled *-ed;* /d/ spelled *-ed;* verb ending *-ing;* *r* clusters; *l* clusters; *s* clusters; silent *k* in *kn;* silent *w* in *wr;* silent *g* in *gn;* triple clusters; digraph *sh;* digraph *th;* digraph *wh;* digraph *ch;* digraph *-tch;* long *a* (CVC*e*); /s/ spelled *c;* /j/ spelled *g;* consonants *-nd;* consonants *-ng;* consonants *-nk*

"I am here!" said Gramp.

"When, when, when can we eat?"

4

When, When, When?

"What is that?" asked Pam.

"It is a cake," said Dad.

1

Pam got a whiff of cake.
Whiff, whiff, whiff.

"When can we eat it?"
she asked.

2

"We can eat it when Gramp
gets here," said Dad.

"When, when, when will
Gramp get here?" asked Pam.

3

Chad and Chet

DECODABLE WORDS

Target Skill: **digraph *ch***

Chad	Chet	chips	such
chat	chill	chug	

Previously Taught Skills

fun	it	quick	sit	wind
get	pals	ship	snack	

SKILLS APPLIED IN WORDS IN STORY: *m, s, c, t,* short *a*; consonant *n*; consonant *f*; consonant *p*; short *i*; consonant *g*; consonant *d*; consonant *w*; consonant *l*; short *e*; short *u*; /kw/ spelled *qu*; /z/ spelled *s*; consonants *-ck*; /l/ spelled *-ll*; *s* clusters; digraph *sh*; consonants *-nd*

HIGH–FREQUENCY WORDS

a	cold	in
and	go	is
are	have	of

HOUGHTON MIFFLIN   BOSTON

Chad and Chet

HIGH-FREQUENCY WORDS TAUGHT TO DATE

Grade 1

a	full	of	walk
all	funny	on	we
also	girl	once	what
and	go	one	where
animal	green	other	who
are	grow	over	why
away	have	own	world
bird	he	paper	would
blue	hear	people	write
brown	here	picture	you
call	hold	play	your
car	house	pull	
children	how	read	
cold	hurt	right	
color	I	room	
come	in	said	
could	is	see	
do	jump	shall	
does	know	she	
down	learn	sing	
eat	light	small	
every	like	so	
fall	live	some	
family	long	the	
father	look	their	
find	love	these	
first	many	they	
five	me	three	
flower	more	to	
for	mother	today	
four	my	too	
friend	never	two	
	not	upon	

Decoding skills taught to date: m, s, c, t, short a; consonant n; consonant f; consonant p; short i; consonant b; consonant r; consonant h; consonant g; short o; consonant d; consonant w; consonant l; consonant x; short e; consonant y; consonant k; consonant v; short u; /kw/ spelled qu; consonant j; consonant z; /z/ spelled s; consonants -ck; /l/ spelled -ll; /f/ spelled -ff; /s/ spelled -ss; /t/ spelled -ed; /d/ spelled -ed; verb ending -ing; r clusters; l clusters; s clusters; silent k in kn; silent w in wr; silent g in gn; triple clusters; digraph sh; digraph th; digraph wh; digraph ch; digraph -tch; long a (CVCe); /s/ spelled c; /j/ spelled g; consonants -nd; consonants -ng; consonants -nk

Chad and Chet

Chad and Chet sit and get
a snack of chips.

Chad and Chet are pals.
Chad and Chet chat, chat, chat.

4

1

Chad and Chet have a ship. Chug, chug, chug! It is such fun!

It is such a cold wind! Chad and Chet get a chill. Chad and Chet go in quick!

Dutch and Kitch

DECODABLE WORDS

Target Skill: **digraph** *-tch*

Dutch	Kitch	match
hutch	latch	patch

Previously Taught Skills

back	has	place
black	his	pets
dish	nap	

SKILLS APPLIED IN WORDS IN STORY: *m, s, c, t,* short *a*; consonant *n*; consonant *p*; short *i*; consonant *b*; consonant *h*; short *o*; consonant *d*; consonant *l*; short *e*; consonant *k*; short *u*; /z/ spelled *s*; consonants *-ck*; *l* clusters; digraph *sh*; long *a* (CVCe); /s/ spelled *c*; consonants *-nd*

HIGH–FREQUENCY WORDS

a	have	live	too
and	I	on	two
for	in	the	

HOUGHTON MIFFLIN   BOSTON

Dutch and Kitch

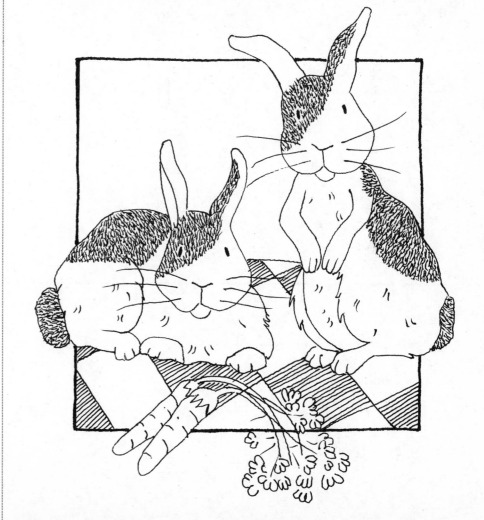

HIGH-FREQUENCY WORDS TAUGHT TO DATE

Grade 1

a	full	of	walk
all	funny	on	we
also	girl	once	what
and	go	one	where
animal	green	other	who
are	grow	over	why
away	have	own	world
bird	he	paper	would
blue	hear	people	write
brown	here	picture	you
call	hold	play	your
car	house	pull	
children	how	read	
cold	hurt	right	
color	I	room	
come	in	said	
could	is	see	
do	jump	shall	
does	know	she	
down	learn	sing	
eat	light	small	
every	like	so	
fall	live	some	
family	long	the	
father	look	their	
find	love	these	
first	many	they	
five	me	three	
flower	more	to	
for	mother	today	
four	my	too	
friend	never	two	
	not	upon	

Decoding skills taught to date: *m, s, c, t,* short *a;* consonant *n;* consonant *f;* consonant *p;* short *i;* consonant *b;* consonant *r;* consonant *h;* consonant *g;* short *o;* consonant *d;* consonant *w;* consonant *l;* consonant *x;* short *e;* consonant *y;* consonant *k;* consonant *v;* short *u;* /kw/ spelled *qu;* consonant *j;* consonant *z;* /z/ spelled *s;* consonants *-ck;* /l/ spelled *-ll;* /f/ spelled *-ff;* /s/ spelled *-ss;* /t/ spelled *-ed;* /d/ spelled *-ed;* verb ending *-ing;* *r* clusters; *l* clusters; *s* clusters; silent *k* in *kn;* silent *w* in *wr;* silent *g* in *gn;* triple clusters; digraph *sh;* digraph *th;* digraph *wh;* digraph *ch;* digraph *-tch;* long *a* (CVC*e*); /s/ spelled *c;* /j/ spelled *g;* consonants *-nd;* consonants *-ng;* consonants *-nk*

The hutch has a latch. Dutch and Kitch nap.

Dutch and Kitch

I have two pets, Dutch and Kitch. Dutch and Kitch live in a hutch.

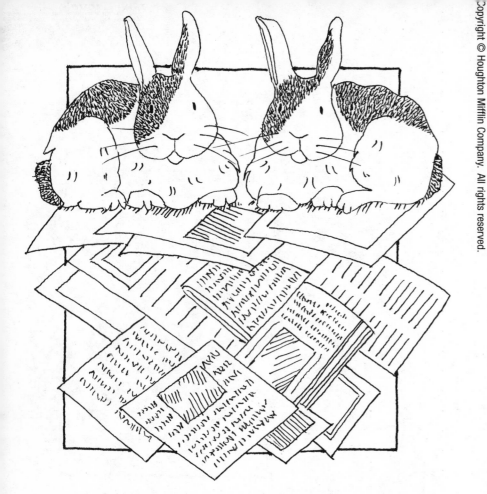

Dutch has a black patch on his back. Kitch has a black patch on his back, too. Dutch and Kitch match!

I place a dish in the hutch for Dutch and Kitch.

Tate, Jane, and Shane

DECODABLE WORDS

Target Skill: long *a* (CVC*e*)

gave	name	shade	tame	wake
Jane	named	shake	Tate	
mane	safe	Shane	Tate's	

Previously Taught Skills

cub	his	naps	up
dad	it	pet	
has	mom	thick	

SKILLS APPLIED IN WORDS IN STORY: *m, s, c, t,* short *a*; consonant *n*; consonant *f*; consonant *p*; short *i*; consonant *b*; consonant *h*; consonant *g*; short *o*; consonant *d*; consonant *w*; short *e*; consonant *k*; consonant *v*; short *u*; consonant *j*; /z/ spelled *s*; consonants *-ck*; /d/ spelled *-ed*; digraph *sh*; digraph *th*; consonants *-nd*

HIGH–FREQUENCY WORDS

a	in	the
and	is	they
are	not	to

HOUGHTON MIFFLIN   BOSTON

Tate, Jane, and Shane

HIGH-FREQUENCY WORDS TAUGHT TO DATE

Grade 1

a	friend	more	three
all	full	mother	to
also	funny	my	today
and	girl	never	too
animal	give	not	try
are	go	of	two
away	good	on	upon
bird	green	once	walk
blue	grow	one	was
brown	have	other	we
call	he	our	what
car	hear	over	where
children	her	own	who
cold	here	paper	why
color	hold	people	world
come	house	picture	would
could	how	play	write
do	hurt	pull	you
does	I	read	your
down	in	right	
eat	is	room	
every	jump	said	
fall	know	see	
family	learn	shall	
father	light	she	
find	like	sing	
first	little	small	
five	live	so	
flower	long	some	
fly	look	the	
for	love	their	
four	many	these	
	me	they	

Decoding skills taught to date: m, s, c, t; short a; consonant n; consonant f; consonant p; short i; consonant b; consonant r; consonant h; consonant g; short o; consonant d; consonant w; consonant l; consonant x; short e; consonant y; consonant k; consonant v; short u; /kw/ spelled qu; consonant j; consonant z; /z/ spelled s; consonants -ck; /l/ spelled -ll; /f/ spelled -ff; /s/ spelled -ss; /t/ spelled -ed; /d/ spelled -ed; verb ending -ing; r clusters; l clusters; s clusters; silent k in kn; silent w in wr; silent g in gn; triple clusters; digraph sh; digraph th; digraph wh; digraph ch; digraph -tch; long a (CVCe); /s/ spelled c; /j/ spelled g; consonants -nd; consonants -ng; consonants -nk; long i (CVCe); contractions

It is not safe to pet Tate,
Jane, and Shane. They are
not tame.

Tate, Jane, and Shane

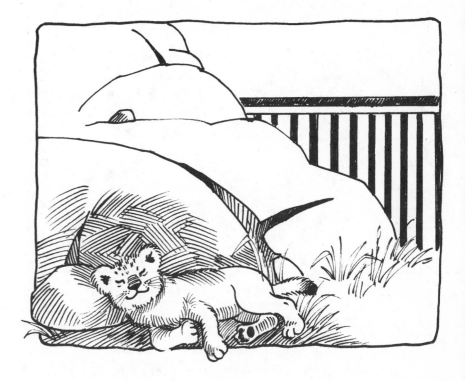

A cub naps in the shade.
His name is Tate.

Tate's mom is named Jane.

Jane gave Tate a shake.

Wake up, Tate!

Tate's dad is named Shane.

Shane has a thick mane.

A Nice Price!

DECODABLE WORDS

Target Skill: /s/ spelled c

cent	Grace	nice	price
cents	ice	place	spice

Previously Taught Skills

cake	drinks	set	switched
can	pops	snacks	ten
did	sell	still	

SKILLS APPLIED IN WORDS IN STORY: *m, s, c, t,* short *a*; consonant *n*; consonant *f*; consonant *p*; short *i*; consonant *r*; consonant *g*; short *o*; consonant *d*; consonant *w*; consonant *l*; short *e*; consonant *k*; consonant *v*; /z/ spelled *s*; consonants *-ck*; /l/ spelled *-ll*; /t/ spelled *-ed*; *r* clusters; *l* clusters; *s* clusters; digraph *-tch*; long *a* (CVC*e*); consonants *-nk*; long *i* (CVC*e*)

HIGH–FREQUENCY WORDS

a	for	is	people	she
could	her	my	said	so
five	in	not	see	the

Underscored high-frequency words are introduced in this week's instruction.

HOUGHTON MIFFLIN   BOSTON

A Nice Price!

10 cents

HIGH-FREQUENCY WORDS TAUGHT TO DATE

Grade 1

a	friend	more	three
all	full	mother	to
also	funny	my	today
and	girl	never	too
animal	give	not	try
are	go	of	two
away	good	on	upon
bird	green	once	walk
blue	grow	one	was
brown	have	other	we
call	he	our	what
car	hear	over	where
children	her	own	who
cold	here	paper	why
color	hold	people	world
come	house	picture	would
could	how	play	write
do	hurt	pull	you
does	I	read	your
down	in	right	
eat	is	room	
every	jump	said	
fall	know	see	
family	learn	shall	
father	light	she	
find	like	sing	
first	little	small	
five	live	so	
flower	long	some	
fly	look	the	
for	love	their	
four	many	these	
	me	they	

Decoding skills taught to date: m, s, c, t, short a; consonant n; consonant f; consonant p; short i; consonant b; consonant r; consonant h; consonant g; short o; consonant d; consonant w; consonant l; consonant x; short e; consonant y; consonant k; consonant v; short u; /kw/ spelled qu; consonant j; consonant z; /z/ spelled s; consonants -ck; /l/ spelled -ll; /f/ spelled -ff; /s/ spelled -ss; /t/ spelled -ed; /d/ spelled -ed; verb ending -ing; r clusters; l clusters; s clusters; silent k in kn; silent w in wr; silent g in gn; triple clusters; digraph sh; digraph th; digraph wh; digraph ch; digraph -tch; long a (CVCe); /s/ spelled c; /j/ spelled g; consonants -nd; consonants -ng; consonants -nk; long i (CVCe); contractions

Grace set her snacks in a nice place. Grace **did** sell her snacks for five cents!

4

A Nice Price!

"Ice pops! Nice drinks! Spice cake! Ten cents!" said Grace.

1

Grace could not sell her
nice snacks, so Grace switched
the price.
She said, "Five cents is nice."

Grace could still not sell
her five-cent snacks. "Can
people see my snacks?"
said Grace.

2

3

Gems, Gems, Gems

DECODABLE WORDS

Target Skill: **/j/ spelled _g_**

gem
gems

Previously Taught Skills

big	chip	make	place	shine
bits	cut	man	ring	this
can	get	must	rocks	will

SKILLS APPLIED IN WORDS IN STORY: _m, s, c, t,_ short _a;_ consonant _n;_ consonant _p;_ short _i;_ consonant _b;_ consonant _r;_ consonant _g;_ short _o;_ consonant _w;_ consonant _l;_ short _e;_ consonant _k;_ short _u;_ /z/ spelled _s;_ consonants _-ck;_ /l/ spelled _-ll;_ _l_ clusters; _s_ clusters; digraph _sh;_ digraph _th;_ digraph _ch;_ long _a_ (CVCe); /s/ spelled _c;_ consonants _-ng;_ long _i_ (CVCe)

HIGH–FREQUENCY WORDS

a	he	is	small	to
are	in	like	the	
find	into	people	these	

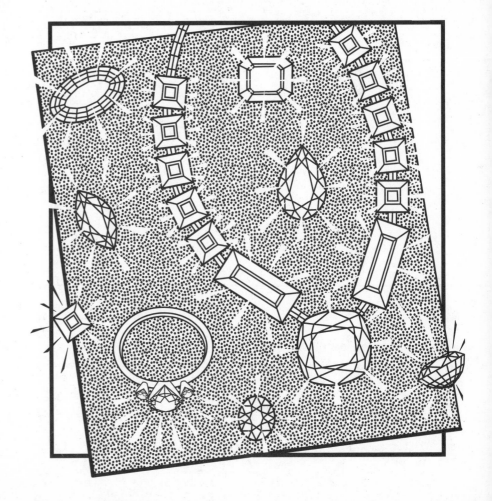

Gems, Gems, Gems

HOUGHTON MIFFLIN   BOSTON

HIGH-FREQUENCY WORDS TAUGHT TO DATE

Grade 1

a	friend	more	three
all	full	mother	to
also	funny	my	today
and	girl	never	too
animal	give	not	try
are	go	of	two
away	good	on	upon
bird	green	once	walk
blue	grow	one	was
brown	have	other	we
call	he	our	what
car	hear	over	where
children	her	own	who
cold	here	paper	why
color	hold	people	world
come	house	picture	would
could	how	play	write
do	hurt	pull	you
does	I	read	your
down	in	right	
eat	is	room	
every	jump	said	
fall	know	see	
family	learn	shall	
father	light	she	
find	like	sing	
first	little	small	
five	live	so	
flower	long	some	
fly	look	the	
for	love	their	
four	many	these	
	me	they	

Decoding skills taught to date: *m, s, c, t,* short *a;* consonant *n;* consonant *f;* consonant *p;* short *i;* consonant *b;* consonant *r;* consonant *h;* consonant *g;* short *o;* consonant *d;* consonant *w;* consonant *l;* consonant *x;* short *e;* consonant *y;* consonant *k;* consonant *v;* short *u;* /kw/ spelled *qu;* consonant *j;* consonant *z;* /z/ spelled *s;* consonants *-ck;* /l/ spelled *-ll;* /f/ spelled *-ff;* /s/ spelled *-ss;* /t/ spelled *-ed;* /d/ spelled *-ed;* verb ending *-ing; r* clusters; *l* clusters; *s* clusters; silent *k* in *kn;* silent *w* in *wr;* silent *g* in *gn;* triple clusters; digraph *sh;* digraph *th;* digraph *wh;* digraph *ch;* digraph *-tch;* long *a* (CVC*e*); /s/ spelled *c;* /j/ spelled *g;* consonants *-nd;* consonants *-ng;* consonants *-nk;* long *i* (CVC*e*); contractions

Gems, Gems, Gems

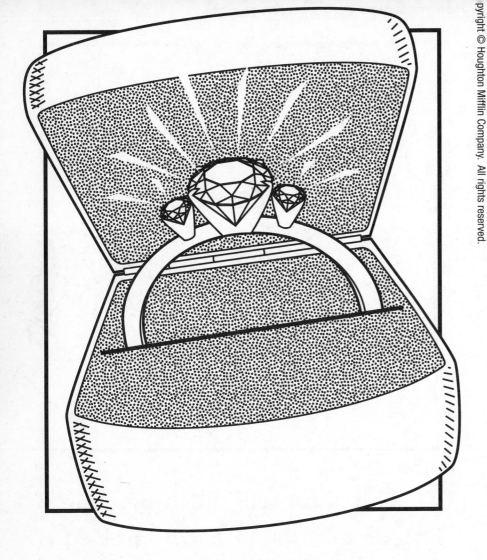

This is a gem ring. The gems make the ring shine.

These are gems. Gems are like rocks. Gems can shine.

4

1

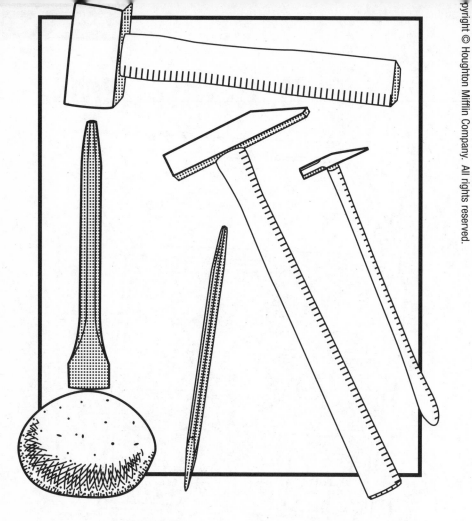

People can find gems in rocks. People must chip the rocks to get gems.

2

This man will cut a big gem into small bits. He will make the gems shine. He will place gems in a ring.

3

DECODABLE WORDS

Target Skill: consonants -nd

bends	grand	sand	strand
fond	Lind	stands	

Previously Taught Skills

get	has	shell	this
gift	it	shells	
Gran	Miss	strings	

SKILLS APPLIED IN WORDS IN STORY: *m, s, c, t,* short *a*; consonant *n*; consonant *f*; short *i*; consonant *b*; consonant *r*; consonant *h*; consonant *g*; short *o*; consonant *d*; consonant *l*; short *e*; /z/ spelled *s*; /l/ spelled *-ll*; /s/ spelled *-ss*; *r* clusters; *s* clusters; triple clusters; digraph *sh*; digraph *th*; consonants *-ng*

HIGH–FREQUENCY WORDS

a	is	the
for	many	to
in	of	

HOUGHTON MIFFLIN   BOSTON

A Strand for Gran

Grade 1

a	friend	more	three
all	full	mother	to
also	funny	my	today
and	girl	never	too
animal	give	not	try
are	go	of	two
away	good	on	upon
bird	green	once	walk
blue	grow	one	was
brown	have	other	we
call	he	our	what
car	hear	over	where
children	her	own	who
cold	here	paper	why
color	hold	people	world
come	house	picture	would
could	how	play	write
do	hurt	pull	you
does	I	read	your
down	in	right	
eat	is	room	
every	jump	said	
fall	know	see	
family	learn	shall	
father	light	she	
find	like	sing	
first	little	small	
five	live	so	
flower	long	some	
fly	look	the	
for	love	their	
four	many	these	
	me	they	

Decoding skills taught to date: *m, s, c, t,* short *a;* consonant *n;* consonant *f;* consonant *p;* short *i;* consonant *b;* consonant *r;* consonant *h;* consonant *g;* short *o;* consonant *d;* consonant *w;* consonant *l;* consonant *x;* short *e;* consonant *y;* consonant *k;* consonant *v;* short *u;* /kw/ spelled *qu;* consonant *j;* consonant *z;* /z/ spelled *s;* consonants *-ck;* /l/ spelled *-ll;* /f/ spelled *-ff;* /s/ spelled *-ss;* /t/ spelled *-ed;* /d/ spelled *-ed;* verb ending *-ing;* *r* clusters; *l* clusters; *s* clusters; silent *k* in *kn;* silent *w* in *wr;* silent *g* in *gn;* triple clusters; digraph *sh;* digraph *th;* digraph *wh;* digraph *ch;* digraph *-tch;* long *a* (CVC*e*); /s/ spelled *c;* /j/ spelled *g;* consonants *-nd;* consonants *-ng;* consonants *-nk;* long *i* (CVC*e*); contractions

This strand is a gift for Gran.

A Strand for Gran

Miss Lind is fond of shells. Miss Lind bends to get a shell in the sand.

Miss Lind stands in the sand.
Miss Lind has many shells.

Miss Lind strings a strand
of shells. It is grand!

DECODABLE WORDS

Target Skill: *consonants -ng*

bang	gang	gongs	Wang
bong	gong	ring	

Previously Taught Skills

chimes	drums	this
drum	Miss	

SKILLS APPLIED IN WORDS IN STORY: *m, s, c, t,* short *a*; consonant *n*; short *i*; consonant *b*; consonant *r*; consonant *g*; short *o*; consonant *d*; consonant *w*; short *u*; /z/ spelled *s*; /s/ spelled *-ss*; *r* clusters; digraph *th*; digraph *ch*; long *i* (CVCe)

HIGH–FREQUENCY WORDS

a	here	the
are	is	these
go	said	we

Ring, Bang, Bong!

HOUGHTON MIFFLIN   BOSTON

HIGH-FREQUENCY WORDS TAUGHT TO DATE

Grade 1

a	friend	more	three
all	full	mother	to
also	funny	my	today
and	girl	never	too
animal	give	not	try
are	go	of	two
away	good	on	upon
bird	green	once	walk
blue	grow	one	was
brown	have	other	we
call	he	our	what
car	hear	over	where
children	her	own	who
cold	here	paper	why
color	hold	people	world
come	house	picture	would
could	how	play	write
do	hurt	pull	you
does	I	read	your
down	in	right	
eat	is	room	
every	jump	said	
fall	know	see	
family	learn	shall	
father	light	she	
find	like	sing	
first	little	small	
five	live	so	
flower	long	some	
fly	look	the	
for	love	their	
four	many	these	
	me	they	

Decoding skills taught to date: *m, s, c, t,* short *a;* consonant *n;* consonant *f;* consonant *p;* short *i;* consonant *b;* consonant *r;* consonant *h;* consonant *g;* short *o;* consonant *d;* consonant *w;* consonant *l;* consonant *x;* short *e;* consonant *y;* consonant *k;* consonant *v;* short *u;* /kw/ spelled *qu;* consonant *j;* consonant *z;* /z/ spelled *s;* consonants *-ck;* /l/ spelled *-ll;* /f/ spelled *-ff;* /s/ spelled *-ss;* /t/ spelled *-ed;* /d/ spelled *-ed;* verb ending *-ing;* *r* clusters; *l* clusters; *s* clusters; silent *k* in *kn;* silent *w* in *wr;* silent *g* in *gn;* triple clusters; digraph *sh;* digraph *th;* digraph *wh;* digraph *ch;* digraph *-tch;* long *a* (CVC*e*); /s/ spelled *c;* /j/ spelled *g;* consonants *-nd;* consonants *-ng;* consonants *-nk;* long *i* (CVC*e*); contractions

"Here we go, gang," said Miss
Wang. "Ring the chimes! Bang
the drum! Bong the gong!"

Ring, Bang, Bong!

Miss Wang said, "These
are chimes. Chimes ring."
Ring, ring, ring!

Miss Wang said, "This is
a drum. Drums bang."
Bang, bang, bang!

Miss Wang said, "This is
a gong. Gongs bong."
Bong, bong, bong!

DECODABLE WORDS

Target Skill: consonants -nk

Hank's	stinks	think	Wink
honk	tank	thinking	Wink's

Previously Taught Skills

back	filled	got	jug	went
fast	from	had	must	yelled
fill	gas	his	this	

SKILLS APPLIED IN WORDS IN STORY: *m, s, c, t,* short *a;* consonant *n;* consonant *f;* short *i;* consonant *b;* consonant *r;* consonant *h;* consonant *g;* short *o;* consonant *d;* consonant *w;* short *e;* consonant *y;* short *u;* consonant *j;* /z/ spelled *s;* consonants *-ck;* /l/ spelled *-ll;* /d/ spelled *-ed;* verb ending *–ing; r* clusters; *s* clusters; digraph *th*

HIGH–FREQUENCY WORDS

a	go	I	not	to
car	<u>good</u>	in	of	would
cars	he	my	said	

Underscored high-frequency words are introduced in this week's instruction.

HOUGHTON MIFFLIN   BOSTON

Think, Wink!

HIGH-FREQUENCY WORDS TAUGHT TO DATE

Grade 1

a	friend	more	three
all	full	mother	to
also	funny	my	today
and	girl	never	too
animal	give	not	try
are	go	of	two
away	good	on	upon
bird	green	once	walk
blue	grow	one	was
brown	have	other	we
call	he	our	what
car	hear	over	where
children	her	own	who
cold	here	paper	why
color	hold	people	world
come	house	picture	would
could	how	play	write
do	hurt	pull	you
does	I	read	your
down	in	right	
eat	is	room	
every	jump	said	
fall	know	see	
family	learn	shall	
father	light	she	
find	like	sing	
first	little	small	
five	live	so	
flower	long	some	
fly	look	the	
for	love	their	
four	many	these	
	me	they	

Decoding skills taught to date: m, s, c, t, short a; consonant n; consonant f; consonant p; short i; consonant b; consonant r; consonant h; consonant g; short o; consonant d; consonant w; consonant l; consonant x; short e; consonant y; consonant k; consonant v; short u; /kw/ spelled qu; consonant j; consonant z; /z/ spelled s; consonants -ck; /l/ spelled -ll; /f/ spelled -ff; /s/ spelled -ss; /t/ spelled -ed; /d/ spelled -ed; verb ending -ing; r clusters; l clusters; s clusters; silent k in kn; silent w in wr; silent g in gn; triple clusters; digraph sh; digraph th; digraph wh; digraph ch; digraph -tch; long a (CVCe); /s/ spelled c; /j/ spelled g; consonants -nd; consonants -ng; consonants -nk; long i (CVCe); contractions

Think, Wink!

Good thinking, Wink!

4

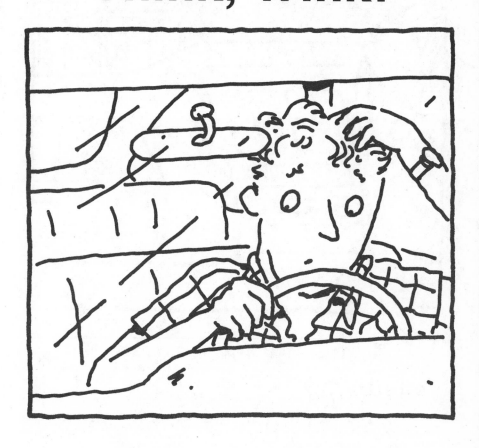

Wink's car would not go.
"This stinks," said Wink.

1

"I must fill my gas tank!"
yelled Wink.

Cars in back of Wink went
honk, honk, honk. Wink had to
think fast.

Wink got a gas jug from
Hank's Gas. He filled his tank.

I ♥ LOVE READING BOOKS

THEME 6
Animal Adventures

My Friend Mike

DECODABLE WORDS

Target Skill: long *i* (CVC*e*)

bike	lime	nice	slice	time
bikes	Mike	rice	slide	
bite	mine	ride	spice	

Previously Taught Skills

fun	his	with
got	let's	
had	went	

SKILLS APPLIED IN WORDS IN STORY: *m, s, c, t,* short *a*; consonant *n*; consonant *f*; consonant *p*; short *i*; consonant *b*; consonant *r*; consonant *h*; consonant *g*; short *o*; consonant *d*; consonant *w*; consonant *l*; short *e*; consonant *k*; short *u*; /z/ spelled *s*; *l* clusters; *s* clusters; digraph *th*; /s/ spelled *c*; consonants *-nd*; contractions; consonants *-nt*

HIGH–FREQUENCY WORDS

a	friend	like	on	the
and	I	my	said	to
down	is	of	see	too

HOUGHTON MIFFLIN   BOSTON

My Friend Mike

HIGH-FREQUENCY WORDS TAUGHT TO DATE

Grade 1

a	for	love	small
all	found	many	so
also	four	me	some
and	friend	more	the
animal	full	morning	their
are	funny	mother	these
away	girl	my	they
bird	give	never	three
blue	go	not	to
brown	good	of	today
by	green	on	too
call	grow	once	try
car	have	one	two
children	he	other	upon
climb	hear	our	walk
cold	her	out	was
color	here	over	we
come	hold	own	what
could	house	paper	where
do	how	people	who
does	hurt	picture	why
down	I	play	world
eat	in	pull	would
every	is	read	write
fall	jump	right	you
family	know	room	your
father	learn	said	
find	light	see	
first	like	shall	
five	little	she	
flower	live	shout	
fly	long	show	
	look	sing	

Decoding skills taught to date: *m, s, c, t,* short *a;* consonant *n;* consonant *f;* consonant *p;* short *i;* consonant *b;* consonant *r;* consonant *h;* consonant *g;* short *o;* consonant *d;* consonant *w;* consonant *l;* consonant *x;* short *e;* consonant *y;* consonant *k;* consonant *v;* short *u;* /kw/ spelled *qu;* consonant *j;* consonant *z;* /z/ spelled *s;* consonants *-ck;* /l/ spelled *-ll;* /f/ spelled *-ff;* /s/ spelled *-ss;* /t/ spelled *-ed;* /d/ spelled *-ed;* verb ending *-ing;* *r* clusters; *l* clusters; *s* clusters; silent *k* in *kn;* silent *w* in *wr;* silent *g* in *gn;* triple clusters; digraph *sh;* digraph *th;* digraph *wh;* digraph *ch;* digraph *-tch;* long *a* (CVC*e*); /s/ spelled *c;* /j/ spelled *g;* consonants *-nd;* consonants *-ng;* consonants *-nk;* long *i* (CVC*e*); contractions; long *o* (CV); long *o* (CVC*e*); /o͞o/ spelled *u* (CVC*e*); /yo͞o/ spelled *u* (CVC*e*); consonants *-ft;* consonants *-lk;* consonants *-nt*

"Let's ride down the slide," said Mike. Mike and I had a fun time.

4

My Friend Mike

I went to see my friend Mike. I had a bite of rice with spice and a slice of lime.

1

I like spice on rice. Lime
is nice, too.

2

"Let's ride bikes," said Mike.
Mike got his bike, and I got mine.

3

Don't Walk

DECODABLE WORDS

Target Skill: contractions

can't	it's
don't	

Previously Taught Skills

but	home	safe	tells	when
cross	it	spot	that	yet
dogs	no	take	this	
him	pet	tell	us	

SKILLS APPLIED IN WORDS IN STORY: *m, s, c, t*, short *a*; consonant *n*; consonant *f*; consonant *p*; short *i*; consonant *b*; consonant *r*; consonant *h*; consonant *g*; short *o*; consonant *d*; consonant *l*; short *e*; consonant *y*; consonant *k*; short *u*; /z/ spelled *s*; /l/ spelled -*ll*; /s/ spelled -*ss*; *r* clusters; *s* clusters; digraph *th*; digraph *wh*; long *a* (CVCe); long *i* (CVCe); long *o* (CV); long *o* (CVCe)

HIGH–FREQUENCY WORDS

animals	like	our	to	we'd
bird	not	play	walk	we'll
isn't	on	she'll	we	

HOUGHTON MIFFLIN   BOSTON

Don't Walk

HIGH-FREQUENCY WORDS TAUGHT TO DATE

Grade 1

a	for	love	small
all	found	many	so
also	four	me	some
and	friend	more	the
animal	full	morning	their
are	funny	mother	these
away	girl	my	they
bird	give	never	three
blue	go	not	to
brown	good	of	today
by	green	on	too
call	grow	once	try
car	have	one	two
children	he	other	upon
climb	hear	our	walk
cold	her	out	was
color	here	over	we
come	hold	own	what
could	house	paper	where
do	how	people	who
does	hurt	picture	why
down	I	play	world
eat	in	pull	would
every	is	read	write
fall	jump	right	you
family	know	room	your
father	learn	said	
find	light	see	
first	like	shall	
five	little	she	
flower	live	shout	
fly	long	show	
	look	sing	

Decoding skills taught to date: *m, s, c, t,* short *a;* consonant *n;* consonant *f;* consonant *p;* short *i;* consonant *b;* consonant *r;* consonant *h;* consonant *g;* short *o;* consonant *d;* consonant *w;* consonant *l;* consonant *x;* short *e;* consonant *y;* consonant *k;* consonant *v;* short *u;* /kw/ spelled *qu;* consonant *j;* consonant *z;* /z/ spelled *s;* consonants *-ck;* /l/ spelled *-ll;* /f/ spelled *-ff;* /s/ spelled *-ss;* /t/ spelled *-ed;* /d/ spelled *-ed;* verb ending *-ing;* *r* clusters; *l* clusters; *s* clusters; silent *k* in *kn;* silent *w* in *wr;* silent *g* in *gn;* triple clusters; digraph *sh;* digraph *th;* digraph *wh;* digraph *ch;* digraph *-tch;* long *a* (CVC*e*); /s/ spelled *c;* /j/ spelled *g;* consonants *-nd;* consonants *-ng;* consonants *-nk;* long *i* (CVC*e*); contractions; long *o* (CV); long *o* (CVC*e*); /o͞o/ spelled *u* (CVC*e*); /yo͞o/ spelled *u* (CVC*e*); consonants *-ft;* consonants *-lk;* consonants *-nt*

Don't Walk

Don't Walk tells us that it isn't safe to cross yet. She'll tell us when it's safe.

1

It's safe to play on this spot. It's our home!

4

Don't Pet Animals tells us that we can't pet this bird. We'd like to pet it, but it's not safe.

2

No Dogs tells us that dogs can't walk on this spot. We'll take him home.

3

Po and Mo

DECODABLE WORDS

Target Skill: **long _o_ (CV)**

Mo   Po
no

Previously Taught Skills

can	hats	let's
dogs	hill	sleds

SKILLS APPLIED IN WORDS IN STORY: *m, s, c, t,* short *a*; consonant *n*; consonant *p*; short *i*; consonant *h*; consonant *g*; short *o*; consonant *d*; consonant *w*; consonant *l*; short *e*; /z/ spelled *s*; /l/ spelled *-ll*; *l* clusters; *s* clusters; consonants *-nd*; contractions; long *e* (CV)

HIGH–FREQUENCY WORDS

a	here	know	said	where
and	house	my	to	
go	I	not	we	

HOUGHTON MIFFLIN   BOSTON

Po and Mo

HIGH-FREQUENCY WORDS TAUGHT TO DATE

Grade 1

a	flower	live	she	your
all	fly	long	shout	
also	for	look	show	
and	found	love	sing	
animal	four	many	small	
are	friend	me	so	
away	full	more	some	
bird	funny	morning	table	
blue	girl	mother	the	
brown	give	my	their	
by	go	never	there	
call	good	not	these	
car	green	now	they	
children	grow	of	three	
climb	have	on	through	
cold	he	once	to	
color	hear	one	today	
come	her	other	too	
could	here	our	try	
cow	hold	out	two	
do	horse	over	upon	
does	house	own	walk	
door	how	paper	wall	
down	hurt	people	was	
eat	I	picture	we	
every	in	play	what	
fall	is	pull	where	
family	jump	read	who	
father	know	right	why	
find	learn	room	world	
first	light	said	would	
five	like	see	write	
	little	shall	you	

Decoding skills taught to date: m, s, c, t, short a; consonant n; consonant f; consonant p; short i; consonant b; consonant r; consonant h; consonant g; short o; consonant d; consonant w; consonant l; consonant x; short e; consonant y; consonant k; consonant v; short u; /kw/ spelled qu; consonant j; consonant z; /z/ spelled s; consonants -ck; /l/ spelled -ll; /f/ spelled -ff; /s/ spelled -ss; /t/ spelled -ed; /d/ spelled -ed; verb ending -ing; r clusters; l clusters; s clusters; silent k in kn; silent w in wr; silent g in gn; triple clusters; digraph sh; digraph th; digraph wh; digraph ch; digraph -tch; long a (CVCe); /s/ spelled c; /j/ spelled g; consonants -nd; consonants -ng; consonants -nk; long i (CVCe); contractions; long o (CV); long o (CVCe); /o͞o/ spelled u (CVCe); /yo͞o/ spelled u (CVCe); consonants -ft; consonants -lk; consonants -nt; long e (CV); long e (CVCe); long e spelled ee; long e spelled ea

"Let's go to my house, Po,"
said Mo.

"I know a hill where we
can go, go, go!"

4

Po and Mo

"Let's go, Mo!" said Po.

"No," said Mo. "No dogs!
We can not go here."

1

"Let's go, Mo!" said Po.

"No," said Mo. "No hats!

We can not go here."

"Let's go, Mo!" said Po.

"No," said Mo. "No sleds!

We can not go here."

King Frode's Robe

DECODABLE WORDS

Target Skill: **long o (CVCe)**

bone	cone	home	throne
broke	Frode	robe	woke
chose	Frode's	slope	

Previously Taught Skills

dressed	King	then	up
him	made	think	went
his	spilled	trip	

SKILLS APPLIED IN WORDS IN STORY: *m, s, c, t,* short *a*; consonant *n*; consonant *f*; consonant *p*; short *i*; consonant *b*; consonant *r*; consonant *h*; short *o*; consonant *d*; consonant *w*; consonant *l*; short *e*; consonant *k*; short *u*; /z/ spelled *s*; /l/ spelled *-ll*; /s/ spelled *-ss*; /t/ spelled *-ed*; /d/ spelled *-ed*; *r* clusters; *l* clusters; *s* clusters; digraph *th*; digraph *ch*; long *a* (CVCe); consonants *-ng*; consonants *-nk*; consonants *-nt*; long *e* (CV)

HIGH–FREQUENCY WORDS

a	in	said
he	long	small
I	on	the

HOUGHTON MIFFLIN   BOSTON

King Frode's Robe

HIGH-FREQUENCY WORDS TAUGHT TO DATE

Grade 1

a	five	like	said	world
all	flower	little	see	would
also	fly	live	shall	write
and	for	long	she	you
animal	found	look	shout	your
are	four	love	show	
away	friend	many	sing	
bird	full	me	small	
blue	funny	more	so	
brown	girl	morning	some	
by	give	mother	table	
call	go	my	the	
car	good	never	their	
children	green	not	there	
climb	grow	now	these	
cold	have	of	they	
color	he	on	three	
come	hear	once	through	
could	her	one	to	
cow	here	other	today	
do	hold	our	too	
does	horse	out	try	
door	house	over	two	
down	how	own	upon	
eat	hurt	paper	walk	
every	I	people	wall	
fall	in	picture	was	
family	is	play	we	
father	jump	pull	what	
find	know	read	where	
first	learn	right	who	
	light	room	why	

Decoding skills taught to date: *m, s, c, t,* short *a;* consonant *n;* consonant *f;* consonant *p;* short *i;* consonant *b;* consonant *r;* consonant *h;* consonant *g;* short *o;* consonant *d;* consonant *w;* consonant *l;* consonant *x;* short *e;* consonant *y;* consonant *k;* consonant *v;* short *u;* /kw/ spelled *qu;* consonant *j;* consonant *z;* /z/ spelled *s;* consonants *-ck;* /l/ spelled *-ll;* /f/ spelled *-ff;* /s/ spelled *-ss;* /t/ spelled *-ed;* /d/ spelled *-ed;* verb ending *-ing;* *r* clusters; *l* clusters; *s* clusters; silent *k* in *kn;* silent *w* in *wr;* silent *g* in *gn;* triple clusters; digraph *sh;* digraph *th;* digraph *wh;* digraph *ch;* digraph *-tch;* long *a* (CVC*e*); /s/ spelled *c;* /j/ spelled *g;* consonants *-nd;* consonants *-ng;* consonants *-nk;* long *i* (CVC*e*); contractions; long *o* (CV); long *o* (CVC*e*); /o͞o/ spelled *u* (CVC*e*); /yo͞o/ spelled *u* (CVC*e*); consonants *-ft;* consonants *-lk;* consonants *-nt;* long *e* (CV); long *e* (CVC*e*); long *e* spelled *ee;* long *e* spelled *ea*

King Frode's Robe

King Frode went home.
Then King Frode chose a
small robe!

King Frode woke up.
He dressed in his long robe.

King Frode broke his throne.
King Frode spilled his cone on
his robe.

2

King Frode's robe made him
trip on the slope.
"I think I broke a bone!"
said King Frode.

3

Spruce Tune

DECODABLE WORDS

Target Skill: /ōō/ spelled *u* (CVCe)

Bruce	June	lute	tune
flute	Luke	Spruce	

Previously Taught Skills

his	makes	Street
it	names	up

SKILLS APPLIED IN WORDS IN STORY: *m, s, c, t,* short *a*; consonant *n*; consonant *f*; consonant *p*; short *i*; consonant *b*; consonant *r*; consonant *h*; short *o*; consonant *l*; consonant *k*; short *u*; consonant *j*; /z/ spelled *s*; *r* clusters; *l* clusters; triple clusters; long *a* (CVCe); /s/ spelled *c*; long *i* (CVCe); long *e* spelled *ee*

HIGH-FREQUENCY WORDS

a	like	lives	people	too
her	likes	on	plays	

HOUGHTON MIFFLIN   BOSTON

Spruce Tune

HIGH-FREQUENCY WORDS TAUGHT TO DATE

Grade 1

a	flower	live	she	your
all	fly	long	shout	
also	for	look	show	
and	found	love	sing	
animal	four	many	small	
are	friend	me	so	
away	full	more	some	
bird	funny	morning	table	
blue	girl	mother	the	
brown	give	my	their	
by	go	never	there	
call	good	not	these	
car	green	now	they	
children	grow	of	three	
climb	have	on	through	
cold	he	once	to	
color	hear	one	today	
come	her	other	too	
could	here	our	try	
cow	hold	out	two	
do	horse	over	upon	
does	house	own	walk	
door	how	paper	wall	
down	hurt	people	was	
eat	I	picture	we	
every	in	play	what	
fall	is	pull	where	
family	jump	read	who	
father	know	right	why	
find	learn	room	world	
first	light	said	would	
five	like	see	write	
	little	shall	you	

Decoding skills taught to date: *m, s, c, t,* short *a;* consonant *n;* consonant *f;* consonant *p;* short *i;* consonant *b;* consonant *r;* consonant *h;* consonant *g;* short *o;* consonant *d;* consonant *w;* consonant *l;* consonant *x;* short *e;* consonant *y;* consonant *k;* consonant *v;* short *u;* /kw/ spelled *qu;* consonant *j;* consonant *z;* /z/ spelled *s;* consonants *-ck;* /l/ spelled *-ll;* /f/ spelled *-ff;* /s/ spelled *-ss;* /t/ spelled *-ed;* /d/ spelled *-ed;* verb ending *-ing;* *r* clusters; *l* clusters; *s* clusters; silent *k* in *kn;* silent *w* in *wr;* silent *g* in *gn;* triple clusters; digraph *sh;* digraph *th;* digraph *wh;* digraph *ch;* digraph *-tch;* long *a* (CVC*e*); /s/ spelled *c;* /j/ spelled *g;* consonants *-nd;* consonants *-ng;* consonants *-nk;* long *i* (CVC*e*); contractions; long *o* (CV); long *o* (CVC*e*); /o͞o/ spelled *u* (CVC*e*); /yo͞o/ spelled *u* (CVC*e*); consonants *-ft;* consonants *-lk;* consonants *-nt;* long *e* (CV); long *e* (CVC*e*); long *e* spelled *ee;* long *e* spelled *ea*

Spruce Tune

Luke lives on Spruce Street.
Luke makes up a tune. Luke
names it "Spruce Tune."

People on Spruce Street
like "Spruce Tune," too!

Bruce likes "Spruce Tune."
Bruce plays "Spruce Tune"
on his flute.

June likes "Spruce Tune."
June plays "Spruce Tune"
on her lute.

The Huge Mule

DECODABLE WORDS

Target Skill: /yōo/ spelled *u* (CVC*e*)

huge
mule

Previously Taught Skills

at	dog	last
big	fit	went
cat	just	wide

SKILLS APPLIED IN WORDS IN STORY: *m, s, c, t,* short *a*; consonant *n*; consonant *f*; short *i*; consonant *b*; consonant *h*; consonant *g*; short *o*; consonant *d*; consonant *w*; consonant *l*; short *e*; short *u*; consonant *j*; *s* clusters; digraph *th*; /j/ spelled *g*; long *i* (CVC*e*); consonants *-nt*; long *e* (CV); long *e* spelled *ee*

HIGH–FREQUENCY WORDS

bird	see	too
<u>horse</u>	the	was
right	to	

Underscored high-frequency words are introduced in this week's instruction.

HOUGHTON MIFFLIN   BOSTON

The Huge Mule

Grade 1

a	friend	never	to
all	full	not	today
also	funny	now	too
and	girl	of	try
animal	give	on	two
are	go	once	upon
away	good	one	walk
bird	green	other	wall
blue	grow	our	was
brown	have	out	we
by	he	over	what
call	hear	own	where
car	her	paper	who
children	here	people	why
climb	hold	picture	world
cold	horse	play	would
color	house	pull	write
come	how	read	you
could	hurt	right	your
cow	I	room	
do	in	said	
does	is	see	
door	jump	shall	
down	know	she	
eat	learn	shout	
every	light	show	
fall	like	sing	
family	little	small	
father	live	so	
find	long	some	
first	look	table	
five	love	the	
flower	many	their	
fly	me	there	
for	more	these	
found	morning	they	
four	mother	three	
	my	through	

Decoding skills taught to date: *m, s, c, t,* short *a;* consonant *n;* consonant *f;* consonant *p;* short *i;* consonant *b;* consonant *r;* consonant *h;* consonant *g;* short *o;* consonant *d;* consonant *w;* consonant *l;* consonant *x;* short *e;* consonant *y;* consonant *k;* consonant *v;* short *u;* /kw/ spelled *qu;* consonant *j;* consonant *z;* /z/ spelled *s;* consonants *-ck;* /l/ spelled *-ll;* /f/ spelled *-ff;* /s/ spelled *-ss;* /t/ spelled *-ed;* /d/ spelled *-ed;* verb ending *–ing;* *r* clusters; *l* clusters; *s* clusters; silent *k* in *kn;* silent *w* in *wr;* silent *g* in *gn;* triple clusters; digraph *sh;* digraph *th;* digraph *wh;* digraph *ch;* digraph *-tch;* long *a* (CVC*e*); /s/ spelled *c;* /j/ spelled *g;* consonants *-nd;* consonants *-ng;* consonants *-nk;* long *i* (CVC*e*); contractions; long *o* (CV); long *o* (CVC*e*); /o͞o/ spelled *u* (CVC*e*); /yo͞o/ spelled *u* (CVC*e*); consonants *-ft;* consonants *-lk;* consonants *-nt;* long *e* (CV); long *e* (CVC*e*); long *e* spelled *ee;* long *e* spelled *ea*

The huge mule went to see
the big horse. At last, the huge
mule fit just right!

The Huge Mule

The huge mule went to see
the cat. The huge mule was
too big.

The huge mule went to see
the dog. The huge mule was
too wide.

The huge mule went to see the
bird. The huge mule was just
too huge!

A Soft, Soft Nest

DECODABLE WORDS

Target Skill: *consonants -ft*

crafts	drift	loft	swift
draft	lifts	soft	tuft

Previously Taught Skills

brings	has	mud	take	will
but	it	nest	that	with
grass	its	snug	this	

SKILLS APPLIED IN WORDS IN STORY: *m, s, c, t,* short *a*; consonant *n*; consonant *f*; short *i*; consonant *b*; consonant *r*; consonant *h*; consonant *g*; short *o*; consonant *d*; consonant *w*; consonant *l*; short *e*; consonant *k*; short *u*; /z/ spelled *s*; /l/ spelled *-ll*; /s/ spelled *-ss*; *r* clusters; *s* clusters; digraph *th*; long *a* (CVCe); consonants *-nd*; consonants *-ng*; long *e* (CV); long *e* spelled *ee*

HIGH–FREQUENCY WORDS

a	cold	in	of	to
and	fly	is	see	
bird	for	not	the	

HOUGHTON MIFFLIN BOSTON

A Soft, Soft Nest

HIGH-FREQUENCY WORDS TAUGHT TO DATE

Grade 1

a	flower	live	she	your
all	fly	long	shout
also	for	look	show
and	found	love	sing
animal	four	many	small
are	friend	me	so
away	full	more	some
bird	funny	morning	table
blue	girl	mother	the
brown	give	my	their
by	go	never	there
call	good	not	these
car	green	now	they
children	grow	of	three
climb	have	on	through
cold	he	once	to
color	hear	one	today
come	her	other	too
could	here	our	try
cow	hold	out	two
do	horse	over	upon
does	house	own	walk
door	how	paper	wall
down	hurt	people	was
eat	I	picture	we
every	in	play	what
fall	is	pull	where
family	jump	read	who
father	know	right	why
find	learn	room	world
first	light	said	would
five	like	see	write
	little	shall	you

Decoding skills taught to date: *m, s, c, t,* short *a;* consonant *n;* consonant *f;* consonant *p;* short *i;* consonant *b;* consonant *r;* consonant *h;* consonant *g;* short *o;* consonant *d;* consonant *w;* consonant *l;* consonant *x;* short *e;* consonant *y;* consonant *k;* consonant *v;* short *u;* /kw/ spelled *qu;* consonant *j;* consonant *z;* /z/ spelled *s;* consonants *-ck;* /l/ spelled *-ll;* /f/ spelled *-ff;* /s/ spelled *-ss;* /t/ spelled *-ed;* /d/ spelled *-ed;* verb ending *-ing;* *r* clusters; *l* clusters; *s* clusters; silent *k* in *kn;* silent *w* in *wr;* silent *g* in *gn;* triple clusters; digraph *sh;* digraph *th;* digraph *wh;* digraph *ch;* digraph *-tch;* long *a* (CVC*e*); /s/ spelled *c;* /j/ spelled *g;* consonants *-nd;* consonants *-ng;* consonants *-nk;* long *i* (CVC*e*); contractions; long *o* (CV); long *o* (CVC*e*); /o͞o/ spelled *u* (CVC*e*); /yo͞o/ spelled *u* (CVC*e*); consonants *-ft;* consonants *-lk;* consonants *-nt;* long *e* (CV); long *e* (CVC*e*); long *e* spelled *ee;* long *e* spelled *ea*

A Soft, Soft Nest

The loft has a swift draft, but the bird is not cold. It is snug in its soft, soft nest.

See that tuft of grass drift? This bird will take that tuft for its nest.

4

1

The bird lifts the tuft of grass. It will fly to its nest.

The swift bird brings the tuft to a loft. It crafts its nest with the tuft of grass and mud.

Milk Sap

DECODABLE WORDS

Target Skill: consonants -*lk*

milk
silk

Previously Taught Skills

bugs	it	sap	takes	tufts
each	land	seed	then	when
eggs	place	seeds	this	will
has	plant	soft	top	wind
hatch	pods	stem	tuft	

SKILLS APPLIED IN WORDS IN STORY: *m, s, c, t,* short *a*; consonant *n*; consonant *f*; consonant *p*; short *i*; consonant *b*; consonant *h*; consonant *g*; short *o*; consonant *d*; consonant *w*; consonant *l*; short *e*; consonant *k*; short *u*; /z/ spelled *s*; /l/ spelled *-ll*; *l* clusters; *s* clusters; digraph *th*; digraph *wh*; digraph *ch*; digraph *-tch*; long *a* (CVCe); /s/ spelled *c*; consonants *-nd*; long *i* (CVCe); consonants *-ft*; consonants *-nt*; long *e* (CV); long *e* (CVCe); long *e* spelled *ee*; long *e* spelled *ea*

HIGH–FREQUENCY WORDS

a	here	on	their
away	in	over	these
eat	is	see	walk
grow	like	the	

HOUGHTON MIFFLIN   BOSTON

Milk Sap

HIGH-FREQUENCY WORDS TAUGHT TO DATE

Grade 1

a	flower	live	she	your
all	fly	long	shout	
also	for	look	show	
and	found	love	sing	
animal	four	many	small	
are	friend	me	so	
away	full	more	some	
bird	funny	morning	table	
blue	girl	mother	the	
brown	give	my	their	
by	go	never	there	
call	good	not	these	
car	green	now	they	
children	grow	of	three	
climb	have	on	through	
cold	he	once	to	
color	hear	one	today	
come	her	other	too	
could	here	our	try	
cow	hold	out	two	
do	horse	over	upon	
does	house	own	walk	
door	how	paper	wall	
down	hurt	people	was	
eat	I	picture	we	
every	in	play	what	
fall	is	pull	where	
family	jump	read	who	
father	know	right	why	
find	learn	room	world	
first	light	said	would	
five	like	see	write	
	little	shall	you	

Decoding skills taught to date: m, s, c, t, short a; consonant n; consonant f; consonant p; short i; consonant b; consonant r; consonant h; consonant g; short o; consonant d; consonant w; consonant l; consonant x; short e; consonant y; consonant k; consonant v; short u; /kw/ spelled qu; consonant j; consonant z; /z/ spelled s; consonants -ck; /l/ spelled -ll; /f/ spelled -ff; /s/ spelled -ss; /t/ spelled -ed; /d/ spelled -ed; verb ending -ing; r clusters; l clusters; s clusters; silent k in kn; silent w in wr; silent g in gn; triple clusters; digraph sh; digraph th; digraph wh; digraph ch; digraph -tch; long a (CVCe); /s/ spelled c; /j/ spelled g; consonants -nd; consonants -ng; consonants -nk; long i (CVCe); contractions; long o (CV); long o (CVCe); /ōō/ spelled u (CVCe); /yōō/ spelled u (CVCe); consonants -ft; consonants -lk; consonants -nt; long e (CV); long e (CVCe); long e spelled ee; long e spelled ea

These bugs will place their eggs on this plant. The eggs will hatch. Then the bugs will eat the milk sap.

4

Milk Sap

Walk over here. See this plant? It has sap like milk.

1

The milk sap is in the stem. On top, the plant has seed pods. Each seed has a soft tuft like silk.

Wind takes the silk tufts away. When the silk tufts land, the seeds will grow.

Ant Jobs

DECODABLE WORDS

Target Skill: consonants -nt

ant	dent	mint
ants	hunt	plant

Previously Taught Skills

an	from	job	queen	will
eggs	has	jobs	things	
fix	hatch	nest	this	

SKILLS APPLIED IN WORDS IN STORY: *m, s, c, t,* short *a*; consonant *n*; consonant *f*; consonant *p*; short *i*; consonant *b*; consonant *r*; consonant *h*; consonant *g*; short *o*; consonant *d*; consonant *w*; consonant *l*; consonant *x*; short *e*; short *u*; /kw/ spelled *qu*; consonant *j*; /z/ spelled *s*; /l/ spelled *-ll*; *r* clusters; *l* clusters; *s* clusters; digraph *th*; digraph *-tch*; consonants *-ng*; long *e* (CV); long *e* (CVCe); long *e* spelled *ee*; long *e* spelled *ea*

HIGH–FREQUENCY WORDS

a	finds	in	on	to
eat	have	is	the	
every	her	more	these	

Ant Jobs

HIGH-FREQUENCY WORDS TAUGHT TO DATE

Grade 1

a	flower	live	she	your
all	fly	long	shout	
also	for	look	show	
and	found	love	sing	
animal	four	many	small	
are	friend	me	so	
away	full	more	some	
bird	funny	morning	table	
blue	girl	mother	the	
brown	give	my	their	
by	go	never	there	
call	good	not	these	
car	green	now	they	
children	grow	of	three	
climb	have	on	through	
cold	he	once	to	
color	hear	one	today	
come	her	other	too	
could	here	our	try	
cow	hold	out	two	
do	horse	over	upon	
does	house	own	walk	
door	how	paper	wall	
down	hurt	people	was	
eat	I	picture	we	
every	in	play	what	
fall	is	pull	where	
family	jump	read	who	
father	know	right	why	
find	learn	room	world	
first	light	said	would	
five	like	see	write	
	little	shall	you	

Decoding skills taught to date: *m, s, c, t,* short *a;* consonant *n;* consonant *f;* consonant *p;* short *i;* consonant *b;* consonant *r;* consonant *h;* consonant *g;* short *o;* consonant *d;* consonant *w;* consonant *l;* consonant *x;* short *e;* consonant *y;* consonant *k;* consonant *v;* short *u;* /kw/ spelled *qu;* consonant *j;* consonant *z;* /z/ spelled *s;* consonants *-ck;* /l/ spelled *-ll;* /f/ spelled *-ff;* /s/ spelled *-ss;* /t/ spelled *-ed;* /d/ spelled *-ed;* verb ending *-ing;* *r* clusters; *l* clusters; *s* clusters; silent *k* in *kn;* silent *w* in *wr;* silent *g* in *gn;* triple clusters; digraph *sh;* digraph *th;* digraph *wh;* digraph *ch;* digraph *-tch;* long *a* (CVC*e*); /s/ spelled *c;* /j/ spelled *g;* consonants *-nd;* consonants *-ng;* consonants *-nk;* long *i* (CVC*e*); contractions; long *o* (CV); long *o* (CVC*e*); /o͞o/ spelled *u* (CVC*e*); /yo͞o/ spelled *u* (CVC*e*); consonants *-ft;* consonants *-lk;* consonants *-nt;* long *e* (CV); long *e* (CVC*e*); long *e* spelled *ee;* long *e* spelled *ea*

Ant Jobs

This is an ant nest.
Every ant has a job.

1

This ant is the queen ant.
More ants will hatch from her
eggs. Every ant in her nest will
have a job!

4

The ant on the mint plant finds things to eat. Hunt, ant, hunt!

The nest has a dent.
These ants will fix the dent.

2

3

Who Will Be in the Play?

DECODABLE WORDS

Target Skill: long *e* (CV)

be

Previously Taught Skills

Ben	class	masks	will
Cass	frog	Mike	
cat	Lin	Miss	

SKILLS APPLIED IN WORDS IN STORY: *m, s, c, t,* short *a;* consonant *n;* consonant *f;* consonant *p;* short *i;* consonant *b;* consonant *g;* short *o;* consonant *w;* consonant *l;* short *e;* consonant *k;* /l/ spelled *-ll;* /s/ spelled *-ss;* *r* clusters; *l* clusters; *s* clusters; digraph *th;* long *i* (CVCe); long *a* spelled *ay*

HIGH–FREQUENCY WORDS

a	have	play	we
all	in	said	who
bird	me	the	

HOUGHTON MIFFLIN   BOSTON

Who Will Be in the Play?

HIGH-FREQUENCY WORDS TAUGHT TO DATE

Grade 1

a	find	jump	pull	what
all	first	know	read	where
also	five	learn	right	who
and	flower	light	room	why
animal	fly	like	said	world
are	for	little	see	would
away	forest	live	shall	write
been	found	long	she	you
bird	four	look	shout	your
blue	friend	love	show	
brown	full	many	sing	
by	funny	me	small	
call	girl	more	so	
car	give	morning	some	
children	go	mother	soon	
climb	goes	my	table	
cold	good	near	the	
color	green	never	their	
come	grow	not	there	
could	have	now	these	
cow	he	of	they	
do	hear	on	three	
does	her	once	through	
door	here	one	to	
down	hold	other	today	
eat	horse	our	too	
evening	house	out	try	
every	how	over	two	
fall	hungry	own	upon	
family	hurt	paper	walk	
far	I	people	wall	
father	in	picture	was	
	is	play	we	

Decoding skills taught to date: m, s, c, t, short a; consonant n; consonant f; consonant p; short i; consonant b; consonant r; consonant h; consonant g; short o; consonant d; consonant w; consonant l; consonant x; short e; consonant y; consonant k; consonant v; short u; /kw/ spelled qu; consonant j; consonant z; /z/ spelled s; consonants -ck; /l/ spelled -ll; /f/ spelled -ff; /s/ spelled -ss; /t/ spelled -ed; /d/ spelled -ed; verb ending -ing; r clusters; l clusters; s clusters; silent k in kn; silent w in wr; silent g in gn; triple clusters; digraph sh; digraph th; digraph wh; digraph ch; digraph -tch; long a (CVCe); /s/ spelled c; /j/ spelled g; consonants -nd; consonants -ng; consonants -nk; long i (CVCe); contractions; long o (CV); long o (CVCe); /o͞o/ spelled u (CVCe); /yo͞o/ spelled u (CVCe); consonants -ft; consonants -lk; consonants -nt; long e (CV); long e (CVCe); long e spelled ee; long e spelled ea; long a spelled ai; long a spelled ay

"Who will be in the play?"
said Miss Cass.

"We will all be in the play!"
said the class.

4

Who Will Be in the Play?

"We will have a play,"
said Miss Cass. "Who will be
the cat?"

"Me, me, me!" said
the class.

"Mike will be the cat,"
said Miss Cass.

1

"Who will be the frog?"
said Miss Cass.

"Me, me, me!" said the class.

"Lin will be the frog,"
said Miss Cass.

"Who will be the bird?"
said Miss Cass.

"Me, me, me!" said the class.

"Ben will be the bird,"
said Miss Cass.

Can Zeke Reach?

DECODABLE WORDS

Target Skill: long *e* (CVC*e*)

Zeke

Previously Taught Skills

can	cubes	ice	them
cannot	cups	no	yes
cans	Dad	reach	

SKILLS APPLIED IN WORDS IN STORY: *m, s, c, t,* short *a*; consonant *n*; consonant *p*; short *i*; consonant *b*; consonant *r*; short *o*; consonant *d*; short *e*; consonant *y*; consonant *k*; short *u*; consonant *z*; /z/ spelled *s*; digraph *th*; digraph *ch*; /s/ spelled *c*; long *i* (CVCe); long *o* (CV); /yōō/ spelled *u* (CVCe); long *e* spelled *ea*

HIGH–FREQUENCY WORDS

I
said
these

HOUGHTON MIFFLIN   BOSTON

Can Zeke Reach?

HIGH-FREQUENCY WORDS TAUGHT TO DATE

Grade 1

a	find	jump	pull	what
all	first	know	read	where
also	five	learn	right	who
and	flower	light	room	why
animal	fly	like	said	world
are	for	little	see	would
away	forest	live	shall	write
been	found	long	she	you
bird	four	look	shout	your
blue	friend	love	show	
brown	full	many	sing	
by	funny	me	small	
call	girl	more	so	
car	give	morning	some	
children	go	mother	soon	
climb	goes	my	table	
cold	good	near	the	
color	green	never	their	
come	grow	not	there	
could	have	now	these	
cow	he	of	they	
do	hear	on	three	
does	her	once	through	
door	here	one	to	
down	hold	other	today	
eat	horse	our	too	
evening	house	out	try	
every	how	over	two	
fall	hungry	own	upon	
family	hurt	paper	walk	
far	I	people	wall	
father	in	picture	was	
	is	play	we	

Decoding skills taught to date: *m, s, c, t,* short *a;* consonant *n;* consonant *f;* consonant *p;* short *i;* consonant *b;* consonant *r;* consonant *h;* consonant *g;* short *o;* consonant *d;* consonant *w;* consonant *l;* consonant *x;* short *e;* consonant *y;* consonant *k;* consonant *v;* short *u;* /kw/ spelled *qu;* consonant *j;* consonant *z;* /z/ spelled *s;* consonants *-ck;* /l/ spelled *-ll;* /f/ spelled *-ff;* /s/ spelled *-ss;* /t/ spelled *-ed;* /d/ spelled *-ed;* verb ending *-ing;* *r* clusters; *l* clusters; *s* clusters; silent *k* in *kn;* silent *w* in *wr;* silent *g* in *gn;* triple clusters; digraph *sh;* digraph *th;* digraph *wh;* digraph *ch;* digraph *-tch;* long *a* (CVC*e*); /s/ spelled *c;* /j/ spelled *g;* consonants *-nd;* consonants *-ng;* consonants *-nk;* long *i* (CVC*e*); contractions; long *o* (CV); long *o* (CVC*e*); /o͞o/ spelled *u* (CVC*e*); /yo͞o/ spelled *u* (CVC*e*); consonants *-ft;* consonants *-lk;* consonants *-nt;* long *e* (CV); long *e* (CVC*e*); long *e* spelled *ee;* long *e* spelled *ea;* long *a* spelled *ai;* long *a* spelled *ay*

Dad said, "I can reach these ice cubes, Zeke."

4

Can Zeke Reach?

Can Zeke reach these cups?
Yes, Zeke can reach them!

1

Can Zeke reach these cans?
Yes, Zeke can reach them!

Can Zeke reach these
ice cubes? No, Zeke cannot
reach them.

Beep, Beep, Beep!

DECODABLE WORDS

Target Skill: *long e spelled ee*

beep	jeep	sheep	Sneed's	sweep
Dee Dee	meet	sleeping	speed	
Dee Dee's	screech	Sneed	street	

Previously Taught Skills

am	got	late	must
came	his	man	sped
glad	home	Mr.	went

SKILLS APPLIED IN WORDS IN STORY: *m, s, c, t,* short *a;* consonant *n;* consonant *p;* short *i;* consonant *b;* consonant *r;* consonant *h;* consonant *g;* short *o;* consonant *d;* consonant *w;* consonant *l;* short *e;* short *u;* consonant *j;* /z/ spelled *s;* verb ending *-ing;* r clusters; l clusters; s clusters; triple clusters; digraph *sh;* digraph *ch;* long *a* (CVCe); long *o* (CVCe); consonants *-nt*

HIGH–FREQUENCY WORDS

a	I	on	to
down	<u>near</u>	out	was
green	not	said	you

Underscored high-frequency words are introduced in this week's instruction.

HOUGHTON MIFFLIN   BOSTON

Beep, Beep, Beep!

HIGH-FREQUENCY WORDS TAUGHT TO DATE

Grade 1

a	find	jump	pull	what
all	first	know	read	where
also	five	learn	right	who
and	flower	light	room	why
animal	fly	like	said	world
are	for	little	see	would
away	forest	live	shall	write
been	found	long	she	you
bird	four	look	shout	your
blue	friend	love	show	
brown	full	many	sing	
by	funny	me	small	
call	girl	more	so	
car	give	morning	some	
children	go	mother	soon	
climb	goes	my	table	
cold	good	near	the	
color	green	never	their	
come	grow	not	there	
could	have	now	these	
cow	he	of	they	
do	hear	on	three	
does	her	once	through	
door	here	one	to	
down	hold	other	today	
eat	horse	our	too	
evening	house	out	try	
every	how	over	two	
fall	hungry	own	upon	
family	hurt	paper	walk	
far	I	people	wall	
father	in	picture	was	
	is	play	we	

Decoding skills taught to date: *m, s, c, t,* short *a;* consonant *n;* consonant *f;* consonant *p;* short *i;* consonant *b;* consonant *r;* consonant *h;* consonant *g;* short *o;* consonant *d;* consonant *w;* consonant *l;* consonant *x;* short *e;* consonant *y;* consonant *k;* consonant *v;* short *u;* /kw/ spelled *qu;* consonant *j;* consonant *z;* /z/ spelled *s;* consonants *-ck;* /l/ spelled *-ll;* /f/ spelled *-ff;* /s/ spelled *-ss;* /t/ spelled *-ed;* /d/ spelled *-ed;* verb ending *-ing;* *r* clusters; *l* clusters; *s* clusters; silent *k* in *kn;* silent *w* in *wr;* silent *g* in *gn;* triple clusters; digraph *sh;* digraph *th;* digraph *wh;* digraph *ch;* digraph *-tch;* long *a* (CVCe); /s/ spelled *c;* /j/ spelled *g;* consonants *-nd;* consonants *-ng;* consonants *-nk;* long *i* (CVCe); contractions; long *o* (CV); long *o* (CVCe); /o͞o/ spelled *u* (CVCe); /yo͞o/ spelled *u* (CVCe); consonants *-ft;* consonants *-lk;* consonants *-nt;* long *e* (CV); long *e* (CVCe); long *e* spelled *ee;* long *e* spelled *ea;* long *a* spelled *ai;* long *a* spelled *ay*

Mr. Sneed got to Dee Dee's
home on Green Street.

Dee Dee was not glad.

"Mr. Sneed! You must not speed
on Green Street!"

4

Beep, Beep, Beep!

"I am late! I must meet
Dee Dee!" said Mr. Sneed.
Mr. Sneed sped down Green
Street. His jeep went, "Screech!"

1

A man on Green Street
came out to sweep. Mr. Sneed's
jeep went, "Beep! Beep!"

A sheep was sleeping near
Green Street. Mr. Sneed's jeep
went, "Screech! Beep!"

Clean Jeans

DECODABLE WORDS

Target Skill: *long e spelled ea*

bleach	cream	Neal's	tea
clean	jeans	neat	teach
cleaned	Neal	peach	

Previously Taught Skills

did	his	sat	this	with
from	ice	suds	time	
got	Mom	sweet	will	

SKILLS APPLIED IN WORDS IN STORY: *m, s, c, t,* short *a*; consonant *n*; consonant *f*; consonant *p*; short *i*; consonant *b*; consonant *r*; consonant *h*; consonant *g*; short *o*; consonant *d*; consonant *w*; consonant *l*; short *u*; consonant *j*; /z/ spelled *s*; /l/ spelled *-ll*; /d/ spelled *-ed*; *r* clusters; *l* clusters; *s* clusters; digraph *th*; digraph *ch*; /s/ spelled *c*; long *i* (CVCe); long *e* (CVCe); long *e* spelled *ee*

HIGH-FREQUENCY WORDS

a	in	on	these	your
how	not	own	to	
I	now	said	you	

HOUGHTON MIFFLIN   BOSTON

Clean Jeans

HIGH-FREQUENCY WORDS TAUGHT TO DATE

Grade 1

a	find	jump	pull	what
all	first	know	read	where
also	five	learn	right	who
and	flower	light	room	why
animal	fly	like	said	world
are	for	little	see	would
away	forest	live	shall	write
been	found	long	she	you
bird	four	look	shout	your
blue	friend	love	show	
brown	full	many	sing	
by	funny	me	small	
call	girl	more	so	
car	give	morning	some	
children	go	mother	soon	
climb	goes	my	table	
cold	good	near	the	
color	green	never	their	
come	grow	not	there	
could	have	now	these	
cow	he	of	they	
do	hear	on	three	
does	her	once	through	
door	here	one	to	
down	hold	other	today	
eat	horse	our	too	
evening	house	out	try	
every	how	over	two	
fall	hungry	own	upon	
family	hurt	paper	walk	
far	I	people	wall	
father	in	picture	was	
	is	play	we	

Decoding skills taught to date: *m, s, c, t,* short *a;* consonant *n;* consonant *f;* consonant *p;* short *i;* consonant *b;* consonant *r;* consonant *h;* consonant *g;* short *o;* consonant *d;* consonant *w;* consonant *l;* consonant *x;* short *e;* consonant *y;* consonant *k;* consonant *v;* short *u;* /kw/ spelled *qu;* consonant *j;* consonant *z;* /z/ spelled *s;* consonants -*ck;* /l/ spelled -*ll;* /f/ spelled -*ff;* /s/ spelled -*ss;* /t/ spelled -*ed;* /d/ spelled -*ed;* verb ending -*ing;* *r* clusters; *l* clusters; *s* clusters; silent *k* in *kn;* silent *w* in *wr;* silent *g* in *gn;* triple clusters; digraph *sh;* digraph *th;* digraph *wh;* digraph *ch;* digraph -*tch;* long *a* (CVCe); /s/ spelled *c;* /j/ spelled *g;* consonants -*nd;* consonants -*ng;* consonants -*nk;* long *i* (CVCe); contractions; long *o* (CV); long *o* (CVCe); /o͞o/ spelled *u* (CVCe); /yo͞o/ spelled *u* (CVCe); consonants -*ft;* consonants -*lk;* consonants -*nt;* long *e* (CV); long *e* (CVCe); long *e* spelled *ee;* long *e* spelled *ea;* long *a* spelled *ai;* long *a* spelled *ay*

Clean Jeans

Neal got ice cream on his neat, clean jeans. Mom cleaned Neal's jeans with bleach.

"Neal," said Mom, "I will teach you how to clean these jeans. From now on, you will clean your **own** jeans!"

Neal got sweet tea on his neat, clean jeans. Mom cleaned Neal's jeans with bleach.

Neal sat on a peach in his neat, clean jeans. This time Mom did **not** clean Neal's jeans with bleach.

I LOVE READING BOOKS

THEME 7
We Can Work It Out

Rain and Hail

DECODABLE WORDS

Target Skill: long *a* spelled *ai*

Gail	mail	rains
hail	rain	waits

Previously Taught Skills

can	get	Jake	stops
drive	his	must	take
end	ice	safe	truck
fast	it	stop	will

SKILLS APPLIED IN WORDS IN STORY: *m, s, c, t,* short *a*; consonant *n*; consonant *f*; consonant *p*; short *i*; consonant *r*; consonant *h*; consonant *g*; short *o*; consonant *d*; consonant *w*; consonant *l*; short *e*; consonant *k*; consonant *v*; short *u*; consonant *j*; /z/ spelled *s*; consonants -*ck*; /l/ spelled -*ll*; *r* clusters; *s* clusters; digraph *th*; long *a* (CVCe); /s/ spelled *c*; consonants -*nd*; long *i* (CVCe); long *o* (CV); long *e* (CV)

HIGH–FREQUENCY WORDS

and	in	of	the	<u>turns</u>
for	is	out	to	
go	not	said	too	

Underscored high-frequency words are introduced in this week's instruction.

HOUGHTON MIFFLIN   BOSTON

Rain and Hail

Grade 1

a	far	hurt	own	two
again	father	I	paper	upon
all	find	in	people	walk
also	first	is	picture	wall
and	five	jump	play	want
animal	flower	know	pull	was
are	fly	learn	read	we
away	for	light	right	what
been	forest	like	room	where
bird	found	little	said	who
blue	four	live	see	why
both	friend	long	shall	world
brown	full	look	she	would
by	funny	love	shout	write
call	girl	many	show	you
car	give	me	sing	your
children	go	more	small	
climb	goes	morning	so	
cold	gone	mother	some	
color	good	my	soon	
come	green	near	table	
could	grow	never	the	
cow	hard	not	their	
do	have	now	there	
does	he	of	these	
door	hear	on	they	
down	her	once	three	
eat	here	one	through	
evening	hold	or	to	
every	horse	other	today	
fall	house	our	too	
family	how	out	try	
	hungry	over	turn	

Decoding skills taught to date: *m, s, c, t*, short *a*; consonant *n*; consonant *f*; consonant *p*; short *i*; consonant *b*; consonant *r*; consonant *h*; consonant *g*; short *o*; consonant *d*; consonant *w*; consonant *l*; consonant *x*; short *e*; consonant *y*; consonant *k*; consonant *v*; short *u*; /kw/ spelled *qu*; consonant *j*; consonant *z*; /z/ spelled *s*; consonants *-ck*; /l/ spelled *-ll*; /f/ spelled *-ff*; /s/ spelled *-ss*; /t/ spelled *-ed*; /d/ spelled *-ed*; verb ending *-ing*; *r* clusters; *l* clusters; *s* clusters; silent *k* in *kn*; silent *w* in *wr*; silent *g* in *gn*; triple clusters; digraph *sh*; digraph *th*; digraph *wh*; digraph *ch*; digraph *-tch*; long *a* (CVC*e*); /s/ spelled *c*; /j/ spelled *g*; consonants *-nd*; consonants *-ng*; consonants *-nk*; long *i* (CVC*e*); contractions; long *o* (CV); long *o* (CVC*e*); /o͞o/ spelled *u* (CVC*e*); /yo͞o/ spelled *u* (CVC*e*); consonants *-ft*; consonants *-lk*; consonants *-nt*; long *e* (CV); long *e* (CVC*e*); long *e* spelled *ee*; long *e* spelled *ea*; long *a* spelled *ai*; long *a* spelled *ay*; long *o* spelled *oa*; long *o* spelled *ow*

Rain and Hail

The rain and hail stop!

Jake can take the mail to Gail.

"Mail! Mail! Mail!" said Gail.

It rains, rains, rains.

The mail truck must not drive too fast.

The rain turns to hail.
Hail is ice. The mail truck stops.
It waits for the hail to end.

It is not safe to go out in
the hail. Jake will not get out
of his mail truck.

A Day at Fay Bay

DECODABLE WORDS

Target Skill: **long *a* spelled *ay***

Bay	gray	ray	stay	yay
day	Kay	say	sway	
Fay	may	spray	way	

Previously Taught Skills

at	can	it	run	will
back	has	Mom	sun	
beg	hot	please	trees	

SKILLS APPLIED IN WORDS IN STORY: *m, s, c, t,* short *a*; consonant *n*; consonant *f*; consonant *p*; short *i*; consonant *b*; consonant *r*; consonant *h*; consonant *g*; short *o*; consonant *d*; consonant *w*; consonant *l*; short *e*; consonant *y*; consonant *k*; short *u*; /z/ spelled *s*; consonants *-ck*; /l/ spelled *-ll*; *r* clusters; *l* clusters; *s* clusters; triple clusters; digraph *th*; long *o* (CV); long *e* (CV); long *e* spelled *ee*; long *e* spelled *ea*

HIGH-FREQUENCY WORDS

a	good	on	so
away	in	play	the
for	is	see	to
gone	looks	sees	we

Underscored high-frequency words are introduced in this week's instruction.

 HOUGHTON MIFFLIN   BOSTON

A Day at Fay Bay

Grade 1

a	first	learn	right	where
again	five	light	room	who
all	flower	like	said	why
also	fly	little	see	world
and	for	live	shall	would
animal	found	long	she	write
are	four	look	shout	you
away	friend	love	show	your
bird	full	many	sing	
blue	funny	me	small	
both	girl	more	so	
brown	give	morning	some	
by	go	mother	table	
call	gone	my	the	
car	good	never	their	
children	green	not	there	
climb	grow	now	these	
cold	hard	of	they	
color	have	on	three	
come	he	once	through	
could	hear	one	to	
cow	her	or	today	
do	here	other	too	
does	hold	our	try	
door	horse	out	turn	
down	house	over	two	
eat	how	own	upon	
every	hurt	paper	walk	
fall	I	people	wall	
family	in	picture	want	
father	is	play	was	
find	jump	pull	we	
	know	read	what	

Decoding skills taught to date: m, s, c, t, short a; consonant n; consonant f; consonant p; short i; consonant b; consonant r; consonant h; consonant g; short o; consonant d; consonant w; consonant l; consonant x; short e; consonant y; consonant k; consonant v; short u; /kw/ spelled qu; consonant j; consonant z; /z/ spelled s; consonants -ck; /l/ spelled -ll; /f/ spelled -ff; /s/ spelled -ss; /t/ spelled -ed; /d/ spelled -ed; verb ending -ing; r clusters; l clusters; s clusters; silent k in kn; silent w in wr; silent g in gn; triple clusters; digraph sh; digraph th; digraph wh; digraph ch; digraph -tch; long a (CVCe); /s/ spelled c; /j/ spelled g; consonants -nd; consonants -ng; consonants -nk; long i (CVCe); contractions; long o (CV); long o (CVCe); /ōo/ spelled u (CVCe); /yōo/ spelled u (CVCe); consonants -ft; consonants -lk; consonants -nt; long e (CV); long e (CVCe); long e spelled ee; long e spelled ea; long a spelled ai; long a spelled ay; long o spelled oa; long o spelled ow

We beg Mom to stay.

Please say we can play!

We can stay at Fay Bay!

Yay, Kay! Yay, May!

4

A Day at
Fay Bay

It is a good day to play.

May we play at Fay Bay?

We may! We may! We will

stay for the day!

1

We see the trees sway on the way to Fay Bay. It is a hot, hot day, so we play in the spray.

Fay Bay looks gray. Has the sun gone away? Kay sees a ray. Run back to Fay Bay!

Miss Joan and the Moat

DECODABLE WORDS

Target Skill: **long *o* spelled *oa***

coach	float	moat
coat	Joan	soaked

Previously Taught Skills

big	get	Lance	rides	swim
cannot	grand	lets	rock	wide
deep	hits	Miss	rows	

SKILLS APPLIED IN WORDS IN STORY: *m, s, c, t,* short *a*; consonant *n*; consonant *f*; consonant *p*; short *i*; consonant *b*; consonant *r*; consonant *h*; consonant *g*; short *o*; consonant *d*; consonant *w*; consonant *l*; short *e*; consonant *k*; consonant *j*; /z/ spelled *s*; consonants *-ck*; /s/ spelled *-ss*; /t/ spelled *-ed*; *r* clusters; *l* clusters; *s* clusters; digraph *sh*; digraph *th*; digraph *ch*; /s/ spelled *c*; consonants *-nd*; long *i* (CVC*e*); long *e* (CV); long *e* spelled *ee*; long *o* spelled *ow*

HIGH–FREQUENCY WORDS

a	have	in	said	to
and	her	is	she	
falls	I	over	the	

HOUGHTON MIFFLIN   BOSTON

Miss Joan and the Moat

HIGH-FREQUENCY WORDS TAUGHT TO DATE

Grade 1

a	every	horse	one	three
afraid	fall	house	or	through
again	family	how	other	to
all	far	hungry	our	today
also	father	hurt	out	too
and	find	I	over	try
animal	first	idea	own	turn
any	five	in	paper	two
are	flower	is	people	upon
away	fly	jump	picture	walk
bear	follow	know	play	wall
been	for	learn	pull	want
bird	forest	light	read	was
blue	found	like	right	water
both	four	little	room	we
brown	friend	live	said	what
by	full	long	see	where
call	funny	look	shall	who
car	girl	love	she	why
children	give	many	shout	world
climb	go	me	show	would
cold	goes	more	sing	write
color	gone	morning	small	you
come	good	most	so	your
could	green	mother	some	
cow	grow	my	soon	
do	hard	near	table	
does	have	never	tall	
door	he	not	the	
down	hear	now	their	
eat	her	of	there	
evening	here	on	these	
	hold	once	they	

Decoding skills taught to date: m, s, c, t, short a; consonant n; consonant f; consonant p; short i; consonant b; consonant r; consonant h; consonant g; short o; consonant d; consonant w; consonant l; consonant x; short e; consonant y; consonant k; consonant v; short u; /kw/ spelled qu; consonant j; consonant z; /z/ spelled s; consonants -ck; /l/ spelled -ll; /f/ spelled -ff; /s/ spelled -ss; /t/ spelled -ed; /d/ spelled -ed; verb ending -ing; r clusters; l clusters; s clusters; silent k in kn; silent w in wr; silent g in gn; triple clusters; digraph sh; digraph th; digraph wh; digraph ch; digraph -tch; long a (CVCe); /s/ spelled c; /j/ spelled g; consonants -nd; consonants -ng; consonants -nk; long i (CVCe); contractions; long o (CV); long o (CVCe); /o͞o/ spelled u (CVCe); /yo͞o/ spelled u (CVCe); consonants -ft; consonants -lk; consonants -nt; long e (CV); long e (CVCe); long e spelled ee; long e spelled ea; long a spelled ai; long a spelled ay; long o spelled oa; long o spelled ow; /o͞o/ spelled oo

Lance rows to get
Miss Joan. She is soaked,
soaked, soaked!

4

Miss Joan
and the Moat

"I have a big, big coat and
a grand coach," said Miss Joan
to Lance.

1

Miss Joan rides over the deep, wide moat in her grand coach. The grand coach hits a rock.

Miss Joan falls in the moat. Miss Joan cannot swim! Her big, big coat lets her float.

Dad's Rowboat

DECODABLE WORDS

Target Skill: **long *o* spelled *ow***

blow	row	rows
blows	rowboat	slow

Previously Taught Skills

Dad	get	need	takes	wind
Dad's	his	Sal	will	

SKILLS APPLIED IN WORDS IN STORY: *m, s, c, t,* short *a*; consonant *n*; short *i*; consonant *b*; consonant *r*; consonant *h*; consonant *g*; short *o*; consonant *d*; consonant *w*; consonant *l*; short *e*; consonant *k*; /z/ spelled *s*; /l/ spelled *-ll*; *l* clusters; *s* clusters; silent *k* in *kn*; digraph *th*; long *a* (CVCe); consonants *-nd*; long *o* (CV); long *e* (CV); long *e* spelled *ee*; long *o* spelled *oa*

HIGH–FREQUENCY WORDS

a	does	on	the
and	he	owns	to
are	knows	said	what
do	not	so	you

HOUGHTON MIFFLIN   BOSTON

Dad's Rowboat

HIGH-FREQUENCY WORDS TAUGHT TO DATE

Grade 1

a	every	horse	one	three
afraid	fall	house	or	through
again	family	how	other	to
all	far	hungry	our	today
also	father	hurt	out	too
and	find	I	over	try
animal	first	idea	own	turn
any	five	in	paper	two
are	flower	is	people	upon
away	fly	jump	picture	walk
bear	follow	know	play	wall
been	for	learn	pull	want
bird	forest	light	read	was
blue	found	like	right	water
both	four	little	room	we
brown	friend	live	said	what
by	full	long	see	where
call	funny	look	shall	who
car	girl	love	she	why
children	give	many	shout	world
climb	go	me	show	would
cold	goes	more	sing	write
color	gone	morning	small	you
come	good	most	so	your
could	green	mother	some	
cow	grow	my	soon	
do	hard	near	table	
does	have	never	tall	
door	he	not	the	
down	hear	now	their	
eat	her	of	there	
evening	here	on	these	
	hold	once	they	

Decoding skills taught to date: *m, s, c, t,* short *a;* consonant *n;* consonant *f;* consonant *p;* short *i;* consonant *b;* consonant *r;* consonant *h;* consonant *g;* short *o;* consonant *d;* consonant *w;* consonant *l;* consonant *x;* short *e;* consonant *y;* consonant *k;* consonant *v;* short *u;* /kw/ spelled *qu;* consonant *j;* consonant *z;* /z/ spelled *s;* consonants -*ck;* /l/ spelled -*ll;* /f/ spelled -*ff;* /s/ spelled -*ss;* /t/ spelled -*ed;* /d/ spelled -*ed;* verb ending -*ing;* *r* clusters; *l* clusters; *s* clusters; silent *k* in *kn;* silent *w* in *wr;* silent *g* in *gn;* triple clusters; digraph *sh;* digraph *th;* digraph *wh;* digraph *ch;* digraph -*tch;* long *a* (CVC*e*); /s/ spelled *c;* /j/ spelled *g;* consonants -*nd;* consonants -*ng;* consonants -*nk;* long *i* (CVC*e*); contractions; long *o* (CV); long *o* (CVC*e*); /o͞o/ spelled *u* (CVC*e*); /yo͞o/ spelled *u* (CVC*e*); consonants -*ft;* consonants -*lk;* consonants -*nt;* long *e* (CV); long *e* (CVC*e*); long *e* spelled *ee;* long *e* spelled *ea;* long *a* spelled *ai;* long *a* spelled *ay;* long *o* spelled *oa;* long *o* spelled *ow;* /o͞o/ spelled *oo*

Dad's Rowboat

The wind blows and blows
and blows. Dad does not need
to row!

Dad owns a rowboat.
He takes Sal on a row.

4

1

Dad rows and rows
and rows.

"Dad, you are so slow!"
said Sal.

The wind blows. Dad knows
what he will do! He will get the
wind to blow his rowboat.

Books, Books, Books!

DECODABLE WORDS

Target Skill: /ŏŏ/ spelled *oo*

book	cookboo	woods
books	k	
Brook	took	

Previously Taught Skills

at	can	had	Jen	pets
Ben	dog	Hal	lot	this
big	dogs	has	Miss	with
bugs	got	it	no	

SKILLS APPLIED IN WORDS IN STORY: *m, s, c, t,* short *a*; consonant *n*; consonant *p*; short *i*; consonant *b*; consonant *r*; consonant *h*; consonant *g*; short *o*; consonant *d*; consonant *w*; consonant *l*; short *e*; consonant *k*; short *u*; consonant *j*; /z/ spelled *s*; /s/ spelled *-ss*; *r* clusters; digraph *sh*; digraph *th*; long *o* (CV); long *e* (CV); long *e* spelled *ea*; /ŏŏ/ spelled *oo*

HIGH–FREQUENCY WORDS

a	I	of	room	the
could	is	one	said	we
good	look	read	she	

HOUGHTON MIFFLIN   BOSTON

Books, Books, Books!

HIGH-FREQUENCY WORDS TAUGHT TO DATE

Grade 1

a	evening	hold	on	the
afraid	every	horse	once	their
again	fall	house	one	there
all	family	how	or	these
also	far	hungry	other	they
and	father	hurt	our	three
animal	find	I	out	through
any	first	idea	over	to
are	five	in	own	today
away	flower	is	paper	too
bear	fly	jump	people	try
been	follow	know	picture	turn
bird	for	learn	piece	two
blue	forest	light	play	under
both	found	like	pull	upon
brown	four	little	read	very
build	friend	live	right	walk
by	full	long	room	wall
call	funny	look	said	want
car	girl	love	see	was
children	give	many	shall	water
climb	go	me	she	we
cold	goes	more	shoe[s]	wear
color	gone	morning	shout	what
come	good	most	show	where
could	green	mother	sing	who
cow	grow	my	small	why
do	hard	near	so	world
does	have	never	some	would
door	he	not	soon	write
down	hear	now	start	you
eat	her	of	table	your
	here	old	tall	

Decoding skills taught to date: *m, s, c, t,* short *a;* consonant *n;* consonant *f;* consonant *p;* short *i;* consonant *b;* consonant *r;* consonant *h;* consonant *g;* short *o;* consonant *d;* consonant *w;* consonant *l;* consonant *x;* short *e;* consonant *y;* consonant *k;* consonant *v;* short *u;* /kw/ spelled *qu;* consonant *j;* consonant *z;* /z/ spelled *s;* consonants *-ck;* /l/ spelled *-ll;* /f/ spelled *-ff;* /s/ spelled *-ss;* /t/ spelled *-ed;* /d/ spelled *-ed;* verb ending *-ing;* *r* clusters; *l* clusters; *s* clusters; silent *k* in *kn;* silent *w* in *wr;* silent *g* in *gn;* triple clusters; digraph *sh;* digraph *th;* digraph *wh;* digraph *ch;* digraph *-tch;* long *a* (CVC*e*); /s/ spelled *c;* /j/ spelled *g;* consonants *-nd;* consonants *-ng;* consonants *-nk;* long *i* (CVC*e*); contractions; long *o* (CV); long *o* (CVC*e*); /o͞o/ spelled *u* (CVC*e*); /yo͞o/ spelled *u* (CVC*e*); consonants *-ft;* consonants *-lk;* consonants *-nt;* long *e* (CV); long *e* (CVC*e*); long *e* spelled *ee;* long *e* spelled *ea;* long *a* spelled *ai;* long *a* spelled *ay;* long *o* spelled *oa;* long *o* spelled *ow;* /o͞o/ spelled *oo;* /o͞o/ spelled *oo;* /o͞o/ spelled *ew;* /o͞o/ spelled *ue;* /o͞o/ spelled *ou;* long *i* spelled *igh;* long *i* spelled *ie*

Ben took a look at
the book.

Ben said, "I can read this
book! It is a good one."

Books,
Books,
Books!

Miss Brook has a room
with a lot of books. She said
we could look at the books.

Hal got a cookbook.
Jen got a dog book. Ben had
no book.

Miss Brook said, "Look at
this book, Ben. It is a good
one." Ben took the book.

I ♥ LOVE READING BOOKS

THEME 8
Our Earth

How to Grow Big Blooms

DECODABLE WORDS

Target Skill: /o͞o/ spelled *oo*

bloom	food	roots
blooms	Joon	scoop
droop	noon	tools

Previously Taught Skills

at	fix	must	sets
big	Hee	need	sun
drops	his	pot	them
gets	lots	pots	then

SKILLS APPLIED IN WORDS IN STORY: *m, s, c, t,* short *a*; consonant *n*; consonant *f*; consonant *p*; short *i*; consonant *b*; consonant *r*; consonant *h*; consonant *g*; short *o*; consonant *d*; consonant *l*; consonant *x*; short *e*; short *u*; consonant *j*; /z/ spelled *s*; *r* clusters; *l* clusters; *s* clusters; digraph *th*; consonants *-nd*; long *o* (CV); long *e* (CV); long *e* spelled *ee*; long *o* spelled *ow*; base words + *-s*

HIGH–FREQUENCY WORDS

a	go	he	of	to
and	grow	how	the	too
gives	grows	in	they	

HOUGHTON MIFFLIN   BOSTON

How to Grow Big Blooms

HIGH-FREQUENCY WORDS TAUGHT TO DATE

Grade 1

a	down	he	not	some	why
about	draw	hear	now	soon	world
afraid	eat	her	of	start	would
again	evening	here	old	table	write
all	every	hold	on	tall	you
also	fall	horse	once	teacher	your
and	family	house	one	the	
animal	far	how	or	their	
any	father	hungry	other	there	
are	find	hurt	our	these	
away	first	I	out	they	
bear	five	idea	over	three	
because	flower	in	own	through	
been	fly	is	paper	tiny	
bird	follow	jump	part	to	
blue	for	know	people	today	
both	forest	learn	picture	too	
brown	found	light	piece	try	
build	four	like	play	turn	
by	friend	little	pull	two	
call	full	live	read	under	
car	funny	long	right	upon	
children	girl	look	room	very	
climb	give	love	said	walk	
cold	go	many	see	wall	
color	goes	me	shall	want	
come	gone	more	she	was	
could	good	morning	shoe[s]	water	
cow	green	most	shout	we	
do	grow	mother	show	wear	
does	happy	my	sing	what	
door	hard	near	small	where	
	have	never	so	who	

Decoding skills taught to date: m, s, c, t, short a; consonant n; consonant f; consonant p; short i; consonant b; consonant r; consonant h; consonant g; short o; consonant d; consonant w; consonant l; consonant x; short e; consonant y; consonant k; consonant v; short u; /kw/ spelled qu; consonant j; consonant z; /z/ spelled s; consonants -ck; /l/ spelled -ll; /f/ spelled -ff; /s/ spelled -ss; /t/ spelled -ed; /d/ spelled -ed; verb ending -ing; r clusters; l clusters; s clusters; silent k in kn; silent w in wr; silent g in gn; triple clusters; digraph sh; digraph th; digraph wh; digraph ch; digraph -tch; long a (CVCe); /s/ spelled c; /j/ spelled g; consonants -nd; consonants -ng; consonants -nk; long i (CVCe); contractions; long o (CV); long o (CVCe); /ōō/ spelled u (CVCe); /yōō/ spelled u (CVCe); consonants -ft; consonants -lk; consonants -nt; long e (CV); long e (CVCe); long e spelled ee; long e spelled ea; long a spelled ai; long a spelled ay; long o spelled oa; long o spelled ow; /ōō/ spelled oo; /ōō/ spelled oo; /ōō/ spelled ew; /ōō/ spelled ue; /ōō/ spelled ou; long i spelled igh; long i spelled ie; /ĕd/ spelled -ed; base words + -ing; base words + -s

Joon Hee sets the blooms in the sun at noon. He gives them food, too. They bloom, bloom, bloom.

How to Grow Big Blooms

Joon Hee grows lots of big blooms in pots.

1

The roots go in a pot.

Then Joon Hee gets his tools.

He drops a big scoop in the pot.

2

The big blooms droop.

Joon Hee must fix the blooms.

They need sun and food.

3

Stew for the Crew

DECODABLE WORDS

Target Skill: /o͞o/ spelled *ew*

chew	new
crew	stew

Previously Taught Skills

best	Cook	make	thank
but	gave	makes	tried
cannot	made	no	will

SKILLS APPLIED IN WORDS IN STORY: *m, s, c, t,* short *a*; consonant *n*; short *i*; consonant *b*; consonant *r*; consonant *g*; short *o*; consonant *d*; consonant *w*; short *e*; consonant *y*; consonant *k*; consonant *v*; short *u*; /l/ spelled *-ll*; *r* clusters; *s* clusters; silent *k* in *kn*; digraph *th*; digraph *ch*; long *a* (CVCe); consonants *-nk*; long *o* (CV); long *e* (CV); long *o* spelled *ow*; /o͞o/ spelled *oo*; /o͞o/ spelled *ou*; long *i* spelled *ie*; base words + *-s*

HIGH–FREQUENCY WORDS

a	for	one	to	you
could	I	said	we	what
do	know	the	what	

HOUGHTON MIFFLIN　　　BOSTON

Stew for the Crew

HIGH-FREQUENCY WORDS TAUGHT TO DATE

Grade 1

a	down	he	not	some	why
about	draw	hear	now	soon	world
afraid	eat	her	of	start	would
again	evening	here	old	table	write
all	every	hold	on	tall	you
also	fall	horse	once	teacher	your
and	family	house	one	the	
animal	far	how	or	their	
any	father	hungry	other	there	
are	find	hurt	our	these	
away	first	I	out	they	
bear	five	idea	over	three	
because	flower	in	own	through	
been	fly	is	paper	tiny	
bird	follow	jump	part	to	
blue	for	know	people	today	
both	forest	learn	picture	too	
brown	found	light	piece	try	
build	four	like	play	turn	
by	friend	little	pull	two	
call	full	live	read	under	
car	funny	long	right	upon	
children	girl	look	room	very	
climb	give	love	said	walk	
cold	go	many	see	wall	
color	goes	me	shall	want	
come	gone	more	she	was	
could	good	morning	shoe[s]	water	
cow	green	most	shout	we	
do	grow	mother	show	wear	
does	happy	my	sing	what	
door	hard	near	small	where	
	have	never	so	who	

Decoding skills taught to date: *m, s, c, t,* short *a;* consonant *n;* consonant *f;* consonant *p;* short *i;* consonant *b;* consonant *r;* consonant *h;* consonant *g;* short *o;* consonant *d;* consonant *w;* consonant *l;* consonant *x;* short *e;* consonant *y;* consonant *k;* consonant *v;* short *u;* /kw/ spelled *qu;* consonant *j;* consonant *z;* /z/ spelled *s;* consonants *-ck;* /l/ spelled *-ll;* /f/ spelled *-ff;* /s/ spelled *-ss;* /t/ spelled *-ed;* /d/ spelled *-ed;* verb ending *-ing;* *r* clusters; *l* clusters; *s* clusters; silent *k* in *kn;* silent *w* in *wr;* silent *g* in *gn;* triple clusters; digraph *sh;* digraph *th;* digraph *wh;* digraph *ch;* digraph *-tch;* long *a* (CVC*e*); /s/ spelled *c;* /j/ spelled *g;* consonants *-nd;* consonants *-ng;* consonants *-nk;* long *i* (CVC*e*); contractions; long *o* (CV); long *o* (CVC*e*); /ōō/ spelled *u* (CVC*e*); /yōō/ spelled *u* (CVC*e*); consonants *-ft;* consonants *-lk;* consonants *-nt;* long *e* (CV); long *e* (CVC*e*); long *e* spelled *ee;* long *e* spelled *ea;* long *a* spelled *ai;* long *a* spelled *ay;* long *o* spelled *oa;* long *o* spelled *ow;* /ōō/ spelled *oo;* /ŏŏ/ spelled *oo;* /ōō/ spelled *ew;* /ōō/ spelled *ue;* /ōō/ spelled *ou;* long *i* spelled *igh;* long *i* spelled *ie;* /ĕd/ spelled *-ed;* base words + *-ing;* base words + *-s*

Cook gave the crew a
new stew.

"Thank you," said the crew.
"You make the best stew."

Stew for the Crew

Cook made stew for the crew.
"Cook makes the best stew,"
said the crew.

The crew tried to chew,
but no one could chew
the stew.

"Cook, we cannot chew
the stew," said the crew.

"I know what to do,"
said Cook. "I will make
new stew."

2

3

Copyright©Houghton Mifflin Company. All rights reserved.

DECODABLE WORDS

Target Skill: /ōo/ spelled *ue*

due	true
Sue	

Previously Taught Skills

asked	box	it	slid	will
be	Dad	Miss	take	
book	dime	must	thank	
books	fines	place	took	

SKILLS APPLIED IN WORDS IN STORY: *m, s, c, t,* short *a*; consonant *n*; consonant *f*; consonant *p*; short *i*; consonant *b*; consonant *r*; short *o*; consonant *d*; consonant *w*; consonant *l*; consonant *x*; consonant *y*; consonant *k*; short *u*; /z/ spelled *s*; /l/ spelled *-ll*; /s/ spelled *-ss*; /t/ spelled *-ed*; *r* clusters; *l* clusters; *s* clusters; digraph *th*; long *a* (CVCe); /s/ spelled *c*; consonants *-nk*; long *i* (CVCe); long *e* (CV); long *e* spelled *ea*; /ōō/ spelled *oo*; /ōō/ spelled *ou*; base words + *-s*

HIGH–FREQUENCY WORDS

a	her	my	said	your
again	here	not	the	
Blue	in	overdue	to	
for	is	read	you	

HOUGHTON MIFFLIN   BOSTON

Your Book Is Due, Sue

HIGH-FREQUENCY WORDS TAUGHT TO DATE

Grade 1

a	down	he	not	some	why
about	draw	hear	now	soon	world
afraid	eat	her	of	start	would
again	evening	here	old	table	write
all	every	hold	on	tall	you
also	fall	horse	once	teacher	your
and	family	house	one	the	
animal	far	how	or	their	
any	father	hungry	other	there	
are	find	hurt	our	these	
away	first	I	out	they	
bear	five	idea	over	three	
because	flower	in	own	through	
been	fly	is	paper	tiny	
bird	follow	jump	part	to	
blue	for	know	people	today	
both	forest	learn	picture	too	
brown	found	light	piece	try	
build	four	like	play	turn	
by	friend	little	pull	two	
call	full	live	read	under	
car	funny	long	right	upon	
children	girl	look	room	very	
climb	give	love	said	walk	
cold	go	many	see	wall	
color	goes	me	shall	want	
come	gone	more	she	was	
could	good	morning	shoe[s]	water	
cow	green	most	shout	we	
do	grow	mother	show	wear	
does	happy	my	sing	what	
door	hard	near	small	where	
	have	never	so	who	

Decoding skills taught to date: m, s, c, t, short a; consonant n; consonant f; consonant p; short i; consonant b; consonant r; consonant h; consonant g; short o; consonant d; consonant w; consonant l; consonant x; short e; consonant y; consonant k; consonant v; short u; /kw/ spelled qu; consonant j; consonant z; /z/ spelled s; consonants -ck; /l/ spelled -ll; /f/ spelled -ff; /s/ spelled -ss; /t/ spelled -ed; /d/ spelled -ed; verb ending -ing; r clusters; l clusters; s clusters; silent k in kn; silent w in wr; silent g in gn; triple clusters; digraph sh; digraph th; digraph wh; digraph ch; digraph -tch; long a (CVCe); /s/ spelled c; /j/ spelled g; consonants -nd; consonants -ng; consonants -nk; long i (CVCe); contractions; long o (CV); long o (CVCe); /o͞o/ spelled u (CVCe); /yo͞o/ spelled u (CVCe); consonants -ft; consonants -lk; consonants -nt; long e (CV); long e (CVCe); long e spelled ee; long e spelled ea; long a spelled ai; long a spelled ay; long o spelled oa; long o spelled ow; /o͞o/ spelled oo; /o͝o/ spelled oo; /o͞o/ spelled ew; /o͞o/ spelled ue; /o͞o/ spelled ou; long i spelled igh; long i spelled ie; /ĕd/ spelled -ed; base words + -ing; base words + -s

Sue slid a dime in the box.
"My books will not be
overdue again," said Sue.
"Thank you!" said Miss Blue.

4

Your Book Is Due, Sue

"Sue, your book is due," said
Dad. "Take it to Miss Blue."

1

Sue took her book to
Miss Blue.

"Miss Blue, is it true my
book is due?" asked Sue.

"Sue, your book is **overdue**,"
said Miss Blue. "You must place
a dime in the box."

2

3

A Good Group

DECODABLE WORDS

Target Skill: /o͞o/ spelled *ou*

group
Lou

Previously Taught Skills

Ben	let's	Sue	with
can	May	us	yes
get	need	will	

SKILLS APPLIED IN WORDS IN STORY: *m, s, c, t,* short *a*; consonant *n*; consonant *p*; short *i*; consonant *b*; consonant *r*; consonant *g*; consonant *d*; consonant *w*; consonant *l*; short *e*; consonant *y*; short *u*; /l/ spelled *-ll*; *r* clusters; *l* clusters; digraph *th*; consonants *nd*; contractions; long *e* (CV); long *e* spelled *ee*; long *a* spelled *ay*; /o͞o/ spelled *oo*; /o͞o/ spelled *ue*

HIGH–FREQUENCY WORDS

a	have	play	we
and	I	said	you
good	now	to	

HOUGHTON MIFFLIN BOSTON

A Good Group

HIGH-FREQUENCY WORDS TAUGHT TO DATE

Grade 1

a	down	he	not	some	why
about	draw	hear	now	soon	world
afraid	eat	her	of	start	would
again	evening	here	old	table	write
all	every	hold	on	tall	you
also	fall	horse	once	teacher	your
and	family	house	one	the	
animal	far	how	or	their	
any	father	hungry	other	there	
are	find	hurt	our	these	
away	first	I	out	they	
bear	five	idea	over	three	
because	flower	in	own	through	
been	fly	is	paper	tiny	
bird	follow	jump	part	to	
blue	for	know	people	today	
both	forest	learn	picture	too	
brown	found	light	piece	try	
build	four	like	play	turn	
by	friend	little	pull	two	
call	full	live	read	under	
car	funny	long	right	upon	
children	girl	look	room	very	
climb	give	love	said	walk	
cold	go	many	see	wall	
color	goes	me	shall	want	
come	gone	more	she	was	
could	good	morning	shoe[s]	water	
cow	green	most	shout	we	
do	grow	mother	show	wear	
does	happy	my	sing	what	
door	hard	near	small	where	
	have	never	so	who	

Decoding skills taught to date: *m, s, c, t,* short *a;* consonant *n;* consonant *f;* consonant *p;* short *i;* consonant *b;* consonant *r;* consonant *h;* consonant *g;* short *o;* consonant *d;* consonant *w;* consonant *l;* consonant *x;* short *e;* consonant *y;* consonant *k;* consonant *v;* short *u;* /kw/ spelled *qu;* consonant *j;* consonant *z;* /z/ spelled *s;* consonants *-ck;* /l/ spelled *-ll;* /f/ spelled *-ff;* /s/ spelled *-ss;* /t/ spelled *-ed;* /d/ spelled *-ed;* verb ending *-ing;* *r* clusters; *l* clusters; *s* clusters; silent *k* in *kn;* silent *w* in *wr;* silent *g* in *gn;* triple clusters; digraph *sh;* digraph *th;* digraph *wh;* digraph *ch;* digraph *-tch;* long *a* (CVC*e*); /s/ spelled *c;* /j/ spelled *g;* consonants *-nd;* consonants *-ng;* consonants *-nk;* long *i* (CVC*e*); contractions; long *o* (CV); long *o* (CVC*e*); /o͞o/ spelled *u* (CVC*e*); /yo͞o/ spelled *u* (CVC*e*); consonants *-ft;* consonants *-lk;* consonants *-nt;* long *e* (CV); long *e* (CVC*e*); long *e* spelled *ee;* long *e* spelled *ea;* long *a* spelled *ai;* long *a* spelled *ay;* long *o* spelled *oa;* long *o* spelled *ow;* /o͞o/ spelled *oo;* /o͞o/ spelled *oo;* /o͞o/ spelled *ew;* /o͞o/ spelled *ue;* /o͞o/ spelled *ou;* long *i* spelled *igh;* long *i* spelled *ie;* /ĕd/ spelled *-ed;* base words + *-ing;* base words + *-s*

A Good Group

"We need a group," said Lou.
"Let's get a group to play
with us," said May.

"We have a good group.
Now we can play!"

"Sue, we need a group.
Will you play with us?" said Lou
and May.

"Yes, I will play with you,"
said Sue.

"Ben, we need a group.
Will you play with us?" said Lou
and May and Sue.

"Yes, I will play with you,"
said Ben.

BOOK 71

DECODABLE WORDS

Target Skill: **long *i* spelled *igh***

bright	night	sunlight
high	sight	

Previously Taught Skills

as	fish	lake	still	wake
at	glass	loons	sun	wings
catch	hills	shines	then	
dive	it	sleep	up	

SKILLS APPLIED IN WORDS IN STORY: *m, s, c, t,* short *a*; consonant *n*; consonant *f*; consonant *p*; short *i*; consonant *b*; consonant *r*; consonant *h*; consonant *g*; short *o*; consonant *d*; consonant *w*; consonant *l*; short *e*; consonant *k*; consonant *v*; short *u*; /z/ spelled *s*; /l/ spelled *-ll*; /s/ spelled *-ss*; *r* clusters; *l* clusters; *s* clusters; digraph *sh*; digraph *th*; digraph *-tch*; long *a* (CVC*e*); consonants *-ng*; long *i* (CVC*e*); long *e* (CV); long *e* spelled *ee*; /oo/ spelled *oo*; base words + *-s*

HIGH–FREQUENCY WORDS

a	is	see	their
fly	on	soon	they
into	over	the	to

HOUGHTON MIFFLIN   BOSTON

High, High Up

a	draw	near	now	soon	world
about	eat	her	of	start	would
afraid	evening	here	old	table	write
again	every	hold	on	tall	you
all	fall	horse	once	teacher	your
also	family	house	one	the	
and	far	how	or	their	
animal	father	hungry	other	there	
any	find	hurt	our	these	
are	first	I	out	they	
away	five	idea	over	three	
bear	flower	in	own	through	
because	fly	is	paper	tiny	
been	follow	jump	part	to	
bird	for	know	people	today	
blue	forest	learn	picture	too	
both	found	light	piece	try	
brown	four	like	play	turn	
build	friend	little	pull	two	
by	full	live	read	under	
call	funny	long	right	upon	
car	girl	look	room	very	
children	give	love	said	walk	
climb	go	many	see	wall	
cold	goes	me	shall	want	
color	gone	more	she	was	
come	good	morning	shoe[s]	water	
could	green	most	shout	we	
cow	grow	mother	show	wear	
do	happy	my	sing	what	
does	hard	near	small	where	
door	have	never	so	who	

Decoding skills taught to date: *m, s, c, t,* short *a*; consonant *n*; consonant *f*; consonant *p*; short *i*; consonant *b*; consonant *r*; consonant *h*; consonant *g*; short *o*; consonant *d*; consonant *w*; consonant *l*; consonant *x*; short *e*; consonant *y*; consonant *k*; consonant *v*; short *u*; /kw/ spelled *qu*; consonant *j*; consonant *z*; /z/ spelled *s*; consonants *-ck*; /l/ spelled *-ll*; /f/ spelled *-ff*; /s/ spelled *-ss*; /t/ spelled *-ed*; /d/ spelled *-ed*; verb ending *-ing*; *r* clusters; *l* clusters; *s* clusters; silent *k* in *kn*; silent *w* in *wr*; silent *g* in *gn*; triple clusters; digraph *sh*; digraph *th*; digraph *wh*; digraph *ch*; digraph *-tch*; long *a* (CVC*e*); /s/ spelled *c*; /j/ spelled *g*; consonants *-nd*; consonants *-ng*; consonants *-nk*; long *i* (CVC*e*); contractions; long *o* (CV); long *o* (CVC*e*); /o͞o/ spelled *u* (CVC*e*); /yo͞o/ spelled *u* (CVC*e*); consonants *-ft*; consonants *-lk*; consonants *-nt*; long *e* (CV); long *e* (CVC*e*); long *e* spelled *ee*; long *e* spelled *ea*; long *a* spelled *ai*; long *a* spelled *ay*; long *o* spelled *oa*; long *o* spelled *ow*; /o͞o/ spelled *oo*; /o͞o/ spelled *oo*; /o͞o/ spelled *ew*; /o͞o/ spelled *ue*; /o͞o/ spelled *ou*; long *i* spelled *igh*; long *i* spelled *ie*; /ĕd/ spelled *-ed*; base words + *-ing*; base words + *-s*

The bright sun shines on
their wings as they fly high,
high, high. It is a sight to see!

High, High Up

At night the lake is as still
as glass. The loons sleep.

Soon, the bright sunlight
shines over the high hills.
The loons wake up.

The loons fly high, high up.
Then they dive into the still lake
to catch fish.

So Many "Ties"

DECODABLE WORDS

Target Skill: long *i* spelled *ie*

tie
ties

Previously Taught Skills

but	ends	his
can	game	it
Dad	has	no

SKILLS APPLIED IN WORDS IN STORY: *m, s, c, t,* short *a*; consonant *n*; consonant *p*; short *i*; consonant *b*; consonant *h*; consonant *g*; consonant *d*; consonant *w*; consonant *l*; short *e*; short *u*; /z/ spelled *s*; *l* clusters; digraph *th*; long *a* (CVCe); consonants *-nd*; long *o* (CV); long *e* (CV); long *a* spelled *ay*; base words + *-s*

HIGH–FREQUENCY WORDS

a	I	many	shoes	two
both	in	my	so	we
have	is	play	the	

HOUGHTON MIFFLIN   BOSTON

So Many "Ties"

HIGH-FREQUENCY WORDS TAUGHT TO DATE

Grade 1

a	down	he	not	some	why
about	draw	hear	now	soon	world
afraid	eat	her	of	start	would
again	evening	here	old	table	write
all	every	hold	on	tall	you
also	fall	horse	once	teacher	your
and	family	house	one	the	
animal	far	how	or	their	
any	father	hungry	other	there	
are	find	hurt	our	these	
away	first	I	out	they	
bear	five	idea	over	three	
because	flower	in	own	through	
been	fly	is	paper	tiny	
bird	follow	jump	part	to	
blue	for	know	people	today	
both	forest	learn	picture	too	
brown	found	light	piece	try	
build	four	like	play	turn	
by	friend	little	pull	two	
call	full	live	read	under	
car	funny	long	right	upon	
children	girl	look	room	very	
climb	give	love	said	walk	
cold	go	many	see	wall	
color	goes	me	shall	want	
come	gone	more	she	was	
could	good	morning	shoe[s]	water	
cow	green	most	shout	we	
do	grow	mother	show	wear	
does	happy	my	sing	what	
door	hard	near	small	where	
	have	never	so	who	

Decoding skills taught to date: *m, s, c, t,* short *a;* consonant *n;* consonant *f;* consonant *p;* short *i;* consonant *b;* consonant *r;* consonant *h;* consonant *g;* short *o;* consonant *d;* consonant *w;* consonant *l;* consonant *x;* short *e;* consonant *y;* consonant *k;* consonant *v;* short *u;* /kw/ spelled *qu;* consonant *j;* consonant *z;* /z/ spelled *s;* consonants *-ck;* /l/ spelled *-ll;* /f/ spelled *-ff;* /s/ spelled *-ss;* /t/ spelled *-ed;* /d/ spelled *-ed;* verb ending *-ing;* *r* clusters; *l* clusters; *s* clusters; silent *k* in *kn;* silent *w* in *wr;* silent *g* in *gn;* triple clusters; digraph *sh;* digraph *th;* digraph *wh;* digraph *ch;* digraph *-tch;* long *a* (CVC*e*); /s/ spelled *c;* /j/ spelled *g;* consonants *-nd;* consonants *-ng;* consonants *-nk;* long *i* (CVC*e*); contractions; long *o* (CV); long *o* (CVC*e*); /o͞o/ spelled *u* (CVC*e*); /yo͞o/ spelled *u* (CVC*e*); consonants *-ft;* consonants *-lk;* consonants *-nt;* long *e* (CV); long *e* (CVC*e*); long *e* spelled *ee;* long *e* spelled *ea;* long *a* spelled *ai;* long *a* spelled *ay;* long *o* spelled *oa;* long *o* spelled *ow;* /o͞o/ spelled *oo;* /o͞o/ spelled *oo;* /o͞o/ spelled *ew;* /o͞o/ spelled *ue;* /o͞o/ spelled *ou;* long *i* spelled *igh;* long *i* spelled *ie;* /ĕd/ spelled *-ed;* base words + *-ing;* base words + *-s*

Dad ties his tie. I tie my
shoes. The game is a tie.
So many ties! **Tie. Tie. Tie.**

So Many "Ties"

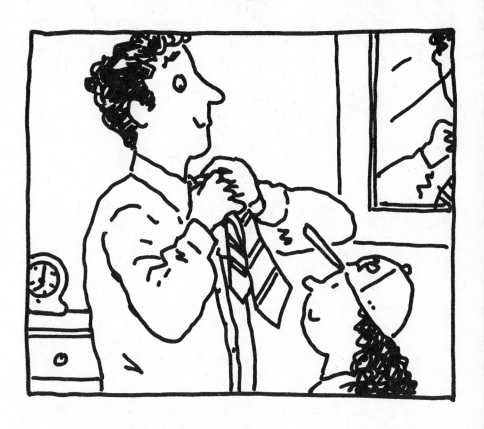

Dad has a tie. Dad can tie
his tie.

I have no tie, but I have two shoes. I can tie both my shoes. **Tie.** **Tie.**

We play a game. It ends in a tie!

I Planted

DECODABLE WORDS

Target Skill: /ĕd/ spelled -*ed*

added   waited
counted
planted

Previously Taught Skills

at	last	such	time
grew	next	them	
had	seeds	then	

SKILLS APPLIED IN WORDS IN STORY: *m, s, c, t,* short *a*; consonant *n*; consonant *p*; consonant *r*; consonant *h*; consonant *g*; short *o*; consonant *d*; consonant *w*; consonant *l*; consonant *x*; short *e*; short *u*; /z/ spelled *s*; *r* clusters; *l* clusters; *s* clusters; digraph *th*; digraph *ch*; consonants -*nd*; consonants -*ng*; long *i* (CVC*e*); long *o* (CV); consonants -*nt*; long *e* spelled *ee*; long *a* spelled *ai*; long *o* spelled *ow*; /ōō/ spelled *ew*; base words + -*s*; /ou/ spelled *ou*

HIGH–FREQUENCY WORDS

a	for	long	three	water
and	grow	my	to	
flowers	I	so	wanted	

HOUGHTON MIFFLIN   BOSTON

I Planted

HIGH-FREQUENCY WORDS TAUGHT TO DATE

Grade 1

a	do	grow	mother	shoe[s]	was
about	does	happy	my	shout	water
afraid	door	hard	near	show	we
again	down	have	never	sing	wear
all	draw	he	not	small	what
also	eat	hear	now	so	where
always	eight	her	of	some	who
and	evening	here	old	soon	why
animal	every	hold	on	start	world
any	fall	horse	once	table	would
are	family	house	one	tall	write
arms	far	how	or	teacher	you
away	father	hungry	other	the	your
bear	find	hurt	our	their	
because	first	I	out	there	
been	five	idea	over	these	
bird	flower	in	own	they	
blue	fly	is	paper	three	
body	follow	jump	part	through	
both	for	know	people	tiny	
brown	forest	learn	picture	to	
build	found	light	piece	today	
by	four	like	play	too	
call	friend	little	pull	try	
car	full	live	read	turn	
children	funny	long	ready	two	
climb	girl	look	right	under	
cold	give	love	room	upon	
color	go	many	said	very	
come	goes	me	see	walk	
could	gone	more	seven	wall	
cow	good	morning	shall	want	
	green	most	she	warm	

Decoding skills taught to date: m, s, c, t, short a; consonant n; consonant f; consonant p; short i; consonant b; consonant r; consonant h; consonant g; short o; consonant d; consonant w; consonant l; consonant x; short e; consonant y; consonant k; consonant v; short u; /kw/ spelled qu; consonant j; consonant z; /z/ spelled s; consonants -ck; /l/ spelled -ll; /f/ spelled -ff; /s/ spelled -ss; /t/ spelled -ed; /d/ spelled -ed; verb ending -ing; r clusters; l clusters; s clusters; silent k in kn; silent w in wr; silent g in gn; triple clusters; digraph sh; digraph th; digraph wh; digraph ch; digraph -tch; long a (CVCe); /s/ spelled c; /j/ spelled g; consonants -nd; consonants -ng; consonants -nk; long i (CVCe); contractions; long o (CV); long o (CVCe); /o͞o/ spelled u (CVCe); /yo͞o/ spelled u (CVCe); consonants -ft; consonants -lk; consonants -nt; long e (CV); long e (CVCe); long e spelled ee; long e spelled ea; long a spelled ai; long a spelled ay; long o spelled oa; long o spelled ow; /o͞o/ spelled oo; /o͞o/ spelled oo; /o͞o/ spelled ew; /o͞o/ spelled ue; /o͞o/ spelled ou; long i spelled igh; long i spelled ie; /ĕd/ spelled -ed; base words + -ing; base words + -s; /ou/ spelled ou; /ou/ spelled ow

I Planted

At last, my flowers grew!
I counted them. I counted
and counted and counted.
I had three flowers!

I wanted to grow flowers.
So, I counted my seeds. Then
I planted them. I planted and
planted and planted.

4

1

Next, I added water to
my seeds. I added and added
and added.

I waited for my seeds
to grow. I waited and waited
and waited. I waited such a
long time!

Squeaking and Creaking

DECODABLE WORDS

Target Skill: base words + -ing

blowing	dreaming	squeaking
brushing	pounding	swishing
creaking	rushing	yelling

Previously Taught Skills

branch	Mom	that
Dad	rain	
Jean	sound	

SKILLS APPLIED IN WORDS IN STORY: *m, s, c, t,* short *a;* consonant *n;* consonant *p;* short *i;* consonant *b;* consonant *r;* short *o;* consonant *d;* consonant *w;* consonant *l;* short *e;* consonant *y;* consonant *k;* short *u;* /kw/ spelled *qu;* consonant *j;* /z/ spelled *s;* /l/ spelled *-ll;* verb ending *-ing;* r clusters; l clusters; s clusters; digraph *sh;* digraph *th;* digraph *ch;* consonants *-nd;* contractions; long *e* (CV); long *e* spelled *ea;* long *a* spelled *ai;* long *o* spelled *ow;* /ou/ spelled *ou*

HIGH–FREQUENCY WORDS

a	falling	shouting	was
and	is	the	what's
calling	said	walking	

HOUGHTON MIFFLIN   BOSTON

Squeaking and Creaking

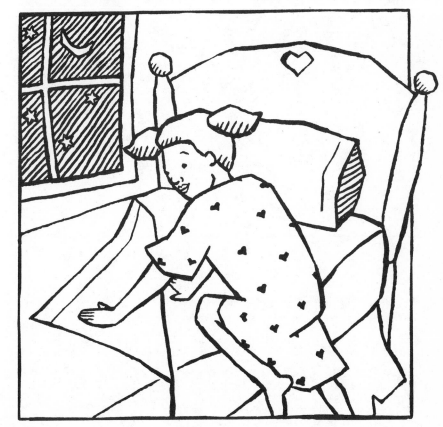

HIGH-FREQUENCY WORDS TAUGHT TO DATE

Grade 1

a	do	grow	mother	shoe[s]	was
about	does	happy	my	shout	water
afraid	door	hard	near	show	we
again	down	have	never	sing	wear
all	draw	he	not	small	what
also	eat	hear	now	so	where
always	eight	her	of	some	who
and	evening	here	old	soon	why
animal	every	hold	on	start	world
any	fall	horse	once	table	would
are	family	house	one	tall	write
arms	far	how	or	teacher	you
away	father	hungry	other	the	your
bear	find	hurt	our	their	
because	first	I	out	there	
been	five	idea	over	these	
bird	flower	in	own	they	
blue	fly	is	paper	three	
body	follow	jump	part	through	
both	for	know	people	tiny	
brown	forest	learn	picture	to	
build	found	light	piece	today	
by	four	like	play	too	
call	friend	little	pull	try	
car	full	live	read	turn	
children	funny	long	ready	two	
climb	girl	look	right	under	
cold	give	love	room	upon	
color	go	many	said	very	
come	goes	me	see	walk	
could	gone	more	seven	wall	
cow	good	morning	shall	want	
	green	most	she	warm	

Decoding skills taught to date: *m, s, c, t,* short *a;* consonant *n;* consonant *f;* consonant *p;* short *i;* consonant *b;* consonant *r;* consonant *h;* consonant *g;* short *o;* consonant *d;* consonant *w;* consonant *l;* consonant *x;* short *e;* consonant *y;* consonant *k;* consonant *v;* short *u;* /kw/ spelled *qu;* consonant *j;* consonant *z;* /z/ spelled *s;* consonants *-ck;* /l/ spelled *-ll;* /f/ spelled *-ff;* /s/ spelled *-ss;* /t/ spelled *-ed;* /d/ spelled *-ed;* verb ending *-ing;* *r* clusters; *l* clusters; *s* clusters; silent *k* in *kn;* silent *w* in *wr;* silent *g* in *gn;* triple clusters; digraph *sh;* digraph *th;* digraph *wh;* digraph *ch;* digraph *-tch;* long *a* (CVC*e*); /s/ spelled *c;* /j/ spelled *g;* consonants *-nd;* consonants *-ng;* consonants *-nk;* long *i* (CVC*e*); contractions; long *o* (CV); long *o* (CVC*e*); /ōō/ spelled *u* (CVC*e*); /yōō/ spelled *u* (CVC*e*); consonants *-ft;* consonants *-lk;* consonants *-nt;* long *e* (CV); long *e* (CVC*e*); long *e* spelled *ee;* long *e* spelled *ea;* long *a* spelled *ai;* long *a* spelled *ay;* long *o* spelled *oa;* long *o* spelled *ow;* /ōō/ spelled *oo;* /ōō/ spelled *oo;* /ōō/ spelled *ew;* /ōō/ spelled *ue;* /ōō/ spelled *ou;* long *i* spelled *igh;* long *i* spelled *ie;* /ĕd/ spelled *-ed;* base words + *-ing;* base words + *-s;* /ou/ spelled *ou;* /ou/ spelled *ow*

The rain was falling, falling, falling. Jean was dreaming, dreaming, dreaming.

Squeaking and Creaking

"Mom!" Jean was calling. "What's that squeaking, creaking sound?"

Mom said, "That sound is Dad walking."

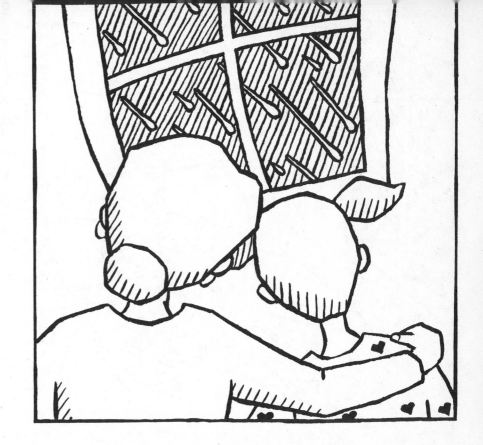

"Mom!" Jean was yelling.
"What's that swishing, brushing
sound?"

Mom said, "That sound is
a branch blowing."

"Mom!" Jean was shouting.
"What's that rushing, pounding
sound?"

Mom said, "That sound is
the rain falling."

DECODABLE WORDS

Target Skill: base words + -s

beds	gets	packs	smells	wraps
cubes	kids	rides	stacks	
cuts	makes	saves	strings	

Previously Taught Skills

as	hay	Kay	when
can	it	nice	with
grass	Jones	sweet	

SKILLS APPLIED IN WORDS IN STORY: *m, s, c, t,* short *a*; consonant *n*; consonant *p*; short *i*; consonant *b*; consonant *r*; consonant *h*; consonant *g*; consonant *d*; consonant *w*; consonant *l*; short *e*; consonant *k*; consonant *v*; short *u*; consonant *j*; /z/ spelled *s*; consonants *-ck*; /l/ spelled *-ll*; /s/ spelled *-ss*; *r* clusters; *s* clusters; silent *w* in *wr*; triple clusters; digraph *sh*; digraph *th*; digraph *wh*; long *a* (CVCe); /s/ spelled *c*; consonants *-nd*; consonants *-ng*; long *i* (CVCe); long *o* (CVCe); /yo͞o/ spelled *u* (CVCe); long *e* (CV); long *e* spelled *ee*; long *e* spelled *ea*; long *a* spelled *ay*; long *o* spelled *ow*; /o͞o/ spelled *oo*; /ou/ spelled *ow*

HIGH-FREQUENCY WORDS

and	eat	horses	some	who
animals	for	into	starts	
cold	grows	like	the	
cows	here	she	too	

HOUGHTON MIFFLIN   BOSTON

Who Makes Hay?

HIGH-FREQUENCY WORDS TAUGHT TO DATE

Grade 1

a	do	grow	mother	shoe[s]	was
about	does	happy	my	shout	water
afraid	door	hard	near	show	we
again	down	have	never	sing	wear
all	draw	he	not	small	what
also	eat	hear	now	so	where
always	eight	her	of	some	who
and	evening	here	old	soon	why
animal	every	hold	on	start	world
any	fall	horse	once	table	would
are	family	house	one	tall	write
arms	far	how	or	teacher	you
away	father	hungry	other	the	your
bear	find	hurt	our	their	
because	first	I	out	there	
been	five	idea	over	these	
bird	flower	in	own	they	
blue	fly	is	paper	three	
body	follow	jump	part	through	
both	for	know	people	tiny	
brown	forest	learn	picture	to	
build	found	light	piece	today	
by	four	like	play	too	
call	friend	little	pull	try	
car	full	live	read	turn	
children	funny	long	ready	two	
climb	girl	look	right	under	
cold	give	love	room	upon	
color	go	many	said	very	
come	goes	me	see	walk	
could	gone	more	seven	wall	
cow	good	morning	shall	want	
	green	most	she	warm	

Decoding skills taught to date: *m, s, c, t,* short *a;* consonant *n;* consonant *f;* consonant *p;* short *i;* consonant *b;* consonant *r;* consonant *h;* consonant *g;* short *o;* consonant *d;* consonant *w;* consonant *l;* consonant *x;* short *e;* consonant *y;* consonant *k;* consonant *v;* short *u;* /kw/ spelled *qu;* consonant *j;* consonant *z;* /z/ spelled *s;* consonants *-ck;* /l/ spelled *-ll;* /f/ spelled *-ff;* /s/ spelled *-ss;* /t/ spelled *-ed;* /d/ spelled *-ed;* verb ending *-ing;* *r* clusters; *l* clusters; *s* clusters; silent *k* in *kn;* silent *w* in *wr;* silent *g* in *gn;* triple clusters; digraph *sh;* digraph *th;* digraph *wh;* digraph *ch;* digraph *-tch;* long *a* (CVC*e*); /s/ spelled *c;* /j/ spelled *g;* consonants *-nd;* consonants *-ng;* consonants *-nk;* long *i* (CVC*e*); contractions; long *o* (CV); long *o* (CVC*e*); /o͞o/ spelled *u* (CVC*e*); /yo͞o/ spelled *u* (CVC*e*); consonants *-ft;* consonants *-lk;* consonants *-nt;* long *e* (CV); long *e* (CVC*e*); long *e* spelled *ee;* long *e* spelled *ea;* long *a* spelled *ai;* long *a* spelled *ay;* long *o* spelled *oa;* long *o* spelled *ow;* /o͞o/ spelled *oo;* /o͞o/ spelled *oo;* /o͞o/ spelled *ew;* /o͞o/ spelled *ue;* /o͞o/ spelled *ou;* long *i* spelled *igh;* long *i* spelled *ie;* /ĕd/ spelled *-ed;* base words + *-ing;* base words + *-s;* /ou/ spelled *ou;* /ou/ spelled *ow*

Who Makes Hay?

Hay grows here. Hay starts as grass. Kay Jones cuts the grass. It smells sweet.

Kids like hay, too.
Kay Jones saves some for hay rides!

Kay Jones packs the hay into cubes. She wraps it with strings and stacks it.

When it gets cold, horses and cows can eat the hay. Hay makes nice beds for animals, too.

Al and Scout

DECODABLE WORDS

Target Skill: /ou/ spelled *ou*

bounded	outside	round
couch	pounding	Scout
ground	pout	slouched

Previously Taught Skills

Al	hat	rain	with
can	his	went	
don't	Mom	wet	

SKILLS APPLIED IN WORDS IN STORY: *m, s, c, t,* short *a*; consonant *n*; consonant *p*; short *i*; consonant *b*; consonant *r*; consonant *h*; consonant *g*; short *o*; consonant *d*; consonant *w*; consonant *l*; short *e*; consonant *y*; /z/ spelled *s*; /t/ spelled *-ed*; verb ending *-ing*; *r* clusters; *l* clusters; *s* clusters; digraph *th*; digraph *ch*; consonants *-nd*; long *i* (CVCe); contractions; long *o* (CV); consonants *-nt*; long *e* (CV); long *a* spelled *ai*; /o͞o/ spelled *ou*; /ĕd/ spelled *-ed*; base words + *-ing*; /ou/ spelled *ow*

HIGH–FREQUENCY WORDS

and	house	out	was
down	of	<u>put</u>	you
go	on	said	
he	onto	the	

Underscored high-frequency words are introduced in this week's instruction.

Al and Scout

HIGH-FREQUENCY WORDS TAUGHT TO DATE

Grade 1

a	could	good	more	said	upon
about	cow	green	morning	saw	very
afraid	do	grow	most	see	walk
again	does	happy	mother	seven	wall
all	door	hard	my	shall	want
also	down	have	near	she	warm
always	draw	he	never	shoe[s]	was
and	eat	hear	not	shout	water
animal	eight	her	now	show	we
any	evening	here	of	sing	wear
are	every	hold	old	small	were
arms	fall	horse	on	so	what
away	family	house	once	some	where
bear	far	how	one	soon	who
because	father	hungry	or	start	why
been	find	hurt	other	table	work
bird	first	I	our	tall	world
blue	five	idea	out	teacher	would
body	flower	in	over	the	write
both	fly	is	own	their	you
brown	follow	jump	paper	there	your
build	for	kind	part	these	
butter	forest	know	people	they	
by	found	learn	person	three	
call	four	light	picture	through	
car	friend	like	piece	tiny	
carry	full	little	play	to	
children	funny	live	pull	today	
climb	girl	long	put	too	
cold	give	look	read	try	
color	go	love	ready	turn	
come	goes	many	right	two	
	gone	me	room	under	

Decoding skills taught to date: *m, s, c, t,* short *a;* consonant *n;* consonant *f;* consonant *p;* short *i;* consonant *b;* consonant *r;* consonant *h;* consonant *g;* short *o;* consonant *d;* consonant *w;* consonant *l;* consonant *x;* short *e;* consonant *y;* consonant *k;* consonant *v;* short *u;* /kw/ spelled *qu;* consonant *j;* consonant *z; /z/ spelled *s;* consonants *-ck;* /l/ spelled *-ll;* /f/ spelled *-ff;* /s/ spelled *-ss;* /t/ spelled *-ed;* /d/ spelled *-ed;* verb ending *-ing;* *r* clusters; *l* clusters; *s* clusters; silent *k* in *kn;* silent *w* in *wr;* silent *g* in *gn;* triple clusters; digraph *sh;* digraph *th;* digraph *wh;* digraph *ch;* digraph *-tch;* long *a* (CVC*e*); /s/ spelled *c;* /j/ spelled *g;* consonants *-nd;* consonants *-ng;* consonants *-nk;* long *i* (CVC*e*); contractions; long *o* (CV); long *o* (CVC*e*); /o͞o/ spelled *u* (CVC*e*); /yo͞o/ spelled *u* (CVC*e*); consonants *-ft;* consonants *-lk;* consonants *-nt;* long *e* (CV); long *e* (CVC*e*); long *e* spelled *ee;* long *e* spelled *ea;* long *a* spelled *ai;* long *a* spelled *ay;* long *o* spelled *oa;* long *o* spelled *ow;* /o͞o/ spelled *oo;* /o͝o/ spelled *oo;* /o͞o/ spelled *ew;* /o͞o/ spelled *ue;* /o͞o/ spelled *ou;* long *i* spelled *igh;* long *i* spelled *ie;* /ĕd/ spelled *-ed;* base words + *-ing;* base words + *-s;* /ou/ spelled *ou;* /ou/ spelled *ow;* *-ing* (spelling changes); *-ed* (spelling changes)

Al and Scout bounded out onto the wet ground.

4

Al and Scout

Al and Scout slouched on the couch. Outside, the rain was pounding down.

1

Mom said, "Don't pout, Al.
You and Scout can go out."

2

Al put on his round hat.
He went out of the house
with Scout.

3

DECODABLE WORDS

Target Skill: /ou/ spelled *ow*

fowl	prowls
howls	town
owl	

Previously Taught Skills

big	flight	peck
cat	grass	takes
dog	ground	this

SKILLS APPLIED IN WORDS IN STORY: *m, s, c, t,* short *a*; consonant *n*; consonant *f*; consonant *p*; short *i*; consonant *b*; consonant *r*; consonant *h*; consonant *g*; short *o*; consonant *d*; consonant *l*; short *e*; consonant *k*; /z/ spelled *s*; consonants *-ck*; /s/ spelled *-ss*; *r* clusters; *l* clusters; digraph *th*; long *a* (CVC*e*); consonants *-nd*; long *e* (CV); long *e* spelled *ee*; long *e* spelled *ea*; long *i* spelled *igh*; base words + *-s*; /ou/ spelled *ou*

HIGH–FREQUENCY WORDS

a	cow	on
and	eats	the
brown	in	three

HOUGHTON MIFFLIN   BOSTON

In This Town

Grade 1

a	could	good	more	said	upon
about	cow	green	morning	saw	very
afraid	do	grow	most	see	walk
again	does	happy	mother	seven	wall
all	door	hard	my	shall	want
also	down	have	near	she	warm
always	draw	he	never	shoe[s]	was
and	eat	hear	not	shout	water
animal	eight	her	now	show	we
any	evening	here	of	sing	wear
are	every	hold	old	small	were
arms	fall	horse	on	so	what
away	family	house	once	some	where
bear	far	how	one	soon	who
because	father	hungry	or	start	why
been	find	hurt	other	table	work
bird	first	I	our	tall	world
blue	five	idea	out	teacher	would
body	flower	in	over	the	write
both	fly	is	own	their	you
brown	follow	jump	paper	there	your
build	for	kind	part	these	
butter	forest	know	people	they	
by	found	learn	person	three	
call	four	light	picture	through	
car	friend	like	piece	tiny	
carry	full	little	play	to	
children	funny	live	pull	today	
climb	girl	long	put	too	
cold	give	look	read	try	
color	go	love	ready	turn	
come	goes	many	right	two	
	gone	me	room	under	

Decoding skills taught to date: *m, s, c, t,* short *a;* consonant *n;* consonant *f;* consonant *p;* short *i;* consonant *b;* consonant *r;* consonant *h;* consonant *g;* short *o;* consonant *d;* consonant *w;* consonant *l;* consonant *x;* short *e;* consonant *y;* consonant *k;* consonant *v;* short *u;* /kw/ spelled *qu;* consonant *j;* consonant *z;* /z/ spelled *s;* consonants *-ck;* /l/ spelled *-ll;* /f/ spelled *-ff;* /s/ spelled *-ss;* /t/ spelled *-ed;* /d/ spelled *-ed;* verb ending *-ing;* *r* clusters; *l* clusters; *s* clusters; silent *k* in *kn;* silent *w* in *wr;* silent *g* in *gn;* triple clusters; digraph *sh;* digraph *th;* digraph *wh;* digraph *ch;* digraph *-tch;* long *a* (CVC*e*); /s/ spelled *c;* /j/ spelled *g;* consonants *-nd;* consonants *-ng;* consonants *-nk;* long *i* (CVC*e*); contractions; long *o* (CV); long *o* (CVC*e*); /ōō/ spelled *u* (CVC*e*); /yōō/ spelled *u* (CVC*e*); consonants *-ft;* consonants *-lk;* consonants *-nt;* long *e* (CV); long *e* (CVC*e*); long *e* spelled *ee;* long *e* spelled *ea;* long *a* spelled *ai;* long *a* spelled *ay;* long *o* spelled *oa;* long *o* spelled *ow;* /ōō/ spelled *oo;* /ōō/ spelled *oo;* /ōō/ spelled *ew;* /ōō/ spelled *ue;* /ōō/ spelled *ou;* long *i* spelled *igh;* long *i* spelled *ie;* /ĕd/ spelled *-ed;* base words + *-ing;* base words + *-s;* /ou/ spelled *ou;* /ou/ spelled *ow;* *-ing* (spelling changes); *-ed* (spelling changes)

In This Town

In this town, a brown cow eats grass.

In this town, a big owl takes flight.

In this town, three fowl
peck on the ground.

In this town, a dog howls
and a cat prowls.

I ♥ LOVE READING BOOKS

THEME 9
Special Friends

Rising, Shining, Setting

Target Skill: *-ing* (spelling changes)

chasing	gliding	humming	shining
dozing	hiding	rising	tapping
flipping	hopping	setting	waking

Previously Taught Skills

bees	hole	moon	toads
bugs	home	rabbit	whoo
cub	its	sun	

SKILLS APPLIED IN WORDS IN STORY: *m, s, c, t,* short *a*; consonant *n*; consonant *f*; consonant *p*; short *i*; consonant *b*; consonant *r*; consonant *h*; consonant *g*; short *o*; consonant *d*; consonant *w*; consonant *l*; short *e*; consonant *k*; short *u*; consonant *z*; /z/ spelled *s*; verb ending *-ing*; *l* clusters; digraph *sh*; digraph *th*; digraph *wh*; digraph *ch*; long *a* (CVCe); consonants *-nd*; long *i* (CVCe); long *o* (CVCe); long *e* (CV); long *e* spelled *ee*; long *o* spelled *oa*; /o͞o/ spelled *oo*; base words + *-ing*; base words + *-s*

HIGH–FREQUENCY WORDS

a	are	in	some
and	bear	is	the
animals	birds	other	

HOUGHTON MIFFLIN   BOSTON

Rising, Shining, Setting

HIGH-FREQUENCY WORDS TAUGHT TO DATE

Grade 1

a	come	give	look	pull	tiny
about	could	go	love	put	to
afraid	cow	goes	many	read	today
again	dance	gone	me	ready	too
all	do	good	more	right	try
also	does	green	morning	room	turn
always	door	grow	most	said	two
and	down	happy	mother	saw	under
animal	draw	hard	my	see	upon
any	eat	have	near	seven	very
are	eight	he	never	shall	walk
arms	else	hear	not	she	wall
around	evening	her	now	shoe[s]	want
away	ever	here	ocean	shout	warm
bear	every	hold	of	show	was
because	fall	horse	old	sing	water
been	family	house	on	small	we
bird	far	how	once	so	wear
blue	father	hungry	one	some	were
body	find	hurt	open	soon	what
both	first	I	or	start	where
brown	five	idea	other	table	who
build	flower	in	our	talk	why
butter	fly	is	out	tall	work
by	follow	jump	over	teacher	world
call	for	kind	own	the	would
car	forest	know	paper	their	write
carry	found	learn	part	there	you
children	four	light	people	these	your
climb	friend	like	person	they	
cold	full	little	picture	though	
color	funny	live	piece	three	
	girl	long	play	through	

Decoding skills taught to date: m, s, c, t, short a; consonant n; consonant f; consonant p; short i; consonant b; consonant r; consonant h; consonant g; short o; consonant d; consonant w; consonant l; consonant x; short e; consonant y; consonant k; consonant v; short u; /kw/ spelled qu; consonant j; consonant z; /z/ spelled s; consonants -ck; /l/ spelled -ll; /f/ spelled -ff; /s/ spelled -ss; /t/ spelled -ed; /d/ spelled -ed; verb ending -ing; r clusters; l clusters; s clusters; silent k in kn; silent w in wr; silent g in gn; triple clusters; digraph sh; digraph th; digraph wh; digraph ch; digraph -tch; long a (CVCe); /s/ spelled c; /j/ spelled g; consonants -nd; consonants -ng; consonants -nk; long i (CVCe); contractions; long o (CV); long o (CVCe); /o͞o/ spelled u (CVCe); /yo͞o/ spelled u (CVCe); consonants -ft; consonants -lk; consonants -nt; long e (CV); long e (CVCe); long e spelled ee; long e spelled ea; long a spelled ai; long a spelled ay; long o spelled oa; long o spelled ow; /o͞o/ spelled oo; /o͞o/ spelled oo; /o͞o/ spelled ew; /o͞o/ spelled ue; /o͞o/ spelled ou; long i spelled igh; long i spelled ie; /ĕd/ spelled -ed; base words + -ing; base words + -s; /ou/ spelled ou; /ou/ spelled ow; -ing (spelling changes); -ed (spelling changes); long e spelled y; long i spelled y

The moon is rising.
Some animals are dozing.
Other animals are waking.
Whoo-whoo!

4

Rising, Shining, Setting

The sun is rising. Bees are humming. Birds are tapping.

1

The sun is shining.
Bugs are flipping and gliding.
A bear is chasing a cub.

The sun is setting. Toads
are hopping home. A rabbit
is hiding in its hole.

I Dotted and Dabbed

DECODABLE WORDS

Target Skill: *-ed* (spelling changes)

dabbed	glued	smiled	used
dotted	hugged	stopped	
dropped	mopped	traced	

Previously Taught Skills

beads	it	red	then	yellow
glue	lot	spilled	up	
Gran	paint	string	with	

SKILLS APPLIED IN WORDS IN STORY: *m, s, c, t,* short *a*; consonant *n*; consonant *p*; short *i*; consonant *b*; consonant *r*; consonant *h*; consonant *g*; short *o*; consonant *d*; consonant *w*; consonant *l*; short *e*; consonant *y*; consonant *k*; short *u*; /z/ spelled *s*; /l/ spelled *-ll*; /t/ spelled *-ed*; /d/ spelled *-ed*; *r* clusters; *l* clusters; *s* clusters; triple clusters; digraph *sh*; digraph *th*; long *a* (CVCe); /s/ spelled *c*; consonants *-nd*; consonants *-ng*; long *i* (CVCe); /yōō/ spelled *u* (CVCe); consonants *-nt*; long *e* (CV); long *e* spelled *ea*; long *a* spelled *ai*; long *o* spelled *ow*; /ōō/ spelled *ue*; /ĕd/ spelled *-ed*; base words + *-s*; long *i* spelled *y*

HIGH–FREQUENCY WORDS

a	blue	me	opened	the
again	I	my	picture	
and	liked	onto	she	

Underscored high-frequency words are introduced in this week's instruction.

HOUGHTON MIFFLIN   BOSTON

HIGH-FREQUENCY WORDS TAUGHT TO DATE

Grade 1					
a	come	give	look	pull	tiny
about	could	go	love	put	to
afraid	cow	goes	many	read	today
again	dance	gone	me	ready	too
all	do	good	more	right	try
also	does	green	morning	room	turn
always	door	grow	most	said	two
and	down	happy	mother	saw	under
animal	draw	hard	my	see	upon
any	eat	have	near	seven	very
are	eight	he	never	shall	walk
arms	else	hear	not	she	wall
around	evening	her	now	shoe[s]	want
away	ever	here	ocean	shout	warm
bear	every	hold	of	show	was
because	fall	horse	old	sing	water
been	family	house	on	small	we
bird	far	how	once	so	wear
blue	father	hungry	one	some	were
body	find	hurt	open	soon	what
both	first	I	or	start	where
brown	five	idea	other	table	who
build	flower	in	our	tall	why
butter	fly	is	out	talk	work
by	follow	jump	over	teacher	world
call	for	kind	own	the	would
car	forest	know	paper	their	write
carry	found	learn	part	there	you
children	four	light	people	these	your
climb	friend	like	person	they	
cold	full	little	picture	though	
color	funny	live	piece	three	
	girl	long	play	through	

Decoding skills taught to date: *m, s, c, t,* short *a;* consonant *n;* consonant *f;* consonant *p;* short *i;* consonant *b;* consonant *r;* consonant *h;* consonant *g;* short *o;* consonant *d;* consonant *w;* consonant *l;* consonant *x;* short *e;* consonant *y;* consonant *k;* consonant *v;* short *u;* /kw/ spelled *qu;* consonant *j;* consonant *z;* /z/ spelled *s;* consonants *-ck;* /l/ spelled *-ll;* /f/ spelled *-ff;* /s/ spelled *-ss;* /t/ spelled *-ed;* /d/ spelled *-ed;* verb ending *-ing;* *r* clusters; *l* clusters; *s* clusters; silent *k* in *kn;* silent *w* in *wr;* silent *g* in *gn;* triple clusters; digraph *sh;* digraph *th;* digraph *wh;* digraph *ch;* digraph *-tch;* long *a* (CVC*e*); /s/ spelled *c;* /j/ spelled *g;* consonants *-nd;* consonants *-ng;* consonants *-nk;* long *i* (CVC*e*); contractions; long *o* (CV); long *o* (CVC*e*); /o͞o/ spelled *u* (CVC*e*); /yo͞o/ spelled *u* (CVC*e*); consonants *-ft;* consonants *-lk;* consonants *-nt;* long *e* (CV); long *e* (CVC*e*); long *e* spelled *ee;* long *e* spelled *ea;* long *a* spelled *ai;* long *a* spelled *ay;* long *o* spelled *oa;* long *o* spelled *ow;* /o͞o/ spelled *oo;* /o͝o/ spelled *oo;* /o͞o/ spelled *ew;* /o͞o/ spelled *ue;* /o͞o/ spelled *ou;* long *i* spelled *igh;* long *i* spelled *ie;* /ĕd/ spelled *-ed;* base words + *-ing;* base words + *-s;* /ou/ spelled *ou;* /ou/ spelled *ow;* *-ing* (spelling changes); *-ed* (spelling changes); long *e* spelled *y;* long *i* spelled *y*

I Dotted and Dabbed

I traced a picture. I dropped the picture. I traced it again.

1

Gran opened my picture. Gran liked it. She smiled and hugged me.

4

I dotted and dabbed my
picture with paint. I used a lot.
I spilled it! I mopped it up.

I glued beads and
string onto my picture.
Then I stopped.

Messy Wally Bunny

DECODABLE WORDS

Target Skill: **long *e* spelled *y***

Bunny	Mommy	taffy
fluffy	sticky	Wally
messy	sudsy	

Previously Taught Skills

am	gave
ate	got
bath	

SKILLS APPLIED IN WORDS IN STORY: *m, s, c, t,* short *a*; consonant *n*; consonant *f*; short *i*; consonant *b*; consonant *g*; short *o*; consonant *d*; consonant *w*; consonant *l*; short *e*; consonant *v*; short *u*; /z/ spelled *s*; consonants *-ck*; /l/ spelled *-ll*; /f/ spelled *-ff*; /s/ spelled *-ss*; *l* clusters; *s* clusters; digraph *th*; long *a* (CVCe); consonants *-nd*; long *o* (CV); /ou/ spelled *ow*

HIGH–FREQUENCY WORDS

a	I	said	very
again	is	so	was
and	now	some	

Messy Wally Bunny

TAFFY

HOUGHTON MIFFLIN   BOSTON

HIGH-FREQUENCY WORDS TAUGHT TO DATE

Grade 1	climb	friend	like	people	their	would
a	cold	full	little	person	there	write
about	color	funny	live	picture	these	you
afraid	come	girl	long	piece	they	your
after	could	give	look	play	though	
again	cow	go	love	pretty	three	
all	dance	goes	many	pull	through	
also	do	gone	me	put	tiny	
always	does	good	more	read	to	
and	done	green	morning	ready	today	
animal	door	grow	most	right	too	
any	down	happy	mother	room	try	
are	draw	hard	my	said	turn	
arms	eat	have	near	saw	two	
around	eight	he	never	school	under	
away	else	hear	not	see	upon	
bear	evening	her	now	seven	very	
because	ever	here	ocean	shall	walk	
been	every	hold	of	she	wall	
before	fall	horse	off	shoe[s]	want	
bird	family	house	old	shout	warm	
blue	far	how	on	show	was	
body	father	hungry	once	sing	wash	
both	find	hurt	one	small	water	
brown	first	I	open	so	we	
build	five	idea	or	some	wear	
butter	flower	in	other	soon	were	
buy	fly	is	our	start	what	
by	follow	jump	out	table	where	
call	for	kind	over	talk	who	
car	forest	know	own	tall	why	
carry	found	learn	paper	teacher	work	
children	four	light	part	the	world	

Decoding skills taught to date: *m, s, c, t,* short *a;* consonant *n;* consonant *f;* consonant *p;* short *i;* consonant *b;* consonant *r;* consonant *h;* consonant *g;* short *o;* consonant *d;* consonant *w;* consonant *l;* consonant *x;* short *e;* consonant *y;* consonant *k;* consonant *v;* short *u;* /kw/ spelled *qu;* consonant *j;* consonant *z;* /z/ spelled *s;* consonants *-ck;* /l/ spelled *-ll;* /f/ spelled *-ff;* /s/ spelled *-ss;* /t/ spelled *-ed;* /d/ spelled *-ed;* verb ending *-ing;* *r* clusters; *l* clusters; *s* clusters; silent *k* in *kn;* silent *w* in *wr;* silent *g* in *gn;* triple clusters; digraph *sh;* digraph *th;* digraph *wh;* digraph *ch;* digraph *-tch;* long *a* (CVC*e*); /s/ spelled *c;* /j/ spelled *g;* consonants *-nd;* consonants *-ng;* consonants *-nk;* long *i* (CVC*e*); contractions; long *o* (CV); long *o* (CVC*e*); /o͞o/ spelled *u* (CVC*e*); /yo͞o/ spelled *u* (CVC*e*); consonants *-ft;* consonants *-lk;* consonants *-nt;* long *e* (CV); long *e* (CVC*e*); long *e* spelled *ee;* long *e* spelled *ea;* long *a* spelled *ai;* long *a* spelled *ay;* long *o* spelled *oa;* long *o* spelled *ow;* /o͝o/ spelled *oo;* /o͞o/ spelled *oo;* /o͞o/ spelled *ew;* /o͞o/ spelled *ue;* /o͞o/ spelled *ou;* long *i* spelled *igh;* long *i* spelled *ie;* /ĕd/ spelled *-ed;* base words + *-ing;* base words + *-s;* /ou/ spelled *ou;* /ou/ spelled *ow;* *-ing* (spelling changes); *-ed* (spelling changes); long *e* spelled *y;* long *i* spelled *y;* /ĕz/ spelled *-es;* /ēz/ spelled *-ies*

Mommy Bunny gave Wally Bunny a sudsy bath. Now Wally Bunny is fluffy again.

4

Messy Wally Bunny

Wally was a very fluffy bunny.

1

Wally Bunny ate some sticky taffy. Wally Bunny got very sticky and messy.

"Mommy Bunny! I am so sticky," said Wally.

The Spy

DECODABLE WORDS

Target Skill: **long *i* spelled *y***

dry
spy

Previously Taught Skills

asked	dad	Lin	must
be	did	milk	will
cup	drank	mom	

SKILLS APPLIED IN WORDS IN STORY: *m, s, c, t,* short *a*; consonant *n*; consonant *p*; short *i*; consonant *b*; consonant *r*; short *o*; consonant *d*; consonant *w*; consonant *l*; consonant *k*; short *u*; /z/ spelled *s*; /l/ spelled *-ll*; /t/ spelled *-ed*; *r* clusters; *s* clusters; silent *k* in *kn*; digraph *th*; digraph *wh*; consonants *-nk*; consonants *-lk*; long *e* (CV); long *o* spelled *ow*; /ou/ spelled *ou*

HIGH–FREQUENCY WORDS

a	is	not	the
find	know	out	why
I	my	said	your

The Spy

HOUGHTON MIFFLIN   BOSTON

HIGH-FREQUENCY WORDS TAUGHT TO DATE

Grade 1

a	climb	friend	like	people	their	would
about	cold	full	little	person	there	write
afraid	color	funny	live	picture	these	you
after	come	girl	long	piece	they	your
again	could	give	look	play	though	
all	cow	go	love	pretty	three	
also	dance	goes	many	pull	through	
always	do	gone	me	put	tiny	
and	does	good	more	read	to	
animal	done	green	morning	ready	today	
any	door	grow	most	right	too	
are	down	happy	mother	room	try	
arms	draw	hard	my	said	turn	
around	eat	have	near	saw	two	
away	eight	he	never	school	under	
bear	else	hear	not	see	upon	
because	evening	her	now	seven	very	
been	ever	here	ocean	shall	walk	
before	every	hold	of	she	wall	
bird	fall	horse	off	shoe[s]	want	
blue	family	house	old	shout	warm	
body	far	how	on	show	was	
both	father	hungry	once	sing	wash	
brown	find	hurt	one	small	water	
build	first	I	open	so	we	
butter	five	idea	or	some	wear	
buy	flower	in	other	soon	were	
by	fly	is	our	start	what	
call	follow	jump	out	table	where	
car	for	kind	over	talk	who	
carry	forest	know	own	tall	why	
children	found	learn	paper	teacher	work	
	four	light	part	the	world	

Decoding skills taught to date: m, s, c, t, short a; consonant n; consonant f; consonant p; short i; consonant b; consonant r; consonant h; consonant g; short o; consonant d; consonant w; consonant l; consonant x; short e; consonant y; consonant k; consonant v; short u; /kw/ spelled qu; consonant j; consonant z; /z/ spelled s; consonants -ck; /l/ spelled -ll; /f/ spelled -ff; /s/ spelled -ss; /t/ spelled -ed; /d/ spelled -ed; verb ending -ing; r clusters; l clusters; s clusters; silent k in kn; silent w in wr; silent g in gn; triple clusters; digraph sh; digraph th; digraph wh; digraph ch; digraph -tch; long a (CVCe); /s/ spelled c; /j/ spelled g; consonants -nd; consonants -ng; consonants -nk; long i (CVCe); contractions; long o (CV); long o (CVCe); /o͞o/ spelled u (CVCe); /yo͞o/ spelled u (CVCe); consonants -ft; consonants -lk; consonants -nt; long e (CV); long e (CVCe); long e spelled ee; long e spelled ea; long a spelled ai; long a spelled ay; long o spelled oa; long o spelled ow; /o͞o/ spelled oo; /o͝o/ spelled oo; /o͞o/ spelled ew; /o͞o/ spelled ue; /o͞o/ spelled ou; long i spelled igh; long i spelled ie; /ĕd/ spelled -ed; base words + -ing; base words + -s; /ou/ spelled ou; /ou/ spelled ow; -ing (spelling changes); -ed (spelling changes); long e spelled y; long i spelled y; /ĕz/ spelled -es; /ēz/ spelled -ies

"I know why your cup
is dry," said Lin. "I drank
your milk!"

The Spy

"I must find out why
my cup is dry," I said.
"I will be a spy."

"Why is my cup dry?"
I asked my dad. Dad did not
know why.

"Why is my cup dry?"
I asked my mom. Mom did not
know why.

2

3

Cassy Rushes

DECODABLE WORDS

Target Skill: /ĕz/ spelled -es

brushes	dishes	snatches
catches	peaches	splashes
dashes	rushes	

Previously Taught Skills

backpac k	bus	face	milk	time
	Cassy	get	teeth	toast
bed	dressed	late	then	

SKILLS APPLIED IN WORDS IN STORY: *m, s, c, t,* short *a;* consonant *n;* consonant *f;* consonant *p;* short *i;* consonant *b;* consonant *r;* consonant *g;* short *o;* consonant *d;* consonant *l;* short *e;* consonant *k;* short *u;* /z/ spelled *s;* consonants *-ck;* /s/ spelled *-ss;* /t/ spelled *-ed; r* clusters; *s* clusters; triple clusters; digraph *sh;* digraph *th;* digraph *ch;* digraph *-tch;* long *a* (CVCe); /s/ spelled *c;* consonants *-nd;* long *i* (CVCe); consonants *-lk;* long *e* (CV); long *e* spelled *ee;* long *e* spelled *ea;* long *o* spelled *oa;* base words + *-s;* /ou/ spelled *ou;* long *e* spelled *y*

HIGH–FREQUENCY WORDS

and	is	out	to
eats	of	she	washes
her	on	the	water

HOUGHTON MIFFLIN   BOSTON

HIGH-FREQUENCY WORDS TAUGHT TO DATE

Grade 1

a	children	forest	kind	out	start	wear
about	climb	found	know	over	table	were
afraid	cold	four	learn	own	talk	what
after	color	friend	light	paper	tall	where
again	come	full	like	part	teacher	who
all	could	funny	little	people	the	why
also	cow	garden	live	person	their	work
always	dance	girl	long	picture	there	world
and	do	give	look	piece	these	would
animal	does	go	love	play	they	write
any	done	goes	many	pretty	though	you
are	door	gone	me	pull	three	your
arms	down	good	more	put	through	
around	draw	green	morning	read	tiny	
away	eat	grow	most	ready	to	
baby	edge	happy	mother	right	today	
bear	eight	hard	my	room	together	
because	else	have	near	said	too	
been	enough	he	never	saw	try	
before	evening	hear	not	school	turn	
bird	ever	her	now	see	two	
blue	every	here	ocean	seven	under	
body	fall	hold	of	shall	upon	
both	family	horse	off	sharp	very	
brown	far	house	old	she	walk	
build	father	how	on	shoe[s]	wall	
butter	find	hungry	once	shout	want	
buy	first	hurt	one	show	warm	
by	five	I	only	sing	was	
call	flower	idea	open	small	wash	
car	fly	in	or	so	watched	
carry	follow	is	other	some	water	
	for	jump	our	soon	we	

Decoding skills taught to date: m, s, c, t; short a; consonant n; consonant f; consonant p; short i; consonant b; consonant r; consonant h; consonant g; short o; consonant d; consonant w; consonant l; consonant x; short e; consonant y; consonant k; consonant v; short u; /kw/ spelled qu; consonant j; consonant z; /z/ spelled s; consonants -ck; /l/ spelled -ll; /f/ spelled -ff; /s/ spelled -ss; /t/ spelled -ed; /d/ spelled -ed; verb ending -ing; r clusters; l clusters; s clusters; silent k in kn; silent w in wr; silent g in gn; triple clusters; digraph sh; digraph th; digraph wh; digraph ch; digraph -tch; long a (CVCe); /s/ spelled c; /j/ spelled g; consonants -nd; consonants -ng; consonants -nk; long i (CVCe); contractions; long o (CV); long o (CVCe); /o͞o/ spelled u (CVCe); /yo͞o/ spelled u (CVCe); consonants -ft; consonants -lk; consonants -nt; long e (CV); long e (CVCe); long e spelled ee; long e spelled ea; long a spelled ai; long a spelled ay; long o spelled oa; long o spelled ow; /o͞o/ spelled oo; /o͞o/ spelled oo; /o͞o/ spelled ew; /o͞o/ spelled ue; /o͞o/ spelled ou; long i spelled igh; long i spelled ie; /ĕd/ spelled -ed; base words + -ing; base words + -s; /ou/ spelled ou; /ou/ spelled ow; -ing (spelling changes); -ed (spelling changes); long e spelled y; long i spelled y; /ĕz/ spelled -es; /ēz/ spelled -ies; /oi/ spelled oi; /oi/ spelled oy; /ô/ spelled aw; /ô/ spelled au

Cassy Rushes

Cassy is late! Cassy dashes out of bed. She rushes to get dressed.

1

Cassy snatches her backpack and rushes to the bus. Cassy catches the bus on time!

4

Cassy brushes her teeth.
She splashes water on
her face.

Cassy eats toast, milk,
and peaches. Then she washes
her dishes.

2

3

Milly Carries the Berries

DECODABLE WORDS

Target Skill: /ēz/ spelled -ies

berries

Previously Taught Skills

at	has	no
but	his	pail
Dad	Milly	pick

SKILLS APPLIED IN WORDS IN STORY: *m, s, c, t,* short *a*; consonant *n*; consonant *p*; short *i*; consonant *b*; consonant *r*; consonant *h*; consonant *d*; consonant *l*; short *e*; short *u*; /z/ spelled *s*; consonants *-ck*; /l/ spelled *-ll*; digraph *th*; consonants *-nd*; long *o* (CV); long *e* (CV); long *e* spelled *ea*; long *a* spelled *ai*; /o͞o/ spelled *oo*; base words + *-s*; /ou/ spelled *ow*; long *e* spelled *y*

HIGH–FREQUENCY WORDS

a	carries	her	some
all	eats	now	the
and	full	of	too

HOUGHTON MIFFLIN   BOSTON

Milly Carries the Berries

HIGH-FREQUENCY WORDS TAUGHT TO DATE

Grade 1

a	children	forest	kind	out	start	wear
about	climb	found	know	over	table	were
afraid	cold	four	learn	own	talk	what
after	color	friend	light	paper	tall	where
again	come	full	like	part	teacher	who
all	could	funny	little	people	the	why
also	cow	garden	live	person	their	work
always	dance	girl	long	picture	there	world
and	do	give	look	piece	these	would
animal	does	go	love	play	they	write
any	done	goes	many	pretty	though	you
are	door	gone	me	pull	three	your
arms	down	good	more	put	through	
around	draw	green	morning	read	tiny	
away	eat	grow	most	ready	to	
baby	edge	happy	mother	right	today	
bear	eight	hard	my	room	together	
because	else	have	near	said	too	
been	enough	he	never	saw	try	
before	evening	hear	not	school	turn	
bird	ever	her	now	see	two	
blue	every	here	ocean	seven	under	
body	fall	hold	of	shall	upon	
both	family	horse	off	sharp	very	
brown	far	house	old	she	walk	
build	father	how	on	shoe[s]	wall	
butter	find	hungry	once	shout	want	
buy	first	hurt	one	show	warm	
by	five	I	only	sing	was	
call	flower	idea	open	small	wash	
car	fly	in	or	so	watched	
carry	follow	is	other	some	water	
	for	jump	our	soon	we	

Decoding skills taught to date: m, s, c, t, short a; consonant n; consonant f; consonant p; short i; consonant b; consonant r; consonant h; consonant g; short o; consonant d; consonant w; consonant l; consonant x; short e; consonant y; consonant k; consonant v; short u; /kw/ spelled qu; consonant j; consonant z; /z/ spelled s; consonants -ck; /l/ spelled -ll; /f/ spelled -ff; /s/ spelled -ss; /t/ spelled -ed; /d/ spelled -ed; verb ending -ing; r clusters; l clusters; s clusters; silent k in kn; silent w in wr; silent g in gn; triple clusters; digraph sh; digraph th; digraph wh; digraph ch; digraph -tch; long a (CVCe); /s/ spelled c; /j/ spelled g; consonants -nd; consonants -ng; consonants -nk; long i (CVCe); contractions; long o (CV); long o (CVCe); /o͞o/ spelled u (CVCe); /yo͞o/ spelled u (CVCe); consonants -ft; consonants -lk; consonants -nt; long e (CV); long e (CVCe); long e spelled ee; long e spelled ea; long a spelled ai; long a spelled ay; long o spelled oa; long o spelled ow; /o͞o/ spelled oo; /o͞o/ spelled oo; /o͞o/ spelled ew; /o͞o/ spelled ue; /o͞o/ spelled ou; long i spelled igh; long i spelled ie; /ĕd/ spelled -ed; base words + -ing; base words + -s; /ou/ spelled ou; /ou/ spelled ow; -ing (spelling changes); -ed (spelling changes); long e spelled y; long i spelled y; /ĕz/ spelled -es; /ēz/ spelled -ies; /oi/ spelled oi; /oi/ spelled oy; /ô/ spelled aw; /ô/ spelled au

Now Dad has a full pail
of berries, but Milly has no
berries at all!

Milly Carries
the Berries

Milly and Dad pick berries.

Dad carries his full pail
of berries. Milly carries her
full pail of berries.

Milly eats some berries, too!

I ❤ LOVE READING BOOKS

THEME 10
We Can Do It!

DECODABLE WORDS

Target Skill: /oi/ spelled *oi*

coins	moist
foil	spoil

Previously Taught Skills

big	gave	lot	Mom	us
Boyd	got	man	shop	went
cake	had	may	sweet	will
did	his	meal	ten	

SKILLS APPLIED IN WORDS IN STORY: *m, s, c, t,* short *a*; consonant *n*; consonant *f*; consonant *p*; short *i*; consonant *b*; consonant *h*; consonant *g*; short *o*; consonant *d*; consonant *w*; consonant *l*; short *e*; consonant *y*; consonant *k*; consonant *v*; short *u*; /z/ spelled *s*; /l/ spelled *-ll*; *s* clusters; digraph *sh*; digraph *th*; long *a* (CVCe); long *o* (CV); consonants *-nt*; long *e* (CV); long *e* spelled *ee*; long *e* spelled *ea*; long *a* spelled *ay*; /o͞o/ spelled *ou*; base words + *-s*; long *i* spelled *y*; /oi/ spelled *oy*; *r*-controlled *or*

HIGH–FREQUENCY WORDS

a	go	not	put	your
all	he	of	said	
do	I	off	the	
eat	in	or	to	
for	my	pulled	you	

HOUGHTON MIFFLIN   BOSTON

Ten Coins

Grade 1

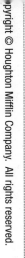

a	car	fly	idea	only	show	want
about	carry	follow	in	open	sing	warm
afraid	children	for	is	or	small	was
after	climb	forest	jump	other	so	wash
again	cold	found	kind	our	some	watched
all	color	four	know	out	soon	water
also	come	friend	laugh[ed]	over	start	we
always	could	full	learn	own	sure	wear
and	cow	funny	light	paper	table	were
animal	dance	garden	like	part	talk	what
any	divide	girl	little	people	tall	where
are	do	give	live	person	teacher	who
arms	does	go	long	picture	the	why
around	done	goes	look	piece	their	work
away	door	gone	love	play	there	world
baby	down	good	many	pretty	these	would
bear	draw	green	me	pull	they	write
because	eat	grow	more	put	though	you
been	edge	happy	morning	read	three	your
before	eight	hard	most	ready	through	
began	else	have	mother	right	tiny	
bird	enough	he	my	room	to	
blue	evening	head[s]	near	said	today	
body	ever	hear	never	saw	together	
both	every	her	not	school	too	
break	fall	here	now	second	try	
brown	family	hold	ocean	see	turn	
build	far	horse	of	seven	two	
butter	father	house	off	shall	under	
buy	find	how	old	sharp	upon	
by	first	hungry	on	she	very	
call	five	hurt	once	shoe[s]	walk	
	flower	I	one	shout	wall	

Decoding skills taught to date: *m, s, c, t,* short *a;* consonant *n;* consonant *f;* consonant *p;* short *i;* consonant *b;* consonant *r;* consonant *h;* consonant *g;* short *o;* consonant *d;* consonant *w;* consonant *l;* consonant *x;* short *e;* consonant *y;* consonant *k;* consonant *v;* short *u;* /kw/ spelled *qu;* consonant *j;* consonant *z;* /z/ spelled *s;* consonants *-ck;* /l/ spelled *-ll;* /f/ spelled *-ff;* /s/ spelled *-ss;* /t/ spelled *-ed;* /d/ spelled *-ed;* verb ending *-ing;* *r* clusters; *l* clusters; *s* clusters; silent *k* in *kn;* silent *w* in *wr;* silent *g* in *gn;* triple clusters; digraph *sh;* digraph *th;* digraph *wh;* digraph *ch;* digraph *-tch;* long *a* (CVC*e*); /s/ spelled *c;* /j/ spelled *g;* consonants *-nd;* consonants *-ng;* consonants *-nk;* long *i* (CVC*e*); contractions; long *o* (CV); long *o* (CVC*e*); /o͞o/ spelled *u* (CVC*e*); /yo͞o/ spelled *u* (CVC*e*); consonants *-ft;* consonants *-lk;* consonants *-nt;* long *e* (CV); long *e* (CVC*e*); long *e* spelled *ee;* long *e* spelled *ea;* long *a* spelled *ai;* long *a* spelled *ay;* long *o* spelled *oa;* long *o* spelled *ow;* /o͞o/ spelled *oo;* /o͝o/ spelled *oo;* /o͞o/ spelled *ew;* /o͞o/ spelled *ue;* /o͞o/ spelled *ou;* long *i* spelled *igh;* long *i* spelled *ie;* /ĕd/ spelled *-ed;* base words + *-ing;* base words + *-s;* /ou/ spelled *ou;* /ou/ spelled *ow;* *-ing* (spelling changes); *-ed* (spelling changes); long *e* spelled *y;* long *i* spelled *y;* /ĕz/ spelled *-es;* /ēz/ spelled *-ies;* /oi/ spelled *oi;* /oi/ spelled *oy;* /ô/ spelled *aw;* /ô/ spelled *au;* r-controlled *or;* r-controlled *ore;* r-controlled *er;* r-controlled *ir;* r-controlled *ur*

Boyd pulled off the foil.
He said, "Mom, I did not spoil
my meal. I got a big, moist
cake for all of us!"

4

Ten Coins

Boyd had ten coins.

1

Mom said, "Boyd, you may go to the Sweet Shop. Do not eat a lot, or you will spoil your meal."

Boyd went to the Sweet Shop. He gave the man his ten coins. He got a big, moist cake. The man put the big, moist cake in foil.

A Toy for Joy

DECODABLE WORDS

Target Skill: /oi/ spelled oy

Joy	Roy
Joy's	toy

Previously Taught Skills

broke	fixed	new
can	got	then
fix	it	with

SKILLS APPLIED IN WORDS IN STORY: *m, s, c, t,* short *a*; consonant *n*; consonant *f*; consonant *p*; short *i*; consonant *b*; consonant *r*; consonant *h*; consonant *g*; short *o*; consonant *w*; consonant *l*; consonant *x*; short *e*; consonant *k*; consonant *j*; /z/ spelled *s*; /t/ spelled *-ed*; /d/ spelled *-ed*; *r* clusters; *l* clusters; digraph *th*; consonants *-nd*; long *o* (CVCe); long *e* (CV); long *a* spelled *ay*; /o͞o/ spelled *ew*; long *i* spelled *y*; *r*-controlled *or*; *r*-controlled *er*

HIGH–FREQUENCY WORDS

a	for	my	the
and	her	played	
both	I	said	

HOUGHTON MIFFLIN BOSTON

A Toy for Joy

HIGH-FREQUENCY WORDS TAUGHT TO DATE

Grade 1

a	car	fly	idea	only	show	want
about	carry	follow	in	open	sing	warm
afraid	children	for	is	or	small	was
after	climb	forest	jump	other	so	wash
again	cold	found	kind	our	some	watched
all	color	four	know	out	soon	water
also	come	friend	laugh[ed]	over	start	we
always	could	full	learn	own	sure	wear
and	cow	funny	light	paper	table	were
animal	dance	garden	like	part	talk	what
any	divide	girl	little	people	tall	where
are	do	give	live	person	teacher	who
arms	does	go	long	picture	the	why
around	done	goes	look	piece	their	work
away	door	gone	love	play	there	world
baby	down	good	many	pretty	these	would
bear	draw	green	me	pull	they	write
because	eat	grow	more	put	though	you
been	edge	happy	morning	read	three	your
before	eight	hard	most	ready	through	
began	else	have	mother	right	tiny	
bird	enough	he	my	room	to	
blue	evening	head[s]	near	said	today	
body	ever	hear	never	saw	together	
both	every	her	not	school	too	
break	fall	here	now	second	try	
brown	family	hold	ocean	see	turn	
build	far	horse	of	seven	two	
butter	father	house	off	shall	under	
buy	find	how	old	sharp	upon	
by	first	hungry	on	she	very	
call	five	hurt	once	shoe[s]	walk	
	flower	I	one	shout	wall	

Decoding skills taught to date: *m, s, c, t,* short *a;* consonant *n;* consonant *f;* consonant *p;* short *i;* consonant *b;* consonant *r;* consonant *h;* consonant *g;* short *o;* consonant *d;* consonant *w;* consonant *l;* consonant *x;* short *e;* consonant *y;* consonant *k;* consonant *v;* short *u;* /kw/ spelled *qu;* consonant *j;* consonant *z;* /z/ spelled *s;* consonants *-ck;* /l/ spelled *-ll;* /f/ spelled *-ff;* /s/ spelled *-ss;* /t/ spelled *-ed;* /d/ spelled *-ed;* verb ending *-ing;* *r* clusters; *l* clusters; *s* clusters; silent *k* in *kn;* silent *w* in *wr;* silent *g* in *gn;* triple clusters; digraph *sh;* digraph *th;* digraph *wh;* digraph *ch;* digraph *-tch;* long *a* (CVC*e*); /s/ spelled *c;* /j/ spelled *g;* consonants *-nd;* consonants *-ng;* consonants *-nk;* long *i* (CVC*e*); contractions; long *o* (CV); long *o* (CVC*e*); /o͞o/ spelled *u* (CVC*e*); /yo͞o/ spelled *u* (CVC*e*); consonants *-ft;* consonants *-lk;* consonants *-nt;* long *e* (CV); long *e* (CVC*e*); long *e* spelled *ee;* long *e* spelled *ea;* long *a* spelled *ai;* long *a* spelled *ay;* long *o* spelled *oa;* long *o* spelled *ow;* /o͝o/ spelled *oo;* /o͞o/ spelled *oo;* /o͞o/ spelled *ew;* /o͞o/ spelled *ue;* /o͞o/ spelled *ou;* long *i* spelled *igh;* long *i* spelled *ie;* /ĕd/ spelled *-ed;* base words + *-ing;* base words + *-s;* /ou/ spelled *ou;* /ou/ spelled *ow;* *-ing* (spelling changes); *-ed* (spelling changes); long *e* spelled *y;* long *i* spelled *y;* /ēz/ spelled *-es;* /ēz/ spelled *-ies;* /oi/ spelled *oi;* /oi/ spelled *oy;* /ô/ spelled *aw;* /ô/ spelled *au;* *r*-controlled *or;* *r*-controlled *ore;* *r*-controlled *er;* *r*-controlled *ir;* *r*-controlled *ur*

Roy fixed it. Then Joy and
Roy both played with the toy.

4

A Toy for Joy

Joy got a new toy. Joy
played with her new toy.

1

Joy's new toy broke!

"I broke my toy!" said Joy.

"I can fix the toy," said Roy.

DECODABLE WORDS

Target Skill: /ô/ spelled *aw*

fawn   lawn

hawk

Previously Taught Skills

Ben   class   Liz

big   has

can   Lee

SKILLS APPLIED IN WORDS IN STORY: *m, s, c, t,* short *a*; consonant *n*; consonant *f*; short *i*; consonant *b*; consonant *r*; consonant *h*; consonant *g*; short *o*; consonant *d*; consonant *l*; short *e*; consonant *k*; consonant *z*; /z/ spelled *s*; /s/ spelled *-ss*; *r* clusters; *l* clusters; digraph *th*; consonants *-nd*; long *e* (CV); long *e* spelled *ee*

HIGH–FREQUENCY WORDS

a   drawn

and   on

draw   the

HOUGHTON MIFFLIN   BOSTON

Draw, Draw, Draw

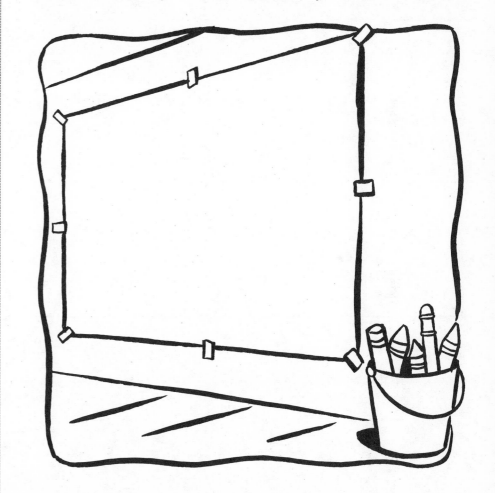

Grade 1

a	car	fly	idea	only	show	want
about	carry	follow	in	open	sing	warm
afraid	children	for	is	or	small	was
after	climb	forest	jump	other	so	wash
again	cold	found	kind	our	some	watched
all	color	four	know	out	soon	water
also	come	friend	laugh[ed]	over	start	we
always	could	full	learn	own	sure	wear
and	cow	funny	light	paper	table	were
animal	dance	garden	like	part	talk	what
any	divide	girl	little	people	tall	where
are	do	give	live	person	teacher	who
arms	does	go	long	picture	the	why
around	done	goes	look	piece	their	work
away	door	gone	love	play	there	world
baby	down	good	many	pretty	these	would
bear	draw	green	me	pull	they	write
because	eat	grow	more	put	though	you
been	edge	happy	morning	read	three	your
before	eight	hard	most	ready	through	
began	else	have	mother	right	tiny	
bird	enough	he	my	room	to	
blue	evening	head[s]	near	said	today	
body	ever	hear	never	saw	together	
both	every	her	not	school	too	
break	fall	here	now	second	try	
brown	family	hold	ocean	see	turn	
build	far	horse	of	seven	two	
butter	father	house	off	shall	under	
buy	find	how	old	sharp	upon	
by	first	hungry	on	she	very	
call	five	hurt	once	shoe[s]	walk	
	flower	I	one	shout	wall	

Decoding skills taught to date: *m, s, c, t;* short *a;* consonant *n;* consonant *f;* consonant *p;* short *i;* consonant *b;* consonant *r;* consonant *h;* consonant *g;* short *o;* consonant *d;* consonant *w;* consonant *l;* consonant *x;* short *e;* consonant *y;* consonant *k;* consonant *v;* short *u;* /kw/ spelled *qu;* consonant *j;* consonant *z;* /z/ spelled *s;* consonants *-ck;* /l/ spelled *-ll;* /f/ spelled *-ff;* /s/ spelled *-ss;* /t/ spelled *-ed;* /d/ spelled *-ed;* verb ending *-ing;* *r* clusters; *l* clusters; *s* clusters; silent *k* in *kn;* silent *w* in *wr;* silent *g* in *gn;* triple clusters; digraph *sh;* digraph *th;* digraph *wh;* digraph *ch;* digraph *-tch;* long *a* (CVC*e*); /s/ spelled *c;* /j/ spelled *g;* consonants *-nd;* consonants *-ng;* consonants *-nk;* long *i* (CVC*e*); contractions; long *o* (CV); long *o* (CVC*e*); /o͞o/ spelled *u* (CVC*e*); /yo͞o/ spelled *u* (CVC*e*); consonants *-ft;* consonants *-lk;* consonants *-nt;* long *e* (CV); long *e* (CVC*e*); long *e* spelled *ee;* long *e* spelled *ea;* long *a* spelled *ai;* long *a* spelled *ay;* long *o* spelled *oa;* long *o* spelled *ow;* /o͞o/ spelled *oo;* /o͝o/ spelled *oo;* /o͞o/ spelled *ew;* /o͞o/ spelled *ue;* /o͞o/ spelled *ou;* long *i* spelled *igh;* long *i* spelled *ie;* /ĕd/ spelled *-ed;* base words + *-ing;* base words + *-s;* /ou/ spelled *ou;* /ou/ spelled *ow;* *-ing* (spelling changes); *-ed* (spelling changes); long *e* spelled *y;* long *i* spelled *y;* /ēz/ spelled *-es;* /ēz/ spelled *-ies;* /oi/ spelled *oi;* /oi/ spelled *oy;* /ô/ spelled *aw;* /ô/ spelled *au;* *r*-controlled *or;* *r*-controlled *ore;* *r*-controlled *er;* *r*-controlled *ir;* *r*-controlled *ur*

Draw, Draw, Draw

Lee can draw a big lawn.

1

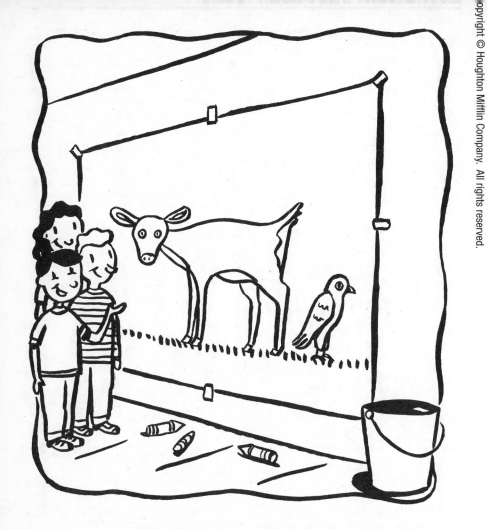

The class has drawn
a hawk and a fawn on a
big lawn!

4

Ben can draw a hawk
on the big lawn.

Liz can draw a fawn
on the big lawn.

Paul

DECODABLE WORDS

Target Skill: /ô/ spelled *au*

cause	Paul
jaunt	pause
launch	

Previously Taught Skills

boat	from	rope
can	his	still
dock	it	will

SKILLS APPLIED IN WORDS IN STORY: *m, s, c, t,* short *a*; consonant *n*; consonant *f*; consonant *p*; short *i*; consonant *b*; consonant *r*; consonant *h*; consonant *g*; short *o*; consonant *d*; consonant *w*; consonant *l*; consonant *k*; consonant *j*; /z/ spelled *s*; consonants *-ck*; /l/ spelled *-ll*; *r* clusters; *s* clusters; digraph *th*; digraph *ch*; long *o* (CV); long *o* (CVCe); consonants *-nt*; long *e* (CV); long *o* spelled *oa*; /o͞o/ spelled *oo*; base words + *s*; *r*-controlled *or*

HIGH–FREQUENCY WORDS

a	in	not	the	wants
for	is	off	there	
go	looks	on	to	

HOUGHTON MIFFLIN   BOSTON

Paul

HIGH-FREQUENCY WORDS TAUGHT TO DATE

Grade 1

a	car	fly	idea	only	show	want
about	carry	follow	in	open	sing	warm
afraid	children	for	is	or	small	was
after	climb	forest	jump	other	so	wash
again	cold	found	kind	our	some	watched
all	color	four	know	out	soon	water
also	come	friend	laugh[ed]	over	start	we
always	could	full	learn	own	sure	wear
and	cow	funny	light	paper	table	were
animal	dance	garden	like	part	talk	what
any	divide	girl	little	people	tall	where
are	do	give	live	person	teacher	who
arms	does	go	long	picture	the	why
around	done	goes	look	piece	their	work
away	door	gone	love	play	there	world
baby	down	good	many	pretty	these	would
bear	draw	green	me	pull	they	write
because	eat	grow	more	put	though	you
been	edge	happy	morning	read	three	your
before	eight	hard	most	ready	through	
began	else	have	mother	right	tiny	
bird	enough	he	my	room	to	
blue	evening	head[s]	near	said	today	
body	ever	hear	never	saw	together	
both	every	her	not	school	too	
break	fall	here	now	second	try	
brown	family	hold	ocean	see	turn	
build	far	horse	of	seven	two	
butter	father	house	off	shall	under	
buy	find	how	old	sharp	upon	
by	first	hungry	on	she	very	
call	five	hurt	once	shoe[s]	walk	
	flower	I	one	shout	wall	

Decoding skills taught to date: m, s, c, t, short a; consonant n; consonant f; consonant p; short i; consonant b; consonant r; consonant h; consonant g; short o; consonant d; consonant w; consonant l; consonant x; short e; consonant y; consonant k; consonant v; short u; /kw/ spelled qu; consonant j; consonant z; /z/ spelled s; consonants -ck; /l/ spelled -ll; /f/ spelled -ff; /s/ spelled -ss; /t/ spelled -ed; /d/ spelled -ed; verb ending -ing; r clusters; l clusters; s clusters; silent k in kn; silent w in wr; silent g in gn; triple clusters; digraph sh; digraph th; digraph wh; digraph ch; digraph -tch; long a (CVCe); /s/ spelled c; /j/ spelled g; consonants -nd; consonants -ng; consonants -nk; long i (CVCe); contractions; long o (CV); long o (CVCe); /o͞o/ spelled u (CVCe); /yo͞o/ spelled u (CVCe); consonants -ft; consonants -lk; consonants -nt; long e (CV); long e (CVCe); long e spelled ee; long e spelled ea; long a spelled ai; long a spelled ay; long o spelled oa; long o spelled ow; /o͝o/ spelled oo; /o͞o/ spelled oo; /o͞o/ spelled ew; /o͞o/ spelled ue; /o͞o/ spelled ou; long i spelled igh; long i spelled ie; /ĕd/ spelled -ed; base words + -ing; base words + -s; /ou/ spelled ou; /ou/ spelled ow; -ing (spelling changes); -ed (spelling changes); long e spelled y; long i spelled y; /ĕz/ spelled -es; /ēz/ spelled -ies; /oi/ spelled oi; /oi/ spelled oy; /ô/ spelled aw; /ô/ spelled au; r-controlled or; r-controlled ore; r-controlled er; r-controlled ir; r-controlled ur

Paul

Paul wants to go for
a jaunt in his boat.

1

Paul is off on his jaunt!

4

Can Paul launch his boat
from the dock?

There is a pause. The boat
will not go.

2

The boat still will not go.
Paul looks for the cause. It is
the rope!

3

North Farm

DECODABLE WORDS

Target Skill: *r-controlled* or

born   shorn
north worn

Previously Taught Skills

at	gets	sheep	when
be	hats	spring	will
big	it	tops	wool
farm	make	used	yarn

SKILLS APPLIED IN WORDS IN STORY: *m, s, c, t,* short *a*; consonant *n*; consonant *f*; consonant *p*; short *i*; consonant *b*; consonant *r*; consonant *h*; consonant *g*; short *o*; consonant *w*; consonant *l*; short *e*; consonant *y*; consonant *k*; /l/ spelled *-ll*; /d/ spelled *-ed*; triple clusters; digraph *sh*; digraph *th*; digraph *wh*; long *a* (CVCe); consonants *-nd*; consonants *-ng*; /yo͞o/ spelled *u* (CVCe); long *e* (CV); long *e* spelled *ee*; /o͞o/ spelled *oo*; base words + *-s*; *-ed* (spelling changes); *r*-controlled *ar*

HIGH–FREQUENCY WORDS

and	becomes	the	to
are	cold	there	
baby	in	they	

HOUGHTON MIFFLIN   BOSTON

North Farm

HIGH-FREQUENCY WORDS TAUGHT TO DATE

Grade 1

a	butter	father	house	of	seven	two
about	buy	find	how	off	shall	under
above	by	first	hungry	old	sharp	upon
afraid	call	five	hurt	on	she	very
after	car	flower	I	once	shoe[s]	walk
again	carry	fly	idea	one	shout	wall
against	caught	follow	in	only	show	want
all	children	for	is	open	sing	warm
also	climb	forest	jump	or	small	was
already	cold	found	kind	other	so	wash
always	color	four	know	our	some	watched
and	come	friend	laugh[ed]	out	soon	water
animal	could	full	learn	over	start	we
any	cow	funny	light	own	sure	wear
are	dance	garden	like	paper	table	were
arms	divide	girl	little	part	talk	what
around	do	give	live	people	tall	where
away	does	go	long	person	teacher	who
baby	done	goes	look	picture	the	why
bear	door	gone	love	piece	their	work
because	down	good	many	play	there	world
been	draw	green	me	pretty	these	would
before	eat	grow	minute[s]	pull	they	write
began	edge	happy	more	put	though	you
begin[s]	eight	hard	morning	read	three	your
bird	else	have	most	ready	through	
blue	enough	he	mother	right	tiny	
body	evening	head[s]	my	room	to	
both	ever	hear	near	said	today	
break	every	her	never	saw	together	
brown	fall	here	not	school	too	
build	family	hold	now	second	try	
	far	horse	ocean	see	turn	

Decoding skills taught to date: m, s, c, t, short a; consonant n; consonant f; consonant p; short i; consonant b; consonant r; consonant h; consonant g; short o; consonant d; consonant w; consonant l; consonant x; short e; consonant y; consonant k; consonant v; short u; /kw/ spelled qu; consonant j; consonant z; /z/ spelled s; consonants -ck; /l/ spelled -ll; /f/ spelled -ff; /s/ spelled -ss; /t/ spelled -ed; /d/ spelled -ed; verb ending -ing; r clusters; l clusters; s clusters; silent k in kn; silent w in wr; silent g in gn; triple clusters; digraph sh; digraph th; digraph wh; digraph ch; digraph -tch; long a (CVCe); /s/ spelled c; /j/ spelled g; consonants -nd; consonants -ng; consonants -nk; long i (CVCe); contractions; long o (CV); long o (CVCe); /ōō/ spelled u (CVCe); /yōō/ spelled u (CVCe); consonants -ft; consonants -lk; consonants -nt; long e (CV); long e (CVCe); long e spelled ee; long e spelled ea; long a spelled ai; long a spelled ay; long o spelled oa; long o spelled ow; /ōō/ spelled oo; /ōō/ spelled oo; /ōō/ spelled ew; /ōō/ spelled ue; /ōō/ spelled ou; long i spelled igh; long i spelled ie; /ēd/ spelled -ed; base words + -ing; base words + -s; /ou/ spelled ou; /ou/ spelled ow; -ing (spelling changes); -ed (spelling changes); long e spelled y; long i spelled y; /ēz/ spelled -es; /ēz/ spelled -ies; /oi/ spelled oi; /oi/ spelled oy; /ô/ spelled aw; /ô/ spelled au; r-controlled or; r-controlled ore; r-controlled er; r-controlled ir; r-controlled ur; r-controlled ar

The yarn will be used to make wool tops and hats. They are worn when it gets cold.

4

North Farm

There are sheep at North Farm.

1

In the spring, baby sheep are born.

The big sheep are shorn.
The wool becomes yarn.

Al's Shorts

DECODABLE WORDS

Target Skill: *r-controlled* *ore*

score	tore
shore	wore
store	

Previously Taught Skills

Al	Dad	need	went
Al's	got	new	with
at	his	shorts	

SKILLS APPLIED IN WORDS IN STORY: *m, s, c, t,* short *a;* consonant *n;* consonant *f;* consonant *p;* short *i;* consonant *h;* consonant *g;* short *o;* consonant *d;* consonant *w;* consonant *l;* short *e;* /z/ spelled *s;* /d/ spelled *-ed; l* clusters; *s* clusters; digraph *sh;* digraph *th;* consonants *-nd;* consonants *-nt;* long *e* (CV); long *e* spelled *ee;* long *a* spelled *ay;* /o͞o/ spelled *ew; r*-controlled *or*

HIGH–FREQUENCY WORDS

and	more	said	to
for	old	the	
I	played	they	

HOUGHTON MIFFLIN   BOSTON

HIGH-FREQUENCY WORDS TAUGHT TO DATE

Grade 1

	butter	father	house	of	seven	two
a	buy	find	how	off	shall	under
about	by	first	hungry	old	sharp	upon
above	call	five	hurt	on	she	very
afraid	car	flower	I	once	shoe[s]	walk
after	carry	fly	idea	one	shout	wall
again	caught	follow	in	only	show	want
against	children	for	is	open	sing	warm
all	climb	forest	jump	or	small	was
also	cold	found	kind	other	so	wash
already	color	four	know	our	some	watched
always	come	friend	laugh[ed]	out	soon	water
and	could	full	learn	over	start	we
animal	cow	funny	light	own	sure	wear
any	dance	garden	like	paper	table	were
are	divide	girl	little	part	talk	what
arms	do	give	live	people	tall	where
around	does	go	long	person	teacher	who
away	done	goes	look	picture	the	why
baby	door	gone	love	piece	their	work
bear	down	good	many	play	there	world
because	draw	green	me	pretty	these	would
been	eat	grow	minute[s]	pull	they	write
before	edge	happy	more	put	though	you
began	eight	hard	morning	read	three	your
begin[s]	else	have	most	ready	through	
bird	enough	he	mother	right	tiny	
blue	evening	head[s]	my	room	to	
body	ever	hear	near	said	today	
both	every	her	never	saw	together	
break	fall	here	not	school	too	
brown	family	hold	now	second	try	
build	far	horse	ocean	see	turn	

Decoding skills taught to date: m, s, c, t, short *a*; consonant *n*; consonant *f*; consonant *p*; short *i*; consonant *b*; consonant *r*; consonant *h*; consonant *g*; short *o*; consonant *d*; consonant *w*; consonant *l*; consonant *x*; short *e*; consonant *y*; consonant *k*; consonant *v*; short *u*; /kw/ spelled *qu*; consonant *j*; consonant *z*; /z/ spelled *s*; consonants -*ck*; /l/ spelled -*ll*; /f/ spelled -*ff*; /s/ spelled -*ss*; /t/ spelled -*ed*; /d/ spelled -*ed*; verb ending -*ing*; *r* clusters; *l* clusters; *s* clusters; silent *k* in *kn*; silent *w* in *wr*; silent *g* in *gn*; triple clusters; digraph *sh*; digraph *th*; digraph *wh*; digraph *ch*; digraph -*tch*; long *a* (CVC*e*); /s/ spelled *c*; /j/ spelled *g*; consonants -*nd*; consonants -*ng*; consonants -*nk*; long *i* (CVC*e*); contractions; long *o* (CV); long *o* (CVC*e*); /ōō/ spelled *u* (CVC*e*); /yōō/ spelled *u* (CVC*e*); consonants -*ft*; consonants -*lk*; consonants -*nt*; long *e* (CV); long *e* (CVC*e*); long *e* spelled *ee*; long *e* spelled *ea*; long *a* spelled *ai*; long *a* spelled *ay*; long *o* spelled *oa*; long *o* spelled *ow*; /ōō/ spelled *oo*; /ōō/ spelled *oo*; /ōō/ spelled *ew*; /ōō/ spelled *ue*; /ōō/ spelled *ou*; long *i* spelled *igh*; long *i* spelled *ie*; /ĕd/ spelled -*ed*; base words + -*ing*; base words + -*s*; /ou/ spelled *ou*; /ou/ spelled *ow*; -*ing* (spelling changes); -*ed* (spelling changes); long *e* spelled *y*; long *i* spelled *y*; /ĕz/ spelled -*es*; /ēz/ spelled -*ies*; /oi/ spelled *oi*; /oi/ spelled *oy*; /ô/ spelled *aw*; /ô/ spelled *au*; *r*-controlled *or*; *r*-controlled *ore*; *r*-controlled *er*; *r*-controlled *ir*; *r*-controlled *ur*; *r*-controlled *ar*

Al and Dad went to the Shorts Store. They got more shorts for Al.

Al's Shorts

Al wore his old shorts to the shore.

Al played with Dad at
the shore. **Score!**

Al tore his old shorts.
"I need new shorts," said Al.

Gert and Her Herd

r-controlled er

REVIEW
BOOK (90)

DECODABLE WORDS

Target Skill: *r-controlled er*

Gert	stern
herd	

Previously Taught Skills

be	brings	has	plain	takes
big	from	home	same	
bring	group	must	steer	

SKILLS APPLIED IN WORDS IN STORY: *m, s, c, t,* short *a*; consonant *n*; consonant *f*; consonant *p*; short *i*; consonant *b*; consonant *r*; consonant *h*; consonant *g*; short *o*; consonant *d*; consonant *l*; consonant *k*; short *u*; /z/ spelled *s*; *r* clusters; *l* clusters; *s* clusters; digraph *th*; long *a* (CVCe); consonants *-nd*; consonants *-ng*; long *o* (CVCe); long *e* (CV); long *e* spelled *ee*; long *a* spelled *ai*; /o͞o/ spelled *ou*; base words + *-s*; *r*-controlled *or*

HIGH–FREQUENCY WORDS

a	her	is	on
and	hold	kind	the
animal	horse	of	

![Houghton Mifflin logo] **HOUGHTON MIFFLIN**   BOSTON

Gert and Her Herd

HIGH-FREQUENCY WORDS TAUGHT TO DATE

Grade 1

a	butter	father	house	of	seven	two
about	buy	find	how	off	shall	under
above	by	first	hungry	old	sharp	upon
afraid	call	five	hurt	on	she	very
after	car	flower	I	once	shoe[s]	walk
again	carry	fly	idea	one	shout	wall
against	caught	follow	in	only	show	want
all	children	for	is	open	sing	warm
also	climb	forest	jump	or	small	was
already	cold	found	kind	other	so	wash
always	color	four	know	our	some	watched
and	come	friend	laugh[ed]	out	soon	water
animal	could	full	learn	over	start	we
any	cow	funny	light	own	sure	wear
are	dance	garden	like	paper	table	were
arms	divide	girl	little	part	talk	what
around	do	give	live	people	tall	where
away	does	go	long	person	teacher	who
baby	done	goes	look	picture	the	why
bear	door	gone	love	piece	their	work
because	down	good	many	play	there	world
been	draw	green	me	pretty	these	would
before	eat	grow	minute[s]	pull	they	write
began	edge	happy	more	put	though	you
begin[s]	eight	hard	morning	read	three	your
bird	else	have	most	ready	through	
blue	enough	he	mother	right	tiny	
body	evening	head[s]	my	room	to	
both	ever	hear	near	said	today	
break	every	her	never	saw	together	
brown	fall	here	not	school	too	
build	family	hold	now	second	try	
	far	horse	ocean	see	turn	

Decoding skills taught to date: *m, s, c, t,* short *a*; consonant *n*; consonant *f*; consonant *p*; short *i*; consonant *b*; consonant *r*; consonant *h*; consonant *g*; short *o*; consonant *d*; consonant *w*; consonant *l*; consonant *x*; short *e*; consonant *y*; consonant *k*; consonant *v*; short *u*; /kw/ spelled *qu*; consonant *j*; consonant *z*; /z/ spelled *s*; consonants *-ck*; /l/ spelled *-ll*; /f/ spelled *-ff*; /s/ spelled *-ss*; /t/ spelled *-ed*; /d/ spelled *-ed*; verb ending *-ing*; *r* clusters; *l* clusters; *s* clusters; silent *k* in *kn*; silent *w* in *wr*; silent *g* in *gn*; triple clusters; digraph *sh*; digraph *th*; digraph *wh*; digraph *ch*; digraph *-tch*; long *a* (CVC*e*); /s/ spelled *c*; /j/ spelled *g*; consonants *-nd*; consonants *-nk*; long *i* (CVC*e*); contractions; long *o* (CV); long *o* (CVC*e*); /o͞o/ spelled *u* (CVC*e*); /yo͞o/ spelled *u* (CVC*e*); consonants *-ft*; consonants *-lk*; consonants *-nt*; long *e* (CV); long *e* (CVC*e*); long *e* spelled *ee*; long *e* spelled *ea*; long *a* spelled *ai*; long *a* spelled *ay*; long *o* spelled *oa*; long *o* spelled *ow*; /o͝o/ spelled *oo*; /o͞o/ spelled *oo*; /o͞o/ spelled *ew*; /o͞o/ spelled *ue*; /o͞o/ spelled *ou*; long *i* spelled *igh*; long *i* spelled *ie*; /ĕd/ spelled *-ed*; base words + *-ing*; base words + *-s*; /ou/ spelled *ou*; /ou/ spelled *ow*; *-ing* (spelling changes); *-ed* (spelling changes); long *e* spelled *y*; long *i* spelled *y*; /ĕz/ spelled *-es*; /ēz/ spelled *-ies*; /oi/ spelled *oi*; /oi/ spelled *oy*; /ô/ spelled *aw*; /ô/ spelled *au*; *r*-controlled *or*; *r*-controlled *ore*; *r*-controlled *er*; *r*-controlled *ir*; *r*-controlled *ur*; *r*-controlled *ar*

Gert and Her Herd

Gert has a herd of steer.
A herd is a big group of the
same kind of animal.

1

Stern Gert brings the
herd home!

4

Gert must bring the herd
home from the plain. Gert
takes her horse.

The herd is big. Gert must
be stern and hold on!

Kirk Chirps

DECODABLE WORDS

Target Skill: *r-controlled ir*

chirp	fir
chirping	Kirk
chirps	

Previously Taught Skills

day	wake
tree	when
up	with

SKILLS APPLIED IN WORDS IN STORY: *m, s, c, t,* short *a*; consonant *n*; consonant *f*; consonant *p*; short *i*; consonant *b*; consonant *r*; consonant *d*; consonant *w*; short *e*; consonant *k*; short *u*; /z/ spelled *s*; verb ending *-ing*; *r* clusters; *s* clusters; digraph *th*; digraph *wh*; digraph *ch*; long *a* (CVCe); long *e* (CV); long *e* spelled *ee*; long *a* spelled *ay*; /o͞o/ spelled *oo*; base words + *-ing*; base words + *-s*

HIGH–FREQUENCY WORDS

a	bird	first	lives	the
all	birds	in	other	to
are	every	is	soon	

Kirk Chirps

HOUGHTON MIFFLIN   BOSTON

HIGH-FREQUENCY WORDS TAUGHT TO DATE

Grade 1

a	butter	father	house	of	seven	two
about	buy	find	how	off	shall	under
above	by	first	hungry	old	sharp	upon
afraid	call	five	hurt	on	she	very
after	car	flower	I	once	shoe[s]	walk
again	carry	fly	idea	one	shout	wall
against	caught	follow	in	only	show	want
all	children	for	is	open	sing	warm
also	climb	forest	jump	or	small	was
already	cold	found	kind	other	so	wash
always	color	four	know	our	some	watched
and	come	friend	laugh[ed]	out	soon	water
animal	could	full	learn	over	start	we
any	cow	funny	light	own	sure	wear
are	dance	garden	like	paper	table	were
arms	divide	girl	little	part	talk	what
around	do	give	live	people	tall	where
away	does	go	long	person	teacher	who
baby	done	goes	look	picture	the	why
bear	door	gone	love	piece	their	work
because	down	good	many	play	there	world
been	draw	green	me	pretty	these	would
before	eat	grow	minute[s]	pull	they	write
began	edge	happy	more	put	though	you
begin[s]	eight	hard	morning	read	three	your
bird	else	have	most	ready	through	
blue	enough	he	mother	right	tiny	
body	evening	head[s]	my	room	to	
both	ever	hear	near	said	today	
break	every	her	never	saw	together	
brown	fall	here	not	school	too	
build	family	hold	now	second	try	
	far	horse	ocean	see	turn	

Decoding skills taught to date: *m, s, c, t,* short *a;* consonant *n;* consonant *f;* consonant *p;* short *i;* consonant *b;* consonant *r;* consonant *h;* consonant *g;* short *o;* consonant *d;* consonant *w;* consonant *l;* consonant *x;* short *e;* consonant *y;* consonant *k;* consonant *v;* short *u;* /kw/ spelled *qu;* consonant *j;* consonant *z;* /z/ spelled *s;* consonants *-ck;* /l/ spelled *-ll;* /f/ spelled *-ff;* /s/ spelled *-ss;* /t/ spelled *-ed;* /d/ spelled *-ed;* verb ending *-ing;* *r* clusters; *l* clusters; *s* clusters; silent *k* in *kn;* silent *w* in *wr;* silent *g* in *gn;* triple clusters; digraph *sh;* digraph *th;* digraph *wh;* digraph *ch;* digraph *-tch;* long *a* (CVC*e*); /s/ spelled *c;* /j/ spelled *g;* consonants *-nd;* consonants *-ng;* consonants *-nk;* long *i* (CVC*e*); contractions; long *o* (CV); long *o* (CVC*e*); /o͞o/ spelled *u* (CVC*e*); /yo͞o/ spelled *u* (CVC*e*); consonants *-ft;* consonants *-lk;* consonants *-nt;* long *e* (CV); long *e* (CVC*e*); long *e* spelled *ee;* long *e* spelled *ea;* long *a* spelled *ai;* long *a* spelled *ay;* long *o* spelled *oa;* long *o* spelled *ow;* /o͞o/ spelled *oo;* /o͞o/ spelled *oo;* /o͞o/ spelled *ew;* /o͞o/ spelled *ue;* /o͞o/ spelled *ou;* long *i* spelled *igh;* long *i* spelled *ie;* /ĕd/ spelled *-ed;* base words + *-ing;* base words + *-s;* /ou/ spelled *ou;* /ou/ spelled *ow;* *-ing* (spelling changes); *-ed* (spelling changes); long *e* spelled *y;* long *i* spelled *y;* /ĕz/ spelled *-es;* /ēz/ spelled *-ies;* /oi/ spelled *oi;* /oi/ spelled *oy;* /ô/ spelled *aw;* /ô/ spelled *au;* *r*-controlled *or;* *r*-controlled *ore;* *r*-controlled *er;* *r*-controlled *ir;* *r*-controlled *ur;* *r*-controlled *ar*

Soon all the birds in the
fir tree are chirping with Kirk.
"Chirp, chirp, chirp!"

Kirk Chirps

Kirk Bird lives in a fir tree.

Every day Kirk is the
first bird to chirp.
"Chirp, chirp, chirp!"

When Kirk chirps, the
other birds in the fir tree
wake up.

The Fur Burr

DECODABLE WORDS

Target Skill: *r-controlled* **ur**

burr	fur	lurking
burrs	Kurt	purr
curled	Kurt's	Zurk

Previously Taught Skills

but	day	his	let	up
came	got	it	might	will
Cat	had	lap	plant	woods

SKILLS APPLIED IN WORDS IN STORY: *m, s, c, t,* short *a*; consonant *n*; consonant *f*; consonant *p*; short *i*; consonant *b*; consonant *r*; consonant *h*; consonant *g*; short *o*; consonant *d*; consonant *w*; consonant *l*; short *e*; consonant *k*; short *u*; consonant *z*; /z/ spelled *s*; /l/ spelled *-ll*; /d/ spelled *-ed*; verb ending *-ing*; *l* clusters; digraph *th*; long *a* (CVCe); consonants *-nt*; long *e* (CV); long *a* spelled *ay*; /o͞o/ spelled *oo*; long *i* spelled *igh*; base words + *-ing*; base words + *-s*; /ou/ spelled *ou*

HIGH–FREQUENCY WORDS

a	in	one	said	your
hurt	of	out	the	
I	on	pull	was	

HOUGHTON MIFFLIN   BOSTON

The Fur Burr

HIGH-FREQUENCY WORDS TAUGHT TO DATE

Grade 1

a	butter	father	house	of	seven	two
about	buy	find	how	off	shall	under
above	by	first	hungry	old	sharp	upon
afraid	call	five	hurt	on	she	very
after	car	flower	I	once	shoe[s]	walk
again	carry	fly	idea	one	shout	wall
against	caught	follow	in	only	show	want
all	children	for	is	open	sing	warm
also	climb	forest	jump	or	small	was
already	cold	found	kind	other	so	wash
always	color	four	know	our	some	watched
and	come	friend	laugh[ed]	out	soon	water
animal	could	full	learn	over	start	we
any	cow	funny	light	own	sure	wear
are	dance	garden	like	paper	table	were
arms	divide	girl	little	part	talk	what
around	do	give	live	people	tall	where
away	does	go	long	person	teacher	who
baby	done	goes	look	picture	the	why
bear	door	gone	love	piece	their	work
because	down	good	many	play	there	world
been	draw	green	me	pretty	these	would
before	eat	grow	minute[s]	pull	they	write
began	edge	happy	more	put	though	you
begin[s]	eight	hard	morning	read	three	your
bird	else	have	most	ready	through	
blue	enough	he	mother	right	tiny	
body	evening	head[s]	my	room	to	
both	ever	hear	near	said	today	
break	every	her	never	saw	together	
brown	fall	here	not	school	too	
build	family	hold	now	second	try	
	far	horse	ocean	see	turn	

Decoding skills taught to date: *m, s, c, t,* short *a*; consonant *n*; consonant *f*; consonant *p*; short *i*; consonant *b*; consonant *r*; consonant *h*; consonant *g*; short *o*; consonant *d*; consonant *w*; consonant *l*; consonant *x*; short *e*; consonant *y*; consonant *k*; consonant *v*; short *u*; /kw/ spelled *qu*; consonant *j*; consonant *z*; /z/ spelled *s*; consonants -*ck*; /l/ spelled -*ll*; /f/ spelled -*ff*; /s/ spelled -*ss*; /t/ spelled -*ed*; /d/ spelled -*ed*; verb ending -*ing*; *r* clusters; *l* clusters; *s* clusters; silent *k* in *kn*; silent *w* in *wr*; silent *g* in *gn*; triple clusters; digraph *sh*; digraph *th*; digraph *wh*; digraph *ch*; digraph -*tch*; long *a* (CVC*e*); /s/ spelled *c*; /j/ spelled *g*; consonants -*nd*; consonants -*ng*; consonants -*nk*; long *i* (CVC*e*); contractions; long *o* (CV); long *o* (CVC*e*); /o͞o/ spelled *u* (CVC*e*); /yo͞o/ spelled *u* (CVC*e*); consonants -*ft*; consonants -*lk*; consonants -*nt*; long *e* (CV); long *e* (CVC*e*); long *e* spelled *ee*; long *e* spelled *ea*; long *a* spelled *ai*; long *a* spelled *ay*; long *o* spelled *oa*; long *o* spelled *ow*; /o͞o/ spelled *oo*; /o͞o/ spelled *oo*; /o͞o/ spelled *ew*; /o͞o/ spelled *ue*; /o͞o/ spelled *ou*; long *i* spelled *igh*; long *i* spelled *ie*; /ĕd/ spelled -*ed*; base words + -*ing*; base words + -*s*; /ou/ spelled *ou*; /ou/ spelled *ow*; -*ing* (spelling changes); -*ed* (spelling changes); long *e* spelled *y*; long *i* spelled *y*; /ĕz/ spelled -*es*; /ēz/ spelled -*ies*; /oi/ spelled *oi*; /oi/ spelled *oy*; /ô/ spelled *aw*; /ô/ spelled *au*; *r*-controlled *or*; *r*-controlled *ore*; *r*-controlled *er*; *r*-controlled *ir*; *r*-controlled *ur*; *r*-controlled *ar*

The Fur Burr

The burr came out. Zurk
Cat curled up on Kurt's lap.
Purr, purr, purr.

One day, Zurk Cat was
lurking in the woods.

A plant in the woods had burrs. Zurk Cat got a burr in his fur.

Kurt said, "I will pull the burr out of your fur, but it might hurt."
Zurk Cat let Kurt pull the burr out of his fur.

Sharks

DECODABLE WORDS

Target Skill: *r-controlled ar*

dark	larger	sharks
harm	largest	
large	shark	

Previously Taught Skills

be	deep	fish	than
bus	dogfish	it	this
can	fast	swim	use
catch	feet	teeth	whale

SKILLS APPLIED IN WORDS IN STORY: *m, s, c, t,* short *a*; consonant *n*; consonant *f*; consonant *p*; short *i*; consonant *b*; consonant *r*; consonant *h*; consonant *g*; short *o*; consonant *d*; consonant *w*; consonant *l*; consonant *k*; short *u*; /z/ spelled *s*; *r* clusters; *l* clusters; *s* clusters; digraph *sh*; digraph *th*; digraph *wh*; digraph *-tch*; long *a* (CVCe); /j/ spelled *g*; consonants *-ng*; /yo͞o/ spelled *u* (CVCe); long *e* (CV); long *e* spelled *ee*; long *o* spelled *ow*; /o͞o/ spelled *ue*; base words + *-s*; *r*-controlled *or*; *-er* (spelling changes); *-est* (spelling changes)

HIGH–FREQUENCY WORDS

a	far	kind	ocean	sharp
all	grow	live	of	small
are	hard	long	or	the
blue	in	most	people	their
do	is	not	school	to

HOUGHTON MIFFLIN   BOSTON

HIGH-FREQUENCY WORDS TAUGHT TO DATE

Grade 1

a	build	family	hold	now	school	together
able	butter	far	horse	ocean	second	too
about	buy	father	house	of	see	try
above	by	find	how	off	seven	turn
afraid	call	first	hungry	old	shall	two
after	car	five	hurt	on	sharp	under
again	carry	flower	I	once	she	upon
against	caught	fly	idea	one	shoe[s]	very
all	children	follow	in	only	shout	walk
also	climb	for	is	open	show	wall
already	cold	forest	jump	or	sing	want
always	color	found	kind	other	small	warm
and	come	four	know	our	so	was
animal	could	friend	laugh[ed]	out	some	wash
any	cow	full	learn	over	soon	watched
are	dance	funny	light	own	start	water
arms	divide	garden	like	paper	sure	we
around	do	girl	little	part	table	wear
away	does	give	live	people	talk	were
baby	done	go	long	person	tall	what
bear	door	goes	look	picture	teacher	where
because	down	gone	love	piece	the	who
been	draw	good	many	play	their	why
before	eat	green	me	present	there	work
began	edge	grow	minute[s]	pretty	these	world
begin[s]	eight	happy	more	pull	they	would
bird	else	hard	morning	put	though	write
blue	enough	have	most	read	thoughts	you
body	evening	he	mother	ready	three	your
both	ever	head[s]	my	right	through	
break	every	hear	near	room	tiny	
brown	eye[s]	her	never	said	to	
	fall	here	not	saw	today	

Decoding skills taught to date: *m, s, c, t,* short *a;* consonant *n;* consonant *f;* consonant *p;* short *i;* consonant *b;* consonant *r;* consonant *h;* consonant *g;* short *o;* consonant *d;* consonant *w;* consonant *l;* consonant *x;* short *e;* consonant *y;* consonant *k;* consonant *v;* short *u;* /kw/ spelled *qu;* consonant *j;* consonant *z;* /z/ spelled *s;* consonants *-ck;* /l/ spelled *-ll;* /f/ spelled *-ff;* /s/ spelled *-ss;* /t/ spelled *-ed;* /d/ spelled *-ed;* verb ending *-ing;* *r* clusters; *l* clusters; *s* clusters; silent *k* in *kn;* silent *w* in *wr;* silent *g* in *gn;* triple clusters; digraph *sh;* digraph *th;* digraph *wh;* digraph *ch;* digraph *-tch;* long *a* (CVC*e*); /s/ spelled *c;* /j/ spelled *g;* consonants *-nd;* consonants *-ng;* consonants *-nk;* long *i* (CVC*e*); contractions; long *o* (CV); long *o* (CVC*e*); /o͞o/ spelled *u* (CVC*e*); /yo͞o/ spelled *u* (CVC*e*); consonants *-ft;* consonants *-lk;* consonants *-nt;* long *e* (CV); long *e* (CVC*e*); long *e* spelled *ee;* long *e* spelled *ea;* long *a* spelled *ai;* long *a* spelled *ay;* long *o* spelled *oa;* long *o* spelled *ow;* /o͞o/ spelled *oo;* /o͝o/ spelled *oo;* /o͞o/ spelled *ew;* /o͞o/ spelled *ue;* /o͞o/ spelled *ou;* long *i* spelled *igh;* long *i* spelled *ie;* /ĕd/ spelled *-ed;* base words + *-ing;* base words + *-s;* /ou/ spelled *ou;* /ou/ spelled *ow;* *-ing* (spelling changes); *-ed* (spelling changes); long *e* spelled *y;* long *i* spelled *y;* /ĕz/ spelled *-es;* /ēz/ spelled *-ies;* /oi/ spelled *oi;* /oi/ spelled *oy;* /ô/ spelled *aw;* /ô/ spelled *au;* *r*-controlled *or;* *r*-controlled *ore;* *r*-controlled *er;* *r*-controlled *ir;* *r*-controlled *ur;* *r*-controlled *ar;* *-er* (spelling changes); *-est* (spelling changes)

Sharks

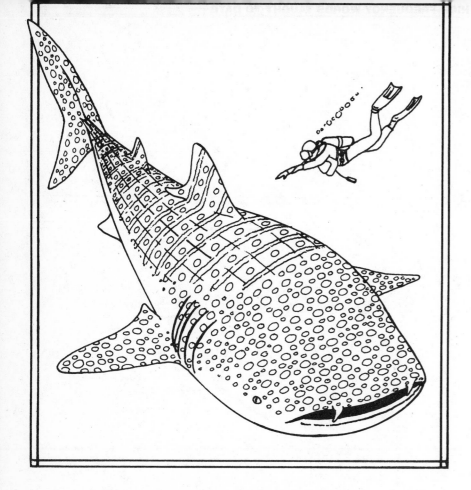

The whale shark is the largest shark of all. This shark can grow to be 40 feet long. It is larger than a school bus!

Sharks are fish. Most sharks live in the deep, dark ocean. Most sharks do not harm people.

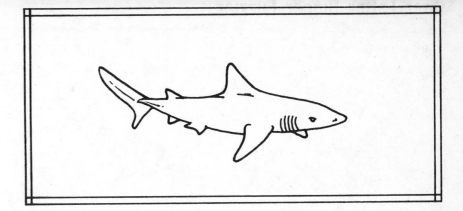

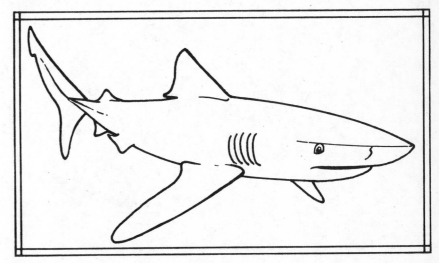

Sharks can swim fast.
Sharks can swim far. Sharks
use their sharp, hard teeth
to catch fish.

Sharks can be large or
small. A dogfish is a small
kind of shark. A blue shark is
a large kind of shark.

2

3

DECODABLE WORDS

Target Skill: *-er* **(spelling changes)**

bigger	fatter	fuzzier
drier	furrier	wetter

Previously Taught Skills

bug	frog
cat	which

SKILLS APPLIED IN WORDS IN STORY: *m, s, c, t,* short *a*; consonant *f*; consonant *p*; short *i*; consonant *b*; consonant *r*; consonant *h*; consonant *g*; short *o*; consonant *d*; consonant *w*; consonant *l*; short *e*; consonant *k*; short *u*; consonant *z*; /z/ spelled *s*; *r* clusters; digraph *wh*; digraph *ch*; consonants *-nd*; /o͞o/ spelled *oo*; long *i* spelled *ie*; base words + *-s*; *r*-controlled *ur*

HIGH–FREQUENCY WORDS

and	happier	looks	tinier
bear	is	one	

HOUGHTON MIFFLIN   BOSTON

Drier, Fatter, Bigger, Fuzzier

HIGH-FREQUENCY WORDS TAUGHT TO DATE

Grade 1

a	build	family	hold	now	school	together
able	butter	far	horse	ocean	second	too
about	buy	father	house	of	see	try
above	by	find	how	off	seven	turn
afraid	call	first	hungry	old	shall	two
after	car	five	hurt	on	sharp	under
again	carry	flower	I	once	she	upon
against	caught	fly	idea	one	shoe[s]	very
all	children	follow	in	only	shout	walk
also	climb	for	is	open	show	wall
already	cold	forest	jump	or	sing	want
always	color	found	kind	other	small	warm
and	come	four	know	our	so	was
animal	could	friend	laugh[ed]	out	some	wash
any	cow	full	learn	over	soon	watched
are	dance	funny	light	own	start	water
arms	divide	garden	like	paper	sure	we
around	do	girl	little	part	table	wear
away	does	give	live	people	talk	were
baby	done	go	long	person	tall	what
bear	door	goes	look	picture	teacher	where
because	down	gone	love	piece	the	who
been	draw	good	many	play	their	why
before	eat	green	me	present	there	work
began	edge	grow	minute[s]	pretty	these	world
begin[s]	eight	happy	more	pull	they	would
bird	else	hard	morning	put	though	write
blue	enough	have	most	read	thoughts	you
body	evening	he	mother	ready	three	your
both	ever	head[s]	my	right	through	
break	every	hear	near	room	tiny	
brown	eye[s]	her	never	said	to	
	fall	here	not	saw	today	

Decoding skills taught to date: *m, s, c, t,* short *a;* consonant *n;* consonant *f;* consonant *p;* short *i;* consonant *b;* consonant *r;* consonant *h;* consonant *g;* short *o;* consonant *d;* consonant *w;* consonant *l;* consonant *x;* short *e;* consonant *y;* consonant *k;* consonant *v;* short *u;* /kw/ spelled *qu;* consonant *j;* consonant *z;* /z/ spelled *s;* consonants *-ck;* /l/ spelled *-ll;* /f/ spelled *-ff;* /s/ spelled *-ss;* /t/ spelled *-ed;* /d/ spelled *-ed;* verb ending *-ing;* *r* clusters; *l* clusters; *s* clusters; silent *k* in *kn;* silent *w* in *wr;* silent *g* in *gn;* triple clusters; digraph *sh;* digraph *th;* digraph *wh;* digraph *ch;* digraph *-tch;* long *a* (CVC*e*); /s/ spelled *c;* /j/ spelled *g;* consonants *-nd;* consonants *-ng;* consonants *-nk;* long *i* (CVC*e*); contractions; long *o* (CV); long *o* (CVC*e*); /o͞o/ spelled *u* (CVC*e*); /yo͞o/ spelled *u* (CVC*e*); consonants *-ft;* consonants *-lk;* consonants *-nt;* long *e* (CV); long *e* (CVC*e*); long *e* spelled *ee;* long *e* spelled *ea;* long *a* spelled *ai;* long *a* spelled *ay;* long *o* spelled *oa;* long *o* spelled *ow;* /o͞o/ spelled *oo;* /o͞o/ spelled *oo;* /o͞o/ spelled *ew;* /o͞o/ spelled *ue;* /o͞o/ spelled *ou;* long *i* spelled *igh;* long *i* spelled *ie;* /ĕd/ spelled *-ed;* base words + *-ing;* base words + *-s;* /ou/ spelled *ou;* /ou/ spelled *ow;* *-ing* (spelling changes); *-ed* (spelling changes); long *e* spelled *y;* long *i* spelled *y;* /ēz/ spelled *-es;* /ēz/ spelled *-ies;* /oi/ spelled *oi;* /oi/ spelled *oy;* /ô/ spelled *aw;* /ô/ spelled *au;* *r*-controlled *or;* *r*-controlled *ore;* *r*-controlled *er;* *r*-controlled *ir;* *r*-controlled *ur;* *r*-controlled *ar;* *-er* (spelling changes); *-est* (spelling changes)

Drier, Fatter, Bigger, Fuzzier

One bug is tinier, and one is fuzzier. Which is tinier? Which is fuzzier?

One frog is wetter, and one is drier. Which is wetter? Which is drier?

One cat is fatter, and one
is furrier. Which is fatter?
Which is furrier?

2

One bear looks bigger,
and one looks happier. Which
looks bigger? Which looks
happier?

3

The Driest Place

DECODABLE WORDS

Target Skill: *-est* **(spelling changes)**

bumpiest	hottest	sandiest
driest	largest	thinnest
fattest	prickliest	

Previously Taught Skills

cactus	frog	plants	toads
desert	get	rain	this
deserts	place	snakes	which

SKILLS APPLIED IN WORDS IN STORY: *m, s, c, t,* short *a*; consonant *n*; consonant *f*; consonant *p*; short *i*; consonant *b*; consonant *r*; consonant *h*; consonant *g*; short *o*; consonant *d*; consonant *l*; short *e*; consonant *k*; short *u*; /z/ spelled *s*; consonants *-ck*; *r* clusters; *l* clusters; *s* clusters; digraph *th*; digraph *wh*; digraph *ch*; long *a* (CVCe); /s/ spelled *c*; /j/ spelled *g*; consonants *-nd*; consonants *-ng*; consonants *-nt*; long *e* (CV); long *e* spelled *ee*; long *a* spelled *ai*; long *o* spelled *oa*; base words + *-s*; *r*-controlled *er*; *r*-controlled *ar*

HIGH–FREQUENCY WORDS

a	here	littlest	one	two
and	is	longest	the	
are	little	of	three	

HOUGHTON MIFFLIN   BOSTON

The Driest Place

HIGH-FREQUENCY WORDS TAUGHT TO DATE

Grade 1

a	build	family	hold	now	school	together
able	butter	far	horse	ocean	second	too
about	buy	father	house	of	see	try
above	by	find	how	off	seven	turn
afraid	call	first	hungry	old	shall	two
after	car	five	hurt	on	sharp	under
again	carry	flower	I	once	she	upon
against	caught	fly	idea	one	shoe[s]	very
all	children	follow	in	only	shout	walk
also	climb	for	is	open	show	wall
already	cold	forest	jump	or	sing	want
always	color	found	kind	other	small	warm
and	come	four	know	our	so	was
animal	could	friend	laugh[ed]	out	some	wash
any	cow	full	learn	over	soon	watched
are	dance	funny	light	own	start	water
arms	divide	garden	like	paper	sure	we
around	do	girl	little	part	table	wear
away	does	give	live	people	talk	were
baby	done	go	long	person	tall	what
bear	door	goes	look	picture	teacher	where
because	down	gone	love	piece	the	who
been	draw	good	many	play	their	why
before	eat	green	me	present	there	work
began	edge	grow	minute[s]	pretty	these	world
begin[s]	eight	happy	more	pull	they	would
bird	else	hard	morning	put	though	write
blue	enough	have	most	read	thoughts	you
body	evening	he	mother	ready	three	your
both	ever	head[s]	my	right	through	
break	every	hear	near	room	tiny	
brown	eye[s]	her	never	said	to	
	fall	here	not	saw	today	

Decoding skills taught to date: m, s, c, t; short a; consonant n; consonant f; consonant p; short i; consonant b; consonant r; consonant h; consonant g; short o; consonant d; consonant w; consonant l; consonant x; short e; consonant y; consonant k; consonant v; short u; /kw/ spelled qu; consonant j; consonant z; /z/ spelled s; consonants -ck; /l/ spelled -ll; /f/ spelled -ff; /s/ spelled -ss; /t/ spelled -ed; /d/ spelled -ed; verb ending -ing; r clusters; l clusters; s clusters; silent k in kn; silent w in wr; silent g in gn; triple clusters; digraph sh; digraph th; digraph wh; digraph ch; digraph -tch; long a (CVCe); /s/ spelled c; /j/ spelled g; consonants -nd; consonants -ng; consonants -nk; long i (CVCe); contractions; long o (CV); long o (CVCe); /o͞o/ spelled u (CVCe); /yo͞o/ spelled u (CVCe); consonants -ft; consonants -lk; consonants -nt; long e (CV); long e (CVCe); long e spelled ee; long e spelled ea; long a spelled ai; long a spelled ay; long o spelled oa; long o spelled ow; /o͞o/ spelled oo; /o͞o/ spelled oo; /o͞o/ spelled ew; /o͞o/ spelled ue; /o͞o/ spelled ou; long i spelled igh; long i spelled ie; /ĕd/ spelled -ed; base words + -ing; base words + -s; /ou/ spelled ou; /ou/ spelled ow; -ing (spelling changes); -ed (spelling changes); long e spelled y; long i spelled y; /ĕz/ spelled -es; /ēz/ spelled -ies; /oi/ spelled oi; /oi/ spelled oy; /ô/ spelled aw; /ô/ spelled au; r-controlled or; r-controlled ore; r-controlled er; r-controlled ir; r-controlled ur; r-controlled ar; -er (spelling changes); -est (spelling changes)

Here are three snakes.
Which is longest? Which is
thinnest?

The Driest Place

Deserts get little rain.
This is one of the hottest, driest,
sandiest deserts.

Here are cactus plants.
Which is largest? Which is
littlest? Which is prickliest?

2

Here are two deserts toads
and a desert frog. Which is
bumpiest? Which is fattest?

The queen asked, "Who is
the finest queen?"

The shiniest looking glass
did not say anything.

2

The queen asked, "Who is
the nicest queen?"

The shiniest looking glass
did not say anything.

3

"You are the silliest looking glass!" said the queen.

"You are the silliest queen!" said the maid. "Looking glasses can't talk!"

4

The Silliest Queen

The queen looked into her shiniest looking glass. She asked, "Who is the prettiest queen of all?"

The shiniest looking glass did not say anything.

1

Grade 1

a	butter	father	house	of	seven	two
about	buy	find	how	off	shall	under
above	by	first	hungry	old	sharp	upon
afraid	call	five	hurt	on	she	very
after	car	flower	I	once	shoe[s]	walk
again	carry	fly	idea	one	shout	wall
against	caught	follow	in	only	show	want
all	children	for	is	open	sing	warm
also	climb	forest	jump	or	small	was
already	cold	found	kind	other	so	wash
always	color	four	know	our	some	watched
and	come	friend	laugh[ed]	out	soon	water
animal	could	full	learn	over	start	we
any	cow	funny	light	own	sure	wear
are	dance	garden	like	paper	table	were
arms	divide	girl	little	part	talk	what
around	do	give	live	people	tall	where
away	does	go	long	person	teacher	who
baby	done	goes	look	picture	the	why
bear	door	gone	love	piece	their	work
because	down	good	many	play	there	world
been	draw	green	me	pretty	these	would
before	eat	grow	minute[s]	pull	they	write
began	edge	happy	more	put	though	you
begin[s]	eight	hard	morning	read	three	your
bird	else	have	most	ready	through	
blue	enough	he	mother	right	tiny	
body	evening	head[s]	my	room	to	
both	ever	hear	near	said	today	
break	every	her	never	saw	together	
brown	fall	here	not	school	too	
build	family	hold	now	second	try	
	far	horse	ocean	see	turn	

Decoding skills taught to date: *m, s, c, t,* short *a;* consonant *n;* consonant *f;* consonant *p;* short *i;* consonant *b;* consonant *r;* consonant *h;* consonant *g;* short *o;* consonant *d;* consonant *w;* consonant *l;* consonant *x;* short *e;* consonant *y;* consonant *k;* consonant *v;* short *u;* /kw/ spelled *qu;* consonant *j;* consonant *z;* /z/ spelled *s;* consonants *-ck;* /l/ spelled *-ll;* /f/ spelled *-ff;* /s/ spelled *-ss;* /t/ spelled *-ed;* /d/ spelled *-ed;* verb ending *-ing;* *r* clusters; *l* clusters; *s* clusters; silent *k* in *kn;* silent *w* in *wr;* silent *g* in *gn;* triple clusters; digraph *sh;* digraph *th;* digraph *wh;* digraph *ch;* digraph *-tch;* long *a* (CVC*e*); /s/ spelled *c;* /j/ spelled *g;* consonants *-nd;* consonants *-ng;* consonants *-nk;* long *i* (CVC*e*); contractions; long *o* (CV); long *o* (CVC*e*); /o͞o/ spelled *u* (CVC*e*); /yo͞o/ spelled *u* (CVC*e*); consonants *-ft;* consonants *-lk;* consonants *-nt;* long *e* (CV); long *e* (CVC*e*); long *e* spelled *ee;* long *e* spelled *ea;* long *a* spelled *ai;* long *a* spelled *ay;* long *o* spelled *oa;* long *o* spelled *ow;* /o͞o/ spelled *oo;* /o͞o/ spelled *oo;* /o͞o/ spelled *ew;* /o͞o/ spelled *ue;* /o͞o/ spelled *ou;* long *i* spelled *igh;* long *i* spelled *ie;* /ĕd/ spelled *-ed;* base words + *-ing;* base words + *-s;* /ou/ spelled *ou;* /ou/ spelled *ow;* *-ing* (spelling changes); *-ed* (spelling changes); long *e* spelled *y;* long *i* spelled *y;* /ĕz/ spelled *-es;* /ēz/ spelled *-ies;* /oi/ spelled *oi;* /oi/ spelled *oy;* /ô/ spelled *aw;* /ô/ spelled *au;* *r*-controlled *or;* *r*-controlled *ore;* *r*-controlled *er;* *r*-controlled *ir;* *r*-controlled *ur;* *r*-controlled *ar;* *-er* (spelling changes); *-est* (spelling changes)

The Silliest Queen

DECODABLE WORDS

Target Skill: *-est* **(spelling changes)**

finest	shiniest
nicest	silliest

Previously Taught Skills

asked	did	glasses	queen
can't	glass	maid	say

SKILLS APPLIED IN WORDS IN STORY: *m, s, c, t,* short *a*; consonant *n*; consonant *f*; short *i*; consonant *h*; consonant *g*; short *o*; consonant *d*; consonant *l*; consonant *y*; consonant *k*; /kw/ spelled *qu*; /z/ spelled *s*; /l/ spelled *-ll*; /s/ spelled *-ss*; /t/ spelled *-ed*; *l* clusters; *s* clusters; digraph *sh*; digraph *th*; /s/ spelled *c*; consonants *-ng*; long *i* (CVCe); contractions; long *e* (CV); long *e* spelled *ee*; long *a* spelled *ai*; long *a* spelled *ay*; /o͞o/ spelled *oo*; /o͞o/ spelled *ou*; base words + *-ing*; long *e* spelled *y*; /ĕz/ spelled *-es*; *r*-controlled *er*

HIGH–FREQUENCY WORDS

all	into	not	she	you
anything	is	of	talk	
are	looked	prettiest	the	
her	looking	said	who	

HOUGHTON MIFFLIN   BOSTON

The Silliest Queen

Munch is hungrier than Dotty. Dotty is getting hotter and thirstier than Munch.

2

Munch is standing! He is the funnier one. Dotty thinks it is safer to sit.

It is hard to tell who's cuter. What do you think?

4

Who's Cuter?

Meet Dotty and Munch. Munch is bigger. Dotty is littler.

1

HIGH-FREQUENCY WORDS TAUGHT TO DATE

Grade 1

a	butter	father	house	of	seven	two
about	buy	find	how	off	shall	under
above	by	first	hungry	old	sharp	upon
afraid	call	five	hurt	on	she	very
after	car	flower	I	once	shoe[s]	walk
again	carry	fly	idea	one	shout	wall
against	caught	follow	in	only	show	want
all	children	for	is	open	sing	warm
also	climb	forest	jump	or	small	was
already	cold	found	kind	other	so	wash
always	color	four	know	our	some	watched
and	come	friend	laugh[ed]	out	soon	water
animal	could	full	learn	over	start	we
any	cow	funny	light	own	sure	wear
are	dance	garden	like	paper	table	were
arms	divide	girl	little	part	talk	what
around	do	give	live	people	tall	where
away	does	go	long	person	teacher	who
baby	done	goes	look	picture	the	why
bear	door	gone	love	piece	their	work
because	down	good	many	play	there	world
been	draw	green	me	pretty	these	would
before	eat	grow	minute[s]	pull	they	write
began	edge	happy	more	put	though	you
begin[s]	eight	hard	morning	read	three	your
bird	else	have	most	ready	through	
blue	enough	he	mother	right	tiny	
body	evening	head[s]	my	room	to	
both	ever	hear	near	said	today	
break	every	her	never	saw	together	
brown	fall	here	not	school	too	
build	family	hold	now	second	try	
	far	horse	ocean	see	turn	

Decoding skills taught to date: m, s, c, t, short a; consonant n; consonant f; consonant p; short i; consonant b; consonant r; consonant h; consonant g; short o; consonant d; consonant w; consonant l; consonant x; short e; consonant y; consonant k; consonant v; short u; /kw/ spelled qu; consonant j; consonant z; /z/ spelled s; consonants -ck; /l/ spelled -ll; /f/ spelled -ff; /s/ spelled -ss; /t/ spelled -ed; /d/ spelled -ed; verb ending -ing; r clusters; l clusters; s clusters; silent k in kn; silent w in wr; silent g in gn; triple clusters; digraph sh; digraph th; digraph wh; digraph ch; digraph -tch; long a (CVCe); /s/ spelled c; /j/ spelled g; consonants -nd; consonants -ng; consonants -nk; long i (CVCe); contractions; long o (CV); long o (CVCe); /ōō/ spelled u (CVCe); /yōō/ spelled u (CVCe); consonants -ft; consonants -lk; consonants -nt; long e (CV); long e (CVCe); long e spelled ee; long e spelled ea; long a spelled ai; long a spelled ay; long o spelled oa; long o spelled ow; /ōō/ spelled oo; /ōō/ spelled oo; /ōō/ spelled ew; /ōō/ spelled ue; /ōō/ spelled ou; long i spelled igh; long i spelled ie; /ĕd/ spelled -ed; base words + -ing; base words + -s; /ou/ spelled ou; /ou/ spelled ow; -ing (spelling changes); -ed (spelling changes); long e spelled y; long i spelled y; /ēz/ spelled -es; /ēz/ spelled -ies; /oi/ spelled oi; /oi/ spelled oy; /ô/ spelled aw; /ô/ spelled au; r-controlled or; r-controlled ore; r-controlled er; r-controlled ir; r-controlled ur; r-controlled ar; -er (spelling changes); -est (spelling changes)

Who's Cuter?

DECODABLE WORDS

Target Skill: *-er* (spelling changes)

bigger	safer
cuter	thirstier
hotter	

Previously Taught Skills

Dotty	Munch	than
getting	sit	think
it	standing	thinks
meet	tell	

SKILLS APPLIED IN WORDS IN STORY: *m, s, c, t,* short *a*; consonant *n*; consonant *f*; short *i*; consonant *b*; consonant *r*; consonant *h*; consonant *g*; short *o*; consonant *d*; consonant *l*; short *e*; consonant *y*; consonant *k*; short *u*; /z/ spelled *s*; /l/ spelled *-ll*; verb ending *-ing*; *s* clusters; digraph *th*; digraph *ch*; long *a* (CVCe); consonants *-nd*; consonants *-nk*; /yo͞o/ spelled *u* (CVCe); long *e* (CV); long *e* spelled *ee*; /o͞o/ spelled *ou*; base words + *-ing*; base words + *-s*; *-ing* (spelling changes); long *e* spelled *y*; *r*-controlled *er*; *r*-controlled *ir*; *r*-controlled *ar*

HIGH–FREQUENCY WORDS

and	hard	is	the	who's
do	he	littler	to	you
funnier	hungrier	one	what	

HOUGHTON MIFFLIN   BOSTON

Who's Cuter?

At the Food Mart, Barb
and Clark park the car and
get a cart.

Barb and Clark put meat,
plums, a jar of jam, and a tart
in the cart. Then they bring
the cart to the line.

Clark puts the jar of jam, the meat, the plums, and the tart into the car. Barb starts the car to go home.

4

At the Food Mart

Barb and Clark drive the car to the Food Mart. It is not too far.

1

HIGH-FREQUENCY WORDS TAUGHT TO DATE

Grade 1

a	car	fly	idea	only	show	want
about	carry	follow	in	open	sing	warm
afraid	children	for	is	or	small	was
after	climb	forest	jump	other	so	wash
again	cold	found	kind	our	some	watched
all	color	four	know	out	soon	water
also	come	friend	laugh[ed]	over	start	we
always	could	full	learn	own	sure	wear
and	cow	funny	light	paper	table	were
animal	dance	garden	like	part	talk	what
any	divide	girl	little	people	tall	where
are	do	give	live	person	teacher	who
arms	does	go	long	picture	the	why
around	done	goes	look	piece	their	work
away	door	gone	love	play	there	world
baby	down	good	many	pretty	these	would
bear	draw	green	me	pull	they	write
because	eat	grow	more	put	though	you
been	edge	happy	morning	read	three	your
before	eight	hard	most	ready	through	
began	else	have	mother	right	tiny	
bird	enough	he	my	room	to	
blue	evening	head[s]	near	said	today	
body	ever	hear	never	saw	together	
both	every	her	not	school	too	
break	fall	here	now	second	try	
brown	family	hold	ocean	see	turn	
build	far	horse	of	seven	two	
butter	father	house	off	shall	under	
buy	find	how	old	sharp	upon	
by	first	hungry	on	she	very	
call	five	hurt	once	shoe[s]	walk	
	flower	I	one	shout	wall	

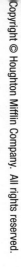

Decoding skills taught to date: *m, s, c, t,* short *a;* consonant *n;* consonant *f;* consonant *p;* short *i;* consonant *b;* consonant *r;* consonant *h;* consonant *g;* short *o;* consonant *d;* consonant *w;* consonant *l;* consonant *x;* short *e;* consonant *y;* consonant *k;* consonant *v;* short *u;* /kw/ spelled *qu;* consonant *j;* consonant *z;* /z/ spelled *s;* consonants -*ck;* /l/ spelled -*ll;* /f/ spelled -*ff;* /s/ spelled -*ss;* /t/ spelled -*ed;* /d/ spelled -*ed;* verb ending -*ing;* *r* clusters; *l* clusters; *s* clusters; silent *k* in *kn;* silent *w* in *wr;* silent *g* in *gn;* triple clusters; digraph *sh;* digraph *th;* digraph *wh;* digraph *ch;* digraph -*tch;* long *a* (CVC*e*); /s/ spelled *c;* /j/ spelled *g;* consonants -*nd;* consonants -*ng;* consonants -*nk;* long *i* (CVC*e*); contractions; long *o* (CV); long *o* (CVC*e*); /ōō/ spelled *u* (CVC*e*); /yōō/ spelled *u* (CVC*e*); consonants -*ft;* consonants -*lk;* consonants -*nt;* long *e* (CV); long *e* (CVC*e*); long *e* spelled *ee;* long *e* spelled *ea;* long *a* spelled *ai;* long *a* spelled *ay;* long *o* spelled *oa;* long *o* spelled *ow;* /ōō/ spelled *oo;* /ōō/ spelled *ew;* /ōō/ spelled *ue;* /ōō/ spelled *ou;* long *i* spelled *igh;* long *i* spelled *ie;* /ĕd/ spelled -*ed;* base words + -*ing;* base words + -*s;* /ou/ spelled *ou;* /ou/ spelled *ow;* -*ing* (spelling changes); -*ed* (spelling changes); long *e* spelled *y;* long *i* spelled *y;* /ēz/ spelled -*es;* /ēz/ spelled -*ies;* /oi/ spelled *oi;* /oi/ spelled *oy;* /ô/ spelled *aw;* /ô/ spelled *au;* r-controlled *or;* r-controlled *ore;* r-controlled *er;* r-controlled *ir;* r-controlled *ur;* r-controlled *ar*

At the Food Mart

DECODABLE WORDS

Target Skill: *r-controlled ar*

Barb	jar	tart
cart	Mart	
Clark	park	

Previously Taught Skills

at	Food	it	meat	then
bring	get	jam	plums	
drive	home	line	sale	

SKILLS APPLIED IN WORDS IN STORY: *m, s, c, t,* short *a*; consonant *n*; consonant *f*; consonant *p*; short *i*; consonant *b*; consonant *r*; consonant *h*; consonant *g*; short *o*; consonant *d*; consonant *l*; short *e*; consonant *k*; consonant *v*; short *u*; consonant *j*; /z/ spelled *s*; *r* clusters; *l* clusters; *s* clusters; digraph *th*; long *a* (CVCe); consonants *-nd*; consonants *-ng*; long *i* (CVCe); long *o* (CV); long *o* (CVCe); long *e* (CV); long *e* spelled *ea*; /o͞o/ spelled *oo*; base words + *-s*

HIGH-FREQUENCY WORDS

a	go	not	puts	to
and	in	of	starts	too
car	into	open	the	
far	is	put	they	

HOUGHTON MIFFLIN   BOSTON

At the Food Mart

Kurt hurls his fishing line
into the surf.

2

The surf starts to churn.
The Blue Spur starts to lurch.
Will Kurt get hurt?

3

No, Kurt will not get hurt.
He turns the Blue Spur out of
the surf.

4

The Blue Spur

Kurt can catch fish in his
boat, the Blue Spur.

1

Grade 1

a	children	forest	kind	out	start	wear
about	climb	found	know	over	table	were
afraid	cold	four	learn	own	talk	what
after	color	friend	light	paper	tall	where
again	come	full	like	part	teacher	who
all	could	funny	little	people	the	why
also	cow	garden	live	person	their	work
always	dance	girl	long	picture	there	world
and	do	give	look	piece	these	would
animal	does	go	love	play	they	write
any	done	goes	many	pretty	though	you
are	door	gone	me	pull	three	your
arms	down	good	more	put	through	
around	draw	green	morning	read	tiny	
away	eat	grow	most	ready	to	
baby	edge	happy	mother	right	today	
bear	eight	hard	my	room	together	
because	else	have	near	said	too	
been	enough	he	never	saw	try	
before	evening	hear	not	school	turn	
bird	ever	her	now	see	two	
blue	every	here	ocean	seven	under	
body	fall	hold	of	shall	upon	
both	family	horse	off	sharp	very	
brown	far	house	old	she	walk	
build	father	how	on	shoe[s]	wall	
butter	find	hungry	once	shout	want	
buy	first	hurt	one	show	warm	
by	five	I	only	sing	was	
call	flower	idea	open	small	wash	
car	fly	in	or	so	watched	
carry	follow	is	other	some	water	
	for	jump	our	soon	we	

Decoding skills taught to date: *m, s, c, t,* short *a;* consonant *n;* consonant *f;* consonant *p;* short *i;* consonant *b;* consonant *r;* consonant *h;* consonant *g;* short *o;* consonant *d;* consonant *w;* consonant *l;* consonant *x;* short *e;* consonant *y;* consonant *k;* consonant *v;* short *u;* /kw/ spelled *qu;* consonant *j;* consonant *z;* /z/ spelled *s;* consonants *-ck;* /l/ spelled *-ll;* /f/ spelled *-ff;* /s/ spelled *-ss;* /t/ spelled *-ed;* /d/ spelled *-ed;* verb ending *-ing;* *r* clusters; *l* clusters; *s* clusters; silent *k* in *kn;* silent *w* in *wr;* silent *g* in *gn;* triple clusters; digraph *sh;* digraph *th;* digraph *wh;* digraph *ch;* digraph *-tch;* long *a* (CVC*e*); /s/ spelled *c;* /j/ spelled *g;* consonants *-nd;* consonants *-ng;* consonants *-nk;* long *i* (CVC*e*); contractions; long *o* (CV); long *o* (CVC*e*); /o͞o/ spelled *u* (CVC*e*); /yo͞o/ spelled *u* (CVC*e*); consonants *-ft;* consonants *-lk;* consonants *-nt;* long *e* (CV); long *e* (CVC*e*); long *e* spelled *ee;* long *e* spelled *ea;* long *a* spelled *ai;* long *a* spelled *ay;* long *o* spelled *oa;* long *o* spelled *ow;* /o͞o/ spelled *oo;* /o͝o/ spelled *oo;* /o͞o/ spelled *ew;* /o͞o/ spelled *ue;* /o͞o/ spelled *ou;* long *i* spelled *igh;* long *i* spelled *ie;* /ĕd/ spelled *-ed;* base words + *-ing;* base words + *-s;* /ou/ spelled *ou;* /ou/ spelled *ow;* *-ing* (spelling changes); *-ed* (spelling changes); long *e* spelled *y;* long *i* spelled *y;* /ĕz/ spelled *-es;* /ēz/ spelled *-ies;* /oi/ spelled *oi;* /oi/ spelled *oy;* /ô/ spelled *aw;* /ô/ spelled *au;* *r*-controlled *or;* *r*-controlled *ore;* *r*-controlled *er;* *r*-controlled *ir;* *r*-controlled *ur*

DECODABLE WORDS

Target Skill: *r-controlled ur*

churn	lurch
hurls	spur
Kurt	surf

Previously Taught Skills

boat	fish	his	will
can	fishing	line	
catch	get	no	

SKILLS APPLIED IN WORDS IN STORY: *m, s, c, t,* short *a;* consonant *n;* consonant *f;* consonant *p;* short *i;* consonant *b;* consonant *r;* consonant *h;* consonant *g;* short *o;* consonant *w;* consonant *l;* short *e;* consonant *k;* /z/ spelled *s;* /l/ spelled *-ll;* *l* clusters; *s* clusters; digraph *sh;* digraph *th;* digraph *ch;* digraph *-tch;* long *i* (CVCe); long *o* (CV); long *e* (CV); long *o* spelled *oa;* /o͞o/ spelled *ue;* base words + *-ing;* base words + *-s;* /ou/ spelled *ou*

HIGH–FREQUENCY WORDS

blue	in	of	the
he	into	out	to
hurt	not	starts	turns

HOUGHTON MIFFLIN   BOSTON

The Blue Spur

Each girl had a shirt with
her name on it.

Sue came in first, Bea
came in next, and Pam
came in third.

After the race, the girls
had a big thirst!

4

The Girls Race

The girls ran a race on
the dirt track.

1

Grade 1

a	children	forest	kind	out	start	wear
about	climb	found	know	over	table	were
afraid	cold	four	learn	own	talk	what
after	color	friend	light	paper	tall	where
again	come	full	like	part	teacher	who
all	could	funny	little	people	the	why
also	cow	garden	live	person	their	work
always	dance	girl	long	picture	there	world
and	do	give	look	piece	these	would
animal	does	go	love	play	they	write
any	done	goes	many	pretty	though	you
are	door	gone	me	pull	three	your
arms	down	good	more	put	through	
around	draw	green	morning	read	tiny	
away	eat	grow	most	ready	to	
baby	edge	happy	mother	right	today	
bear	eight	hard	my	room	together	
because	else	have	near	said	too	
been	enough	he	never	saw	try	
before	evening	hear	not	school	turn	
bird	ever	her	now	see	two	
blue	every	here	ocean	seven	under	
body	fall	hold	of	shall	upon	
both	family	horse	off	sharp	very	
brown	far	house	old	she	walk	
build	father	how	on	shoe[s]	wall	
butter	find	hungry	once	shout	want	
buy	first	hurt	one	show	warm	
by	five	I	only	sing	was	
call	flower	idea	open	small	wash	
car	fly	in	or	so	watched	
carry	follow	is	other	some	water	
	for	jump	our	soon	we	

Decoding skills taught to date: *m, s, c, t,* short *a;* consonant *n;* consonant *f;* consonant *p;* short *i;* consonant *b;* consonant *r;* consonant *h;* consonant *g;* short *o;* consonant *d;* consonant *w;* consonant *l;* consonant *x;* short *e;* consonant *y;* consonant *k;* consonant *v;* short *u;* /kw/ spelled *qu;* consonant *j;* consonant *z;* /z/ spelled *s;* consonants *-ck;* /l/ spelled *-ll;* /f/ spelled *-ff;* /s/ spelled *-ss;* /t/ spelled *-ed;* /d/ spelled *-ed;* verb ending *-ing;* *r* clusters; *l* clusters; *s* clusters; silent *k* in *kn;* silent *w* in *wr;* silent *g* in *gn;* triple clusters; digraph *sh;* digraph *th;* digraph *wh;* digraph *ch;* digraph *-tch;* long *a* (CVC*e*); /s/ spelled *c;* /j/ spelled *g;* consonants *-nd;* consonants *-ng;* consonants *-nk;* long *i* (CVC*e*); contractions; long *o* (CV); long *o* (CVC*e*); /o͞o/ spelled *u* (CVC*e*); /yo͞o/ spelled *u* (CVC*e*); consonants *-ft;* consonants *-lk;* consonants *-nt;* long *e* (CV); long *e* (CVC*e*); long *e* spelled *ee;* long *e* spelled *ea;* long *a* spelled *ai;* long *a* spelled *ay;* long *o* spelled *oa;* long *o* spelled *ow;* /o͞o/ spelled *oo;* /o͞o/ spelled *oo;* /o͞o/ spelled *ew;* /o͞o/ spelled *ue;* /o͞o/ spelled *ou;* long *i* spelled *igh;* long *i* spelled *ie;* /ĕd/ spelled *-ed;* base words + *-ing;* base words + *-s;* /ou/ spelled *ou;* /ou/ spelled *ow;* *-ing* (spelling changes); *-ed* (spelling changes); long *e* spelled *y;* long *i* spelled *y;* /ēz/ spelled *-es;* /ēz/ spelled *-ies;* /oi/ spelled *oi;* /oi/ spelled *oy;* /ô/ spelled *aw;* /ô/ spelled *au;* *r*-controlled *or;* *r*-controlled *ore;* *r*-controlled *er;* *r*-controlled *ir;* *r*-controlled *ur*

The Girls Race

DECODABLE WORDS

Target Skill: *r-controlled ir*

dirt   thirst
shirt
third

Previously Taught Skills

Bea	each	name	race	track
big	had	next	ran	with
came	it	Pam	Sue	

SKILLS APPLIED IN WORDS IN STORY: *m, s, c, t,* short *a*; consonant *n*; consonant *f*; consonant *p*; short *i*; consonant *b*; consonant *r*; consonant *h*; consonant *g*; short *o*; consonant *d*; consonant *w*; consonant *l*; consonant *x*; short *e*; /z/ spelled *s*; consonants *-ck*; *r* clusters; *s* clusters; digraph *sh*; digraph *th*; digraph *ch*; long *a* (CVCe); /s/ spelled *c*; consonants *-nd*; long *e* (CV); long *e* spelled *ea*; /oo/ spelled *ue*; base words + *-s*; *r*-controlled *er*

HIGH–FREQUENCY WORDS

a	first	her	the
after	girl	in	
and	girls	on	

HOUGHTON MIFFLIN   BOSTON

The Girls Race

Herb works in a fern
shop. He sells ferns.

Herb waters the ferns
once per day.

2

3

Herb has big ferns. Herb has small ferns. Do you like ferns?

4

Herb the Clerk

Herb is a clerk.

1

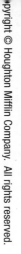

Grade 1

a	children	forest	kind	out	start	wear
about	climb	found	know	over	table	were
afraid	cold	four	learn	own	talk	what
after	color	friend	light	paper	tall	where
again	come	full	like	part	teacher	who
all	could	funny	little	people	the	why
also	cow	garden	live	person	their	work
always	dance	girl	long	picture	there	world
and	do	give	look	piece	these	would
animal	does	go	love	play	they	write
any	done	goes	many	pretty	though	you
are	door	gone	me	pull	three	your
arms	down	good	more	put	through	
around	draw	green	morning	read	tiny	
away	eat	grow	most	ready	to	
baby	edge	happy	mother	right	today	
bear	eight	hard	my	room	together	
because	else	have	near	said	too	
been	enough	he	never	saw	try	
before	evening	hear	not	school	turn	
bird	ever	her	now	see	two	
blue	every	here	ocean	seven	under	
body	fall	hold	of	shall	upon	
both	family	horse	off	sharp	very	
brown	far	house	old	she	walk	
build	father	how	on	shoe[s]	wall	
butter	find	hungry	once	shout	want	
buy	first	hurt	one	show	warm	
by	five	I	only	sing	was	
call	flower	idea	open	small	wash	
car	fly	in	or	so	watched	
carry	follow	is	other	some	water	
	for	jump	our	soon	we	

Decoding skills taught to date: m, s, c, t, short a; consonant n; consonant f; consonant p; short i; consonant b; consonant r; consonant h; consonant g; short o; consonant d; consonant w; consonant l; consonant x; short e; consonant y; consonant k; consonant v; short u; /kw/ spelled qu; consonant j; consonant z; /z/ spelled s; consonants -ck; /l/ spelled -ll; /f/ spelled -ff; /s/ spelled -ss; /t/ spelled -ed; /d/ spelled -ed; verb ending -ing; r clusters; l clusters; s clusters; silent k in kn; silent w in wr; silent g in gn; triple clusters; digraph sh; digraph th; digraph wh; digraph ch; digraph -tch; long a (CVCe); /s/ spelled c; /j/ spelled g; consonants -nd; consonants -ng; consonants -nk; long i (CVCe); contractions; long o (CV); long o (CVCe); /o͞o/ spelled u (CVCe); /yo͞o/ spelled u (CVCe); consonants -ft; consonants -lk; consonants -nt; long e (CV); long e (CVCe); long e spelled ee; long e spelled ea; long a spelled ai; long a spelled ay; long o spelled oa; long o spelled ow; /o͞o/ spelled oo; /o͞o/ spelled oo; /o͞o/ spelled ew; /o͞o/ spelled ue; /o͞o/ spelled ou; long i spelled igh; long i spelled ie; /ĕd/ spelled -ed; base words + -ing; base words + -s; /ou/ spelled ou; /ou/ spelled ow; -ing (spelling changes); -ed (spelling changes); long e spelled y; long i spelled y; /ĕz/ spelled -es; /ĕz/ spelled -ies; /oi/ spelled oi; /oi/ spelled oy; /ô/ spelled aw; /ô/ spelled au; r-controlled or; r-controlled ore; r-controlled er; r-controlled ir; r-controlled ur

Herb the Clerk

DECODABLE WORDS

Target Skill: *r-controlled er*

clerk	Herb
fern	per
ferns	

Previously Taught Skills

big	sells
day	shop
has	

SKILLS APPLIED IN WORDS IN STORY: *m, s, c, t,* short *a*; consonant *n*; consonant *f*; consonant *p*; short *i*; consonant *b*; consonant *r*; consonant *h*; consonant *g*; short *o*; consonant *d*; consonant *l*; short *e*; consonant *y*; consonant *k*; /z/ spelled *s*; /l/ spelled *-ll*; *l* clusters; digraph *sh*; digraph *th*; long *i* (CVCe); long *e* (CV); long *a* spelled *ay*; /o͞o/ spelled *ou*; base words + *-s*

HIGH–FREQUENCY WORDS

a	in	once	waters
do	is	small	works
he	like	the	you

Herb the Clerk

HOUGHTON MIFFLIN   BOSTON

Grandma's mom and dad wore matching smocks at the store.

Grandma had chores at the store.

2

3

The Store

After her chores in the store were done, Grandma went to the shore.

4

When Grandma was little, her mom and dad had a store.

1

HIGH-FREQUENCY WORDS TAUGHT TO DATE

Grade 1

a	children	forest	kind	out	start	wear
about	climb	found	know	over	table	were
afraid	cold	four	learn	own	talk	what
after	color	friend	light	paper	tall	where
again	come	full	like	part	teacher	who
all	could	funny	little	people	the	why
also	cow	garden	live	person	their	work
always	dance	girl	long	picture	there	world
and	do	give	look	piece	these	would
animal	does	go	love	play	they	write
any	done	goes	many	pretty	though	you
are	door	gone	me	pull	three	your
arms	down	good	more	put	through	
around	draw	green	morning	read	tiny	
away	eat	grow	most	ready	to	
baby	edge	happy	mother	right	today	
bear	eight	hard	my	room	together	
because	else	have	near	said	too	
been	enough	he	never	saw	try	
before	evening	hear	not	school	turn	
bird	ever	her	now	see	two	
blue	every	here	ocean	seven	under	
body	fall	hold	of	shall	upon	
both	family	horse	off	sharp	very	
brown	far	house	old	she	walk	
build	father	how	on	shoe[s]	wall	
butter	find	hungry	once	shout	want	
buy	first	hurt	one	show	warm	
by	five	I	only	sing	was	
call	flower	idea	open	small	wash	
car	fly	in	or	so	watched	
carry	follow	is	other	some	water	
	for	jump	our	soon	we	

Decoding skills taught to date: m, s, c, t, short a; consonant n; consonant f; consonant p; short i; consonant b;
consonant r; consonant h; consonant g; short o; consonant d; consonant w; consonant l; consonant x; short e;
consonant y; consonant k; consonant v; short u; /kw/ spelled qu; consonant j; consonant z; /z/ spelled s;
consonants -ck; /l/ spelled -ll; /f/ spelled -ff; /s/ spelled -ss; /t/ spelled -ed; /d/ spelled -ed; verb ending -ing;
r clusters; l clusters; s clusters; silent k in kn; silent w in wr; silent g in gn; triple clusters; digraph sh;
digraph th; digraph wh; digraph ch; digraph -tch; long a (CVCe); /s/ spelled c; /j/ spelled g; consonants -nd;
consonants -ng; consonants -nk; long i (CVCe); contractions; long o (CV); long o (CVCe); /o͞o/ spelled u (CVCe);
/yo͞o/ spelled u (CVCe); consonants -ft; consonants -lk; consonants -nt; long e (CV); long e (CVCe);
long e spelled ee; long e spelled ea; long a spelled ai; long a spelled ay; long o spelled oa; long o spelled ow;
/o͞o/ spelled oo; /o͞o/ spelled oo; /o͞o/ spelled ew; /o͞o/ spelled ue; /o͞o/ spelled ou; long i spelled igh;
long i spelled ie; /ĕd/ spelled -ed; base words + -ing; base words + -s; /ou/ spelled ou; /ou/ spelled ow;
-ing (spelling changes); -ed (spelling changes); long e spelled y; long i spelled y; /ēz/ spelled -es;
/ēz/ spelled -ies; /oi/ spelled oi; /oi/ spelled oy; /ô/ spelled aw; /ô/ spelled au; r-controlled or; r-controlled ore;
r-controlled er; r-controlled ir; r-controlled ur

DECODABLE WORDS

Target Skill: *r-controlled ore*

chores	store
shore	wore

Previously Taught Skills

at	Grandma's	mom	went
dad	had	smocks	when
Grandma	matching	town	

SKILLS APPLIED IN WORDS IN STORY: *m, s, c, t,* short *a*; consonant *n*; consonant *f*; short *i*; consonant *r*; consonant *h*; consonant *g*; short *o*; consonant *d*; consonant *w*; short *e*; /z/ spelled *s*; consonants *-ck*; *r* clusters; *s* clusters; digraph *sh*; digraph *th*; digraph *wh*; digraph *ch*; digraph *-tch*; consonants *-nd*; consonants *-nt*; long *e* (CV); base words + *-ing*; base words + *-s*; /ou/ spelled *ow*; *r*-controlled *er*

HIGH–FREQUENCY WORDS

a	done	little	was
after	her	the	were
and	in	to	

HOUGHTON MIFFLIN   BOSTON

The Store

Wind and rain blow in from the north. The ship finds a safe port.

The men tie cords to the dock. The ship will be safe in the port.

The storm is short.
Soon, the ship can go forth
from the port.

4

Storm at Sea

There is a storm at sea.
The ship blows its horn.

1

HIGH-FREQUENCY WORDS TAUGHT TO DATE

Grade 1	children	forest	kind	out	start	wear
a	climb	found	know	over	table	were
about	cold	four	learn	own	talk	what
afraid	color	friend	light	paper	tall	where
after	come	full	like	part	teacher	who
again	could	funny	little	people	the	why
all	cow	garden	live	person	their	work
also	dance	girl	long	picture	there	world
always	do	give	look	piece	these	would
and	does	go	love	play	they	write
animal	done	goes	many	pretty	though	you
any	door	gone	me	pull	three	your
are	down	good	more	put	through	
arms	draw	green	morning	read	tiny	
around	eat	grow	most	ready	to	
away	edge	happy	mother	right	today	
baby	eight	hard	my	room	together	
bear	else	have	near	said	too	
because	enough	he	never	saw	try	
been	evening	hear	not	school	turn	
before	ever	her	now	see	two	
bird	every	here	ocean	seven	under	
blue	fall	hold	of	shall	upon	
body	family	horse	off	sharp	very	
both	far	house	old	she	walk	
brown	father	how	on	shoe[s]	wall	
build	find	hungry	once	shout	want	
butter	first	hurt	one	show	warm	
buy	five	I	only	sing	was	
by	flower	idea	open	small	wash	
call	fly	in	or	so	watched	
car	follow	is	other	some	water	
carry	for	jump	our	soon	we	

Decoding skills taught to date: *m, s, c, t,* short *a;* consonant *n;* consonant *f;* consonant *p;* short *i;* consonant *b;* consonant *r;* consonant *h;* consonant *g;* short *o;* consonant *d;* consonant *w;* consonant *l;* consonant *x;* short *e;* consonant *y;* consonant *k;* consonant *v;* short *u;* /kw/ spelled *qu;* consonant *j;* consonant *z;* /z/ spelled *s;* consonants *-ck;* /l/ spelled *-ll;* /f/ spelled *-ff;* /s/ spelled *-ss;* /t/ spelled *-ed;* /d/ spelled *-ed;* verb ending *-ing;* *r* clusters; *l* clusters; *s* clusters; silent *k* in *kn;* silent *w* in *wr;* silent *g* in *gn;* triple clusters; digraph *sh;* digraph *th;* digraph *wh;* digraph *ch;* digraph *-tch;* long *a* (CVC*e*); /s/ spelled *c;* /j/ spelled *g;* consonants *-nd;* consonants *-ng;* consonants *-nk;* long *i* (CVC*e*); contractions; long *o* (CV); long *o* (CVC*e*); /o͞o/ spelled *u* (CVC*e*); /yo͞o/ spelled *u* (CVC*e*); consonants *-ft;* consonants *-lk;* consonants *-nt;* long *e* (CV); long *e* (CVC*e*); long *e* spelled *ee;* long *e* spelled *ea;* long *a* spelled *ai;* long *a* spelled *ay;* long *o* spelled *oa;* long *o* spelled *ow;* /o͞o/ spelled *oo;* /o͝o/ spelled *oo;* /o͞o/ spelled *ew;* /o͞o/ spelled *ue;* /o͞o/ spelled *ou;* long *i* spelled *igh;* long *i* spelled *ie;* /ĕd/ spelled *-ed;* base words + *-ing;* base words + *-s;* /ou/ spelled *ou;* /ou/ spelled *ow;* *-ing* (spelling changes); *-ed* (spelling changes); long *e* spelled *y;* long *i* spelled *y;* /ēz/ spelled *-es;* /ēz/ spelled *-ies;* /oi/ spelled *oi;* /oi/ spelled *oy;* /ô/ spelled *aw;* /ô/ spelled *au;* *r*-controlled *or;* *r*-controlled *ore;* *r*-controlled *er;* *r*-controlled *ir;* *r*-controlled *ur*

Storm at Sea

DECODABLE WORDS

Target Skill: *r-controlled* or

cords	north	storm
forth	port	
horn	short	

Previously Taught Skills

at	can	men	ship
be	dock	rain	tie
blow	from	safe	will
blows	its	sea	wind

SKILLS APPLIED IN WORDS IN STORY: *m, s, c, t,* short *a*; consonant *n*; consonant *f*; consonant *p*; short *i*; consonant *b*; consonant *r*; consonant *h*; consonant *g*; short *o*; consonant *d*; consonant *w*; consonant *l*; short *e*; /z/ spelled *s*; consonants -*ck*; /l/ spelled -*ll*; *r* clusters; *l* clusters; *s* clusters; digraph *sh*; digraph *th*; long *a* (CVCe); consonants -*nd*; long *o* (CV); long *e* (CV); long *e* spelled *ea*; long *a* spelled *ai*; long *o* spelled *ow*; /o͞o/ spelled *oo*; long *i* spelled *ie*; base words + -*s*

HIGH–FREQUENCY WORDS

a	go	soon	to
and	in	the	
finds	is	there	

HOUGHTON MIFFLIN   BOSTON

Storm at Sea

I ♥ READING BOOKS

THEME 10
We Can Do It!

The bench tipped.
It caused Meg's lunch to
launch up, up, up!

Meg's milk spilled down,
down, down. It caused Paul
and Meg to get wet, wet, wet.

Paul Caused It All!

Paul sat. He caused the
bench to tip!

1

"It was my fault," said Paul.
"I caused it all!"

4

Grade 1

a	climb	friend	like	people	their	would
about	cold	full	little	person	there	write
afraid	color	funny	live	picture	these	you
after	come	girl	long	piece	they	your
again	could	give	look	play	though	
all	cow	go	love	pretty	three	
also	dance	goes	many	pull	through	
always	do	gone	me	put	tiny	
and	does	good	more	read	to	
animal	done	green	morning	ready	today	
any	door	grow	most	right	too	
are	down	happy	mother	room	try	
arms	draw	hard	my	said	turn	
around	eat	have	near	saw	two	
away	eight	he	never	school	under	
bear	else	hear	not	see	upon	
because	evening	her	now	seven	very	
been	ever	here	ocean	shall	walk	
before	every	hold	of	she	wall	
bird	fall	horse	off	shoe[s]	want	
blue	family	house	old	shout	warm	
body	far	how	on	show	was	
both	father	hungry	once	sing	wash	
brown	find	hurt	one	small	water	
build	first	I	open	so	we	
butter	five	idea	or	some	wear	
buy	flower	in	other	soon	were	
by	fly	is	our	start	what	
call	follow	jump	out	table	where	
car	for	kind	over	talk	who	
carry	forest	know	own	tall	why	
children	found	learn	paper	teacher	work	
	four	light	part	the	world	

Decoding skills taught to date: *m, s, c, t,* short *a;* consonant *n;* consonant *f;* consonant *p;* short *i;* consonant *b;* consonant *r;* consonant *h;* consonant *g;* short *o;* consonant *d;* consonant *w;* consonant *l;* consonant *x;* short *e;* consonant *y;* consonant *k;* consonant *v;* short *u;* /kw/ spelled *qu;* consonant *j;* consonant *z;* /z/ spelled *s;* consonants *-ck;* /l/ spelled *-ll;* /f/ spelled *-ff;* /s/ spelled *-ss;* /t/ spelled *-ed;* /d/ spelled *-ed;* verb ending *-ing;* *r* clusters; *l* clusters; *s* clusters; silent *k* in *kn;* silent *w* in *wr;* silent *g* in *gn;* triple clusters; digraph *sh;* digraph *th;* digraph *wh;* digraph *ch;* digraph *-tch;* long *a* (CVC*e*); /s/ spelled *c;* /j/ spelled *g;* consonants *-nd;* consonants *-ng;* consonants *-nk;* long *i* (CVC*e*); contractions; long *o* (CV); long *o* (CVC*e*); /o͞o/ spelled *u* (CVC*e*); /yo͞o/ spelled *u* (CVC*e*); consonants *-ft;* consonants *-lk;* consonants *-nt;* long *e* (CV); long *e* (CVC*e*); long *e* spelled *ee;* long *e* spelled *ea;* long *a* spelled *ai;* long *a* spelled *ay;* long *o* spelled *oa;* long *o* spelled *ow;* /o͞o/ spelled *oo;* /o͞o/ spelled *oo;* /o͞o/ spelled *ew;* /o͞o/ spelled *ue;* /o͞o/ spelled *ou;* long *i* spelled *igh;* long *i* spelled *ie;* /ĕd/ spelled *-ed;* base words + *-ing;* base words + *-s;* /ou/ spelled *ou;* /ou/ spelled *ow;* *-ing* (spelling changes); *-ed* (spelling changes); long *e* spelled *y;* long *i* spelled *y;* /ĕz/ spelled *-es;* /ēz/ spelled *-ies;* /oi/ spelled *oi;* /oi/ spelled *oy;* /ô/ spelled *aw;* /ô/ spelled *au*

DECODABLE WORDS

Target Skill: /ô/ spelled *au*

caused   launch

fault   Paul

Previously Taught Skills

bench	lunch	milk	tip	wet
get	Meg	sat	tipped	
it	Meg's	spilled	up	

SKILLS APPLIED IN WORDS IN STORY: *m, s, c, t,* short *a;* consonant *n;* consonant *f;* consonant *p;* short *i;* consonant *b;* consonant *h;* consonant *g;* consonant *d;* consonant *w;* consonant *l;* short *e;* consonant *k;* short *u;* /z/ spelled *s;* /l/ spelled *-ll;* /t/ spelled *-ed;* /d/ spelled *-ed; s* clusters; digraph *th;* digraph *ch;* consonants *-nd;* consonants *-lk;* long *e* (CV); /ou/ spelled *ow; -ed* (spelling changes); long *i* spelled *y*

HIGH-FREQUENCY WORDS

all	he	said	was
and	I	the	
down	my	to	

HOUGHTON MIFFLIN   BOSTON

/ô/ spelled *au*

BOOK 87

Paul Caused It All!

At dawn, the bunny hops
on the lawn.

At dawn, the little hawks
squawk.

2

3

At dawn, the boy yawns.

4

At Dawn

At dawn, the crow caws.

1

HIGH-FREQUENCY WORDS TAUGHT TO DATE

Grade 1

a	climb	friend	like	people	their	would
about	cold	full	little	person	there	write
afraid	color	funny	live	picture	these	you
after	come	girl	long	piece	they	your
again	could	give	look	play	though	
all	cow	go	love	pretty	three	
also	dance	goes	many	pull	through	
always	do	gone	me	put	tiny	
and	does	good	more	read	to	
animal	done	green	morning	ready	today	
any	door	grow	most	right	too	
are	down	happy	mother	room	try	
arms	draw	hard	my	said	turn	
around	eat	have	near	saw	two	
away	eight	he	never	school	under	
bear	else	hear	not	see	upon	
because	evening	her	now	seven	very	
been	ever	here	ocean	shall	walk	
before	every	hold	of	she	wall	
bird	fall	horse	off	shoe[s]	want	
blue	family	house	old	shout	warm	
body	far	how	on	show	was	
both	father	hungry	once	sing	wash	
brown	find	hurt	one	small	water	
build	first	I	open	so	we	
butter	five	idea	or	some	wear	
buy	flower	in	other	soon	were	
by	fly	is	our	start	what	
call	follow	jump	out	table	where	
car	for	kind	over	talk	who	
carry	forest	know	own	tall	why	
children	found	learn	paper	teacher	work	
	four	light	part	the	world	

Decoding skills taught to date: *m, s, c, t,* short *a;* consonant *n;* consonant *f;* consonant *p;* short *i;* consonant *b;* consonant *r;* consonant *h;* consonant *g;* short *o;* consonant *d;* consonant *w;* consonant *l;* consonant *x;* short *e;* consonant *y;* consonant *k;* consonant *v;* short *u;* /kw/ spelled *qu;* consonant *j;* consonant *z;* /z/ spelled *s;* consonants -*ck;* /l/ spelled -*ll;* /f/ spelled -*ff;* /s/ spelled -*ss;* /t/ spelled -*ed;* /d/ spelled -*ed;* verb ending -*ing;* *r* clusters; *l* clusters; *s* clusters; silent *k* in *kn;* silent *w* in *wr;* silent *g* in *gn;* triple clusters; digraph *sh;* digraph *th;* digraph *wh;* digraph *ch;* digraph -*tch;* long *a* (CVC*e*); /s/ spelled *c;* /j/ spelled *g;* consonants -*nd;* consonants -*ng;* consonants -*nk;* long *i* (CVC*e*); contractions; long *o* (CV); long *o* (CVC*e*); /o͞o/ spelled *u* (CVC*e*); /yo͞o/ spelled *u* (CVC*e*); consonants -*ft;* consonants -*lk;* consonants -*nt;* long *e* (CV); long *e* (CVC*e*); long *e* spelled *ee;* long *e* spelled *ea;* long *a* spelled *ai;* long *a* spelled *ay;* long *o* spelled *oa;* long *o* spelled *ow;* /o͞o/ spelled *oo;* /o͞o/ spelled *ew;* /o͞o/ spelled *ue;* /o͞o/ spelled *ou;* long *i* spelled *igh;* long *i* spelled *ie;* /ĕd/ spelled -*ed;* base words + -*ing;* base words + -*s;* /ou/ spelled *ou;* /ou/ spelled *ow;* -*ing* (spelling changes); -*ed* (spelling changes); long *e* spelled *y;* long *i* spelled *y;* /ĕz/ spelled -*es;* /ēz/ spelled -*ies;* /oi/ spelled *oi;* /oi/ spelled *oy;* /ô/ spelled *aw;* /ô/ spelled *au*

At Dawn

DECODABLE WORDS

Target Skill: /ô/ spelled *aw*

caws	hawks	squawk
dawn	lawn	yawns

Previously Taught Skills

at	bunny	hops
boy	crow	

SKILLS APPLIED IN WORDS IN STORY: *m, s, c, t,* short *a*; consonant *n*; consonant *p*; consonant *b*; consonant *r*; consonant *h*; short *o*; consonant *d*; consonant *l*; consonant *y*; consonant *k*; short *u*; /kw/ spelled *qu*; /z/ spelled *s*; digraph *th*; *r* clusters; long *e* (CV); long *o* spelled *ow*; base words + -*s*; long *e* spelled *y*; /oi/ spelled *oy*

HIGH–FREQUENCY WORDS

little	the
on	

At Dawn

HOUGHTON MIFFLIN   BOSTON

Miss Troy said, "I am your teacher, Miss Troy." Miss Troy was nice.

Miss Troy said, "Class, this is Roy. He is new here."
Joy said, "Sit here, Roy!"

BOOK 85

The New Boy

Roy went to his new school.
Roy was sad. "Mom, I don't
want to be the new boy,"
said Roy.

Roy sat with Joy. Roy did
not feel like the new boy
anymore.

HIGH-FREQUENCY WORDS TAUGHT TO DATE

Grade 1

a	climb	friend	like	people	their	would
about	cold	full	little	person	there	write
afraid	color	funny	live	picture	these	you
after	come	girl	long	piece	they	your
again	could	give	look	play	though	
all	cow	go	love	pretty	three	
also	dance	goes	many	pull	through	
always	do	gone	me	put	tiny	
and	does	good	more	read	to	
animal	done	green	morning	ready	today	
any	door	grow	most	right	too	
are	down	happy	mother	room	try	
arms	draw	hard	my	said	turn	
around	eat	have	near	saw	two	
away	eight	he	never	school	under	
bear	else	hear	not	see	upon	
because	evening	her	now	seven	very	
been	ever	here	ocean	shall	walk	
before	every	hold	of	she	wall	
bird	fall	horse	off	shoe[s]	want	
blue	family	house	old	shout	warm	
body	far	how	on	show	was	
both	father	hungry	once	sing	wash	
brown	find	hurt	one	small	water	
build	first	I	open	so	we	
butter	five	idea	or	some	wear	
buy	flower	in	other	soon	were	
by	fly	is	our	start	what	
call	follow	jump	out	table	where	
car	for	kind	over	talk	who	
carry	forest	know	own	tall	why	
children	found	learn	paper	teacher	work	
	four	light	part	the	world	

Decoding skills taught to date: m, s, c, t, short a; consonant n; consonant f; consonant p; short i; consonant b; consonant r; consonant h; consonant g; short o; consonant d; consonant w; consonant l; consonant x; short e; consonant y; consonant k; consonant v; short u; /kw/ spelled qu; consonant j; consonant z; /z/ spelled s; consonants -ck; /l/ spelled -ll; /f/ spelled -ff; /s/ spelled -ss; /t/ spelled -ed; /d/ spelled -ed; verb ending -ing; r clusters; l clusters; s clusters; silent k in kn; silent w in wr; silent g in gn; triple clusters; digraph sh; digraph th; digraph wh; digraph ch; digraph -tch; long a (CVCe); /s/ spelled c; /j/ spelled g; consonants -nd; consonants -ng; consonants -nk; long i (CVCe); contractions; long o (CV); long o (CVCe); /o͞o/ spelled u (CVCe); /yo͞o/ spelled u (CVCe); consonants -ft; consonants -lk; consonants -nt; long e (CV); long e (CVCe); long e spelled ee; long e spelled ea; long a spelled ai; long a spelled ay; long o spelled oa; long o spelled ow; /o͞o/ spelled oo; /o͝o/ spelled oo; /o͞o/ spelled ew; /o͞o/ spelled ue; /o͞o/ spelled ou; long i spelled igh; long i spelled ie; /ĕd/ spelled -ed; base words + -ing; base words + -s; /ou/ spelled ou; /ou/ spelled ow; -ing (spelling changes); -ed (spelling changes); long e spelled y; long i spelled y; /ĕz/ spelled -es; /ēz/ spelled -ies; /oi/ spelled oi; /oi/ spelled oy; /ô/ spelled aw; /ô/ spelled au

The New Boy

DECODABLE WORDS

Target Skill: **/oi/ spelled** *oy*

boy	Troy
Joy	Troy's
Roy	

Previously Taught Skills

am	don't	Mom	sat	with
be	feel	new	sit	
class	his	nice	this	
did	Miss	sad	went	

SKILLS APPLIED IN WORDS IN STORY: *m, s, c, t,* short *a*; consonant *n*; consonant *f*; short *i*; consonant *b*; consonant *r*; consonant *h*; short *o*; consonant *d*; consonant *w*; consonant *l*; short *e*; consonant *k*; consonant *j*; /z/ spelled *s*; /s/ spelled *-ss*; *r* clusters; *l* clusters; digraph *th*; /s/ spelled *c*; long *i* (CVCe); contractions; consonants *-nt*; long *e* (CV); long *e* spelled *ee*; /o͞o/ spelled *oo*; /o͞o/ spelled *ew*

HIGH–FREQUENCY WORDS

anymore	is	said	to
he	like	school	want
here	not	teacher	was
I	room	the	your

HOUGHTON MIFFLIN   BOSTON

The New Boy

We set a pot to boil. Then
we add moist greens and oil.

When the stove coil is hot,
we broil the meat.

BOOK 84

Join the Feast!

We all toil to cook the feast.

Yum, yum! Will you join the feast?

HIGH-FREQUENCY WORDS TAUGHT TO DATE

Grade 1

a	climb	friend	like	people	their	would
about	cold	full	little	person	there	write
afraid	color	funny	live	picture	these	you
after	come	girl	long	piece	they	your
again	could	give	look	play	though	
all	cow	go	love	pretty	three	
also	dance	goes	many	pull	through	
always	do	gone	me	put	tiny	
and	does	good	more	read	to	
animal	done	green	morning	ready	today	
any	door	grow	most	right	too	
are	down	happy	mother	room	try	
arms	draw	hard	my	said	turn	
around	eat	have	near	saw	two	
away	eight	he	never	school	under	
bear	else	hear	not	see	upon	
because	evening	her	now	seven	very	
been	ever	here	ocean	shall	walk	
before	every	hold	of	she	wall	
bird	fall	horse	off	shoe[s]	want	
blue	family	house	old	shout	warm	
body	far	how	on	show	was	
both	father	hungry	once	sing	wash	
brown	find	hurt	one	small	water	
build	first	I	open	so	we	
butter	five	idea	or	some	wear	
buy	flower	in	other	soon	were	
by	fly	is	our	start	what	
call	follow	jump	out	table	where	
car	for	kind	over	talk	who	
carry	forest	know	own	tall	why	
children	found	learn	paper	teacher	work	
	four	light	part	the	world	

Decoding skills taught to date: m, s, c, t, short a; consonant n; consonant f; consonant p; short i; consonant b; consonant r; consonant h; consonant g; short o; consonant d; consonant w; consonant l; consonant x; short e; consonant y; consonant k; consonant v; short u; /kw/ spelled qu; consonant j; consonant z; /z/ spelled s; consonants -ck; /l/ spelled -ll; /f/ spelled -ff; /s/ spelled -ss; /t/ spelled -ed; /d/ spelled -ed; verb ending -ing; r clusters; l clusters; s clusters; silent k in kn; silent w in wr; silent g in gn; triple clusters; digraph sh; digraph th; digraph wh; digraph ch; digraph -tch; long a (CVCe); /s/ spelled c; /j/ spelled g; consonants -nd; consonants -ng; consonants -nk; long i (CVCe); contractions; long o (CV); long o (CVCe); /o͞o/ spelled u (CVCe); /yo͞o/ spelled u (CVCe); consonants -ft; consonants -lk; consonants -nt; long e (CV); long e (CVCe); long e spelled ee; long e spelled ea; long a spelled ai; long a spelled ay; long o spelled oa; long o spelled ow; /o͞o/ spelled oo; /o͝o/ spelled oo; /o͞o/ spelled ew; /o͞o/ spelled ue; /o͞o/ spelled ou; long i spelled igh; long i spelled ie; /ĕd/ spelled -ed; base words + -ing; base words + -s; /ou/ spelled ou; /ou/ spelled ow; -ing (spelling changes); -ed (spelling changes); long e spelled y; long i spelled y; /ēz/ spelled -es; /ēz/ spelled -ies; /oi/ spelled oi; /oi/ spelled oy; /ô/ spelled aw; /ô/ spelled au

Join the Feast!

DECODABLE WORDS

Target Skill: /oi/ spelled *oi*

boil	join	toil
broil	moist	
coil	oil	

Previously Taught Skills

add	hot	set	when
cook	meat	stove	will
feast	pot	then	yum

SKILLS APPLIED IN WORDS IN STORY: *m, s, c, t,* short *a*; consonant *n*; consonant *f*; consonant *p*; short *i*; consonant *b*; consonant *r*; consonant *h*; consonant *g*; short *o*; consonant *d*; consonant *w*; consonant *l*; short *e*; consonant *y*; consonant *k*; consonant *v*; short *u*; consonant *j*; /z/ spelled *s*; /l/ spelled *-ll*; *r* clusters; *s* clusters; digraph *th*; digraph *wh*; consonants *-nd*; long *o* (CVCe); long *e* (CV); long *e* spelled *ee*; long *e* spelled *ea*; /o͞o/ spelled *oo*; /o͞o/ spelled *ou*; base words + *-s*

HIGH–FREQUENCY WORDS

a	greens	to
all	is	we
and	the	you

Join the Feast!

Jenny carries her spelling book as she walks. She studies, studies, studies.

2

Jenny
1. cities
2. pennies
3. studies
4. hobbies
5. berries

A

Jenny takes the test. She gets an A!

3

BOOK 83

Jenny Studies

Jenny studies for a big spelling test. Jenny studies, studies, studies.

Jenny carries her test home. Mom tells Jenny, "Good job!"

HIGH-FREQUENCY WORDS TAUGHT TO DATE

Grade 1

a	come	give	look	pull	tiny
about	could	go	love	put	to
afraid	cow	goes	many	read	today
again	dance	gone	me	ready	too
all	do	good	more	right	try
also	does	green	morning	room	turn
always	door	grow	most	said	two
and	down	happy	mother	saw	under
animal	draw	hard	my	see	upon
any	eat	have	near	seven	very
are	eight	he	never	shall	walk
arms	else	hear	not	she	wall
around	evening	her	now	shoe[s]	want
away	ever	here	ocean	shout	warm
bear	every	hold	of	show	was
because	fall	horse	old	sing	water
been	family	house	on	small	we
bird	far	how	once	so	wear
blue	father	hungry	one	some	were
body	find	hurt	open	soon	what
both	first	I	or	start	where
brown	five	idea	other	table	who
build	flower	in	our	talk	why
butter	fly	is	out	tall	work
by	follow	jump	over	teacher	world
call	for	kind	own	the	would
car	forest	know	paper	their	write
carry	found	learn	part	there	you
children	four	light	people	these	your
climb	friend	like	person	they	
cold	full	little	picture	though	
color	funny	live	piece	three	
	girl	long	play	through	

Decoding skills taught to date: *m, s, c, t,* short *a;* consonant *n;* consonant *f;* consonant *p;* short *i;* consonant *b;* consonant *r;* consonant *h;* consonant *g;* short *o;* consonant *d;* consonant *w;* consonant *l;* consonant *x;* short *e;* consonant *y;* consonant *k;* consonant *v;* short *u;* /kw/ spelled *qu;* consonant *j;* consonant *z;* /z/ spelled *s;* consonants *-ck;* /l/ spelled *-ll;* /f/ spelled *-ff;* /s/ spelled *-ss;* /t/ spelled *-ed;* /d/ spelled *-ed;* verb ending *-ing;* *r* clusters; *l* clusters; *s* clusters; silent *k* in *kn;* silent *w* in *wr;* silent *g* in *gn;* triple clusters; digraph *sh;* digraph *th;* digraph *wh;* digraph *ch;* digraph *-tch;* long *a* (CVC*e*); /s/ spelled *c;* /j/ spelled *g;* consonants *-nd;* consonants *-ng;* consonants *-nk;* long *i* (CVC*e*); contractions; long *o* (CV); long *o* (CVC*e*); /o͞o/ spelled *u* (CVC*e*); /yo͞o/ spelled *u* (CVC*e*); consonants *-ft;* consonants *-lk;* consonants *-nt;* long *e* (CV); long *e* (CVC*e*); long *e* spelled *ee;* long *e* spelled *ea;* long *a* spelled *ai;* long *a* spelled *ay;* long *o* spelled *oa;* long *o* spelled *ow;* /o͞o/ spelled *oo;* /o͞o/ spelled *oo;* /o͞o/ spelled *ew;* /o͞o/ spelled *ue;* /o͞o/ spelled *ou;* long *i* spelled *igh;* long *i* spelled *ie;* /ĕd/ spelled *-ed;* base words + *-ing;* base words + *-s;* /ou/ spelled *ou;* /ou/ spelled *ow;* *-ing* (spelling changes); *-ed* (spelling changes); long *e* spelled *y;* long *i* spelled *y;* /ĕz/ spelled *-es;* /ēz/ spelled *-ies*

Jenny Studies

DECODABLE WORDS

Target Skill: /ēz/ spelled *-ies*

berries   pennies
cities   studies
hobbies

Previously Taught Skills

an	book	Jenny	spelling	test
as	gets	job	takes	
big	home	Mom	tells	

SKILLS APPLIED IN WORDS IN STORY: *m, s, c, t,* short *a;* consonant *n;* consonant *p;* short *i;* consonant *b;* consonant *r;* consonant *h;* consonant *g;* short *o;* consonant *d;* consonant *l;* short *e;* consonant *k;* short *u;* consonant *j;* /z/ spelled *s;* /l/ spelled *-ll;* s clusters; digraph *sh;* digraph *th;* long *a* (CVC*e*); /s/ spelled *c;* long *o* (CVC*e*); long *e* (CV); /o͞o/ spelled *oo;* base words + *-ing;* base words + *-s;* long *e* spelled *y*

HIGH–FREQUENCY WORDS

a	good	the
carries	her	walks
for	she	

Jenny Studies

HOUGHTON MIFFLIN   BOSTON

Max reaches for Dad's
pitches. Dad pitches and
Max catches.

Max reaches for two peaches.
Max tosses one of the peaches
to Lily.

Max Reaches

Max reaches for the dishes.
Max passes the dishes to Mom.

Max reaches for Patches,
the dog. Patches kisses Max.
Kisses! Kisses! Kisses!

HIGH-FREQUENCY WORDS TAUGHT TO DATE

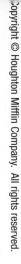

Grade 1

a	come	give	look	pull	tiny
about	could	go	love	put	to
afraid	cow	goes	many	read	today
again	dance	gone	me	ready	too
all	do	good	more	right	try
also	does	green	morning	room	turn
always	door	grow	most	said	two
and	down	happy	mother	saw	under
animal	draw	hard	my	see	upon
any	eat	have	near	seven	very
are	eight	he	never	shall	walk
arms	else	hear	not	she	wall
around	evening	her	now	shoe[s]	want
away	ever	here	ocean	shout	warm
bear	every	hold	of	show	was
because	fall	horse	old	sing	water
been	family	house	on	small	we
bird	far	how	once	so	wear
blue	father	hungry	one	some	were
body	find	hurt	open	soon	what
both	first	I	or	start	where
brown	five	idea	other	table	who
build	flower	in	our	talk	why
butter	fly	is	out	tall	work
by	follow	jump	over	teacher	world
call	for	kind	own	the	would
car	forest	know	paper	their	write
carry	found	learn	part	there	you
children	four	light	people	these	your
climb	friend	like	person	they	
cold	full	little	picture	though	
color	funny	live	piece	three	
	girl	long	play	through	

Decoding skills taught to date: *m, s, c, t,* short *a;* consonant *n;* consonant *f;* consonant *p;* short *i;* consonant *b;* consonant *r;* consonant *h;* consonant *g;* short *o;* consonant *d;* consonant *w;* consonant *l;* consonant *x;* short *e;* consonant *y;* consonant *k;* consonant *v;* short *u;* /kw/ spelled *qu;* consonant *j;* consonant *z;* /z/ spelled *s;* consonants *-ck;* /l/ spelled *-ll;* /f/ spelled *-ff;* /s/ spelled *-ss;* /t/ spelled *-ed;* /d/ spelled *-ed;* verb ending *-ing;* *r* clusters; *l* clusters; *s* clusters; silent *k* in *kn;* silent *w* in *wr;* silent *g* in *gn;* triple clusters; digraph *sh;* digraph *th;* digraph *wh;* digraph *ch;* digraph *-tch;* long *a* (CVC*e*); /s/ spelled *c;* /j/ spelled *g;* consonants *-nd;* consonants *-ng;* consonants *-nk;* long *i* (CVC*e*); contractions; long *o* (CV); long *o* (CVC*e*); /o͞o/ spelled *u* (CVC*e*); /yo͞o/ spelled *u* (CVC*e*); consonants *-ft;* consonants *-lk;* consonants *-nt;* long *e* (CV); long *e* (CVC*e*); long *e* spelled *ee;* long *e* spelled *ea;* long *a* spelled *ai;* long *a* spelled *ay;* long *o* spelled *oa;* long *o* spelled *ow;* /o͞o/ spelled *oo;* /o͝o/ spelled *oo;* /o͞o/ spelled *ew;* /o͞o/ spelled *ue;* /o͞o/ spelled *ou;* long *i* spelled *igh;* long *i* spelled *ie;* /ĕd/ spelled *-ed;* base words + *-ing;* base words + *-s;* /ou/ spelled *ou;* /ou/ spelled *ow;* *-ing* (spelling changes); *-ed* (spelling changes); long *e* spelled *y;* long *i* spelled *y;* /ēz/ spelled *-es;* /ēz/ spelled *-ies*

Max Reaches

DECODABLE WORDS

Target Skill: /ĕz/ spelled -es

catches	passes	pitches
dishes	Patches	reaches
kisses	peaches	tosses

Previously Taught Skills

Dad	Lily
Dad's	Max
dog	Mom

SKILLS APPLIED IN WORDS IN STORY: *m, s, c, t,* short *a*; consonant *p*; short *i*; consonant *r*; consonant *g*; short *o*; consonant *d*; consonant *l*; consonant *x*; consonant *k*; /s/ spelled *-ss*; digraph *sh*; digraph *th*; digraph *ch*; digraph *-tch*; consonants *-nd*; long *e* (CV); long *e* spelled *ea*; long *e* spelled *y*

HIGH–FREQUENCY WORDS

and	one	two
for	the	
of	to	

Copyright©Houghton Mifflin Company.

HOUGHTON MIFFLIN   BOSTON

Max Reaches

"Go away fly!" said Vy.

The fly took the fry. It flew into the sky.

BOOK 81

Vy and the Fly

Can Vy try to get her fry?

No, the fly is up, up in the sky.

Vy saw a fly in the sky.

The fly sat on her fry.

4

1

Grade 1

a	could	good	more	said	upon
about	cow	green	morning	saw	very
afraid	do	grow	most	see	walk
again	does	happy	mother	seven	wall
all	door	hard	my	shall	want
also	down	have	near	she	warm
always	draw	he	never	shoe[s]	was
and	eat	hear	not	shout	water
animal	eight	her	now	show	we
any	evening	here	of	sing	wear
are	every	hold	old	small	were
arms	fall	horse	on	so	what
away	family	house	once	some	where
bear	far	how	one	soon	who
because	father	hungry	or	start	why
been	find	hurt	other	table	work
bird	first	I	our	tall	world
blue	five	idea	out	teacher	would
body	flower	in	over	the	write
both	fly	is	own	their	you
brown	follow	jump	paper	there	your
build	for	kind	part	these	
butter	forest	know	people	they	
by	found	learn	person	three	
call	four	light	picture	through	
car	friend	like	piece	tiny	
carry	full	little	play	to	
children	funny	live	pull	today	
climb	girl	long	put	too	
cold	give	look	read	try	
color	go	love	ready	turn	
come	goes	many	right	two	
	gone	me	room	under	

Decoding skills taught to date: *m, s, c, t*, short *a*; consonant *n*; consonant *f*; consonant *p*; short *i*; consonant *b*; consonant *r*; consonant *h*; consonant *g*; short *o*; consonant *d*; consonant *w*; consonant *l*; consonant *x*; short *e*; consonant *y*; consonant *k*; consonant *v*; short *u*; /kw/ spelled *qu*; consonant *j*; consonant *z*; /z/ spelled *s*; consonants *-ck*; /l/ spelled *-ll*; /f/ spelled *-ff*; /s/ spelled *-ss*; /t/ spelled *-ed*; /d/ spelled *-ed*; verb ending *-ing*; *r* clusters; *l* clusters; *s* clusters; silent *k* in *kn*; silent *w* in *wr*; silent *g* in *gn*; triple clusters; digraph *sh*; digraph *th*; digraph *wh*; digraph *ch*; digraph *-tch*; long *a* (CVC*e*); /s/ spelled *c*; /j/ spelled *g*; consonants *-nd*; consonants *-ng*; consonants *-nk*; long *i* (CVC*e*); contractions; long *o* (CV); long *o* (CVC*e*); /ōō/ spelled *u* (CVC*e*); /yōō/ spelled *u* (CVC*e*); consonants *-ft*; consonants *-lk*; consonants *-nt*; long *e* (CV); long *e* (CVC*e*); long *e* spelled *ee*; long *e* spelled *ea*; long *a* spelled *ai*; long *a* spelled *ay*; long *o* spelled *oa*; long *o* spelled *ow*; /ōō/ spelled *oo*; /ōō/ spelled *oo*; /ōō/ spelled *ew*; /ōō/ spelled *ue*; /ōō/ spelled *ou*; long *i* spelled *igh*; long *i* spelled *ie*; /ĕd/ spelled *-ed*; base words + *-ing*; base words + *-s*; /ou/ spelled *ou*; /ou/ spelled *ow*; *-ing* (spelling changes); *-ed* (spelling changes); long *e* spelled *y*; long *i* spelled *y*

DECODABLE WORDS

Target Skill: long *i* spelled *y*

fry   Vy
sky

Previously Taught Skills

can	it	took
flew	no	up
get	sat	

SKILLS APPLIED IN WORDS IN STORY: *m, s, c, t,* short *a*; consonant *n*; consonant *f*; consonant *p*; short *i*; consonant *r*; consonant *g*; short *o*; consonant *l*; short *e*; consonant *k*; consonant *v*; short *u*; /z/ spelled *s*; *r* clusters; *l* clusters; *s* clusters; digraph *th*; consonants -*nd*; long *o* (CV); long *e* (CV); /ō͞o/ spelled *oo*; /ō͞o/ spelled *ew*

HIGH–FREQUENCY WORDS

a	fly	in	on	the
and	go	into	said	to
away	her	is	saw	try

HOUGHTON MIFFLIN   BOSTON

Vy and the Fly

The ride was very long.
Manny got sleepy.

Soon, Manny and Daddy got
to the city. The city streets were
very hilly.

2

3

Manny and Daddy went
to see Granny. Granny was
very happy.

4

Manny in the City

Manny and Daddy went
to see the city.

1

HIGH-FREQUENCY WORDS TAUGHT TO DATE

Grade 1

a	could	good	more	said	upon
about	cow	green	morning	saw	very
afraid	do	grow	most	see	walk
again	does	happy	mother	seven	wall
all	door	hard	my	shall	want
also	down	have	near	she	warm
always	draw	he	never	shoe[s]	was
and	eat	hear	not	shout	water
animal	eight	her	now	show	we
any	evening	here	of	sing	wear
are	every	hold	old	small	were
arms	fall	horse	on	so	what
away	family	house	once	some	where
bear	far	how	one	soon	who
because	father	hungry	or	start	why
been	find	hurt	other	table	work
bird	first	I	our	tall	world
blue	five	idea	out	teacher	would
body	flower	in	over	the	write
both	fly	is	own	their	you
brown	follow	jump	paper	there	your
build	for	kind	part	these	
butter	forest	know	people	they	
by	found	learn	person	three	
call	four	light	picture	through	
car	friend	like	piece	tiny	
carry	full	little	play	to	
children	funny	live	pull	today	
climb	girl	long	put	too	
cold	give	look	read	try	
color	go	love	ready	turn	
come	goes	many	right	two	
	gone	me	room	under	

Decoding skills taught to date: *m, s, c, t,* short *a;* consonant *n;* consonant *f;* consonant *p;* short *i;* consonant *b;* consonant *r;* consonant *h;* consonant *g;* short *o;* consonant *d;* consonant *w;* consonant *l;* consonant *x;* short *e;* consonant *y;* consonant *k;* consonant *v;* short *u;* /kw/ spelled *qu;* consonant *j;* consonant *z;* /z/ spelled *s;* consonants *-ck;* /l/ spelled *-ll;* /f/ spelled *-ff;* /s/ spelled *-ss;* /t/ spelled *-ed;* /d/ spelled *-ed;* verb ending *-ing;* *r* clusters; *l* clusters; *s* clusters; silent *k* in *kn;* silent *w* in *wr;* silent *g* in *gn;* triple clusters; digraph *sh;* digraph *th;* digraph *wh;* digraph *ch;* digraph *-tch;* long *a* (CVC*e*); /s/ spelled *c;* /j/ spelled *g;* consonants *-nd;* consonants *-ng;* consonants *-nk;* long *i* (CVC*e*); contractions; long *o* (CV); long *o* (CVC*e*); /o͞o/ spelled *u* (CVC*e*); /yo͞o/ spelled *u* (CVC*e*); consonants *-ft;* consonants *-lk;* consonants *-nt;* long *e* (CV); long *e* (CVC*e*); long *e* spelled *ee;* long *e* spelled *ea;* long *a* spelled *ai;* long *a* spelled *ay;* long *o* spelled *oa;* long *o* spelled *ow;* /o͝o/ spelled *oo;* /o͞o/ spelled *oo;* /o͞o/ spelled *ew;* /o͞o/ spelled *ue;* /o͞o/ spelled *ou;* long *i* spelled *igh;* long *i* spelled *ie;* /ĕd/ spelled *-ed;* base words + *-ing;* base words + *-s;* /ou/ spelled *ou;* /ou/ spelled *ow;* *-ing* (spelling changes); *-ed* (spelling changes); long *e* spelled *y;* long *i* spelled *y*

Manny in the City

DECODABLE WORDS

Target Skill: **long *e* spelled *y***

city	hilly
Daddy	Manny
Granny	sleepy

Previously Taught Skills

got	streets
ride	went

SKILLS APPLIED IN WORDS IN STORY: *m, s, c, t,* short *a;* consonant *n;* consonant *p;* short *i;* consonant *r;* consonant *h;* consonant *g;* short *o;* consonant *d;* consonant *w;* consonant *l;* short *e;* /l/ spelled -*ll;* *r* clusters; *l* clusters; *s* clusters; triple clusters; digraph *th;* /s/ spelled *c;* consonants -*nd;* consonants -*ng;* long *i* (CVCe); consonants -*nt;* long *e* (CV); long *e* spelled *ee;* /o͞o/ spelled *oo;* base words + -*s*

HIGH-FREQUENCY WORDS

and	long	the	was
happy	see	to	were
in	soon	very	

HOUGHTON MIFFLIN   BOSTON

Manny in the City

I ♥ LOVE READING BOOKS

THEME 9
Special Friends

We rubbed, rubbed, rubbed. We rubbed a pan with fat. We baked, baked, baked. We baked a nice big cake.

We iced, iced, iced. We iced our nice, baked cake. We sliced, sliced, sliced. We sliced our baked, iced cake.

We Baked, Baked, Baked

We tasted, tasted, tasted. We tasted our baked, iced cake. We begged, begged, begged. We begged for more iced cake!

4

We shopped, shopped, shopped. We shopped for things to eat. We whipped, whipped, whipped. We whipped a lot of eggs.

1

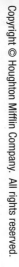

HIGH-FREQUENCY WORDS TAUGHT TO DATE

Grade 1

a	do	grow	mother	shoe[s]	was
about	does	happy	my	shout	water
afraid	door	hard	near	show	we
again	down	have	never	sing	wear
all	draw	he	not	small	what
also	eat	hear	now	so	where
always	eight	her	of	some	who
and	evening	here	old	soon	why
animal	every	hold	on	start	world
any	fall	horse	once	table	would
are	family	house	one	tall	write
arms	far	how	or	teacher	you
away	father	hungry	other	the	your
bear	find	hurt	our	their	
because	first	I	out	there	
been	five	idea	over	these	
bird	flower	in	own	they	
blue	fly	is	paper	three	
body	follow	jump	part	through	
both	for	know	people	tiny	
brown	forest	learn	picture	to	
build	found	light	piece	today	
by	four	like	play	too	
call	friend	little	pull	try	
car	full	live	read	turn	
children	funny	long	ready	two	
climb	girl	look	right	under	
cold	give	love	room	upon	
color	go	many	said	very	
come	goes	me	see	walk	
could	gone	more	seven	wall	
cow	good	morning	shall	want	
	green	most	she	warm	

Decoding skills taught to date: m, s, c, t, short a; consonant n; consonant f; consonant p; short i; consonant b; consonant r; consonant h; consonant g; short o; consonant d; consonant w; consonant l; consonant x; short e; consonant y; consonant k; consonant v; short u; /kw/ spelled qu; consonant j; consonant z; /z/ spelled s; consonants -ck; /l/ spelled -ll; /f/ spelled -ff; /s/ spelled -ss; /t/ spelled -ed; /d/ spelled -ed; verb ending -ing; r clusters; l clusters; s clusters; silent k in kn; silent w in wr; silent g in gn; triple clusters; digraph sh; digraph th; digraph wh; digraph ch; digraph -tch; long a (CVCe); /s/ spelled c; /j/ spelled g; consonants -nd; consonants -ng; consonants -nk; long i (CVCe); contractions; long o (CV); long o (CVCe); /o͞o/ spelled u (CVCe); /yo͞o/ spelled u (CVCe); consonants -ft; consonants -lk; consonants -nt; long e (CV); long e (CVCe); long e spelled ee; long e spelled ea; long a spelled ai; long a spelled ay; long o spelled oa; long o spelled ow; /o͞o/ spelled oo; /o͞o/ spelled oo; /o͞o/ spelled ew; /o͞o/ spelled ue; /o͞o/ spelled ou; long i spelled igh; long i spelled ie; /ĕd/ spelled -ed; base words + -ing; base words + -s; /ou/ spelled ou; /ou/ spelled ow; -ing (spelling changes); -ed (spelling changes)

We Baked, Baked, Baked

DECODABLE WORDS

Target Skill: *-ed* (spelling changes)

baked	iced	shopped	tasted
begged	rubbed	sliced	whipped

Previously Taught Skills

big	fat	pan
cake	lot	things
eggs	nice	with

SKILLS APPLIED IN WORDS IN STORY: *m, s, c, t,* short *a;* consonant *n;* consonant *f;* consonant *p;* short *i;* consonant *b;* consonant *r;* consonant *g;* short *o;* consonant *d;* consonant *w;* consonant *l;* short *e;* consonant *k;* short *u;* /z/ spelled *s;* /t/ spelled *-ed;* /d/ spelled *-ed;* *l* clusters; *s* clusters; digraph *sh;* digraph *th;* digraph *wh;* long *a* (CVCe); /s/ spelled *c;* consonants *-ng;* long *i* (CVCe); long *e* (CV); long *e* spelled *ea;* /ĕd/ spelled *-ed;* base words + *-s;* /ou/ spelled *ou*

HIGH-FREQUENCY WORDS

a	more	to
eat	of	we
for	our	

HOUGHTON MIFFLIN   BOSTON

We Baked, Baked, Baked

Nate is at his table. He is dining, munching, crunching, and sipping.

2

Kim is in her bedroom. She is skipping, hopping, jumping, and springing.

3

Now what are these children doing? They are smiling, chatting, joking, and playing!

4

The Clapping, Tapping House

Tess is in her living room. She is clapping, tapping, dancing, and spinning.

1

HIGH-FREQUENCY WORDS TAUGHT TO DATE

Grade 1

a
about
afraid
again
all
also
always
and
animal
any
are
arms
away
bear
because
been
bird
blue
body
both
brown
build
by
call
car
children
climb
cold
color
come
could
cow
do
does
door
down
draw
eat
eight
evening
every
fall
family
far
father
find
first
five
flower
fly
follow
for
forest
found
four
friend
full
funny
girl
give
go
goes
gone
good
green
grow
happy
hard
have
he
hear
her
here
hold
horse
house
how
hungry
hurt
I
idea
in
is
jump
know
learn
light
like
little
live
long
look
love
many
me
more
morning
most
mother
my
near
never
not
now
of
old
on
once
one
or
other
our
out
over
own
paper
part
people
picture
piece
play
pull
read
ready
right
room
said
see
seven
shall
she
shoe[s]
shout
show
sing
small
so
some
soon
start
table
tall
teacher
the
their
there
these
they
three
through
tiny
to
today
too
try
turn
two
under
upon
very
walk
wall
want
warm
was
water
we
wear
what
where
who
why
world
would
write
you
your

Decoding skills taught to date: *m, s, c, t,* short *a;* consonant *n;* consonant *f;* consonant *p;* short *i;* consonant *b;* consonant *r;* consonant *h;* consonant *g;* short *o;* consonant *d;* consonant *w;* consonant *l;* consonant *x;* short *e;* consonant *y;* consonant *k;* consonant *v;* short *u;* /kw/ spelled *qu;* consonant *j;* consonant *z;* /z/ spelled *s;* consonants *-ck;* /l/ spelled *-ll;* /f/ spelled *-ff;* /s/ spelled *-ss;* /t/ spelled *-ed;* /d/ spelled *-ed;* verb ending *-ing;* *r* clusters; *l* clusters; *s* clusters; silent *k* in *kn;* silent *w* in *wr;* silent *g* in *gn;* triple clusters; digraph *sh;* digraph *th;* digraph *wh;* digraph *ch;* digraph *-tch;* long *a* (CVC*e*); /s/ spelled *c;* /j/ spelled *g;* consonants *-nd;* consonants *-ng;* consonants *-nk;* long *i* (CVC*e*); contractions; long *o* (CV); long *o* (CVC*e*); /o͞o/ spelled *u* (CVC*e*); /yo͞o/ spelled *u* (CVC*e*); consonants *-ft;* consonants *-lk;* consonants *-nt;* long *e* (CV); long *e* (CVC*e*); long *e* spelled *ee;* long *e* spelled *ea;* long *a* spelled *ai;* long *a* spelled *ay;* long *o* spelled *oa;* long *o* spelled *ow;* /o͝o/ spelled *oo;* /o͞o/ spelled *oo;* /o͞o/ spelled *ew;* /o͞o/ spelled *ue;* /o͞o/ spelled *ou;* long *i* spelled *igh;* long *i* spelled *ie;* /ĕd/ spelled *-ed;* base words + *-ing;* base words + *-s;* /ou/ spelled *ou;* /ou/ spelled *ow;* *-ing* (spelling changes); *-ed* (spelling changes)

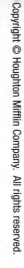

The Clapping, Tapping House

DECODABLE WORDS

Target Skill: *-ing* (spelling changes)

chatting	dining	sipping	spinning
clapping	hopping	skipping	tapping
dancing	joking	smiling	

Previously Taught Skills

at	his	Nate
bedroom	Kim	springing
crunching	munching	Tess

SKILLS APPLIED IN WORDS IN STORY: *m, s, c, t,* short *a;* consonant *n;* consonant *p;* short *i;* consonant *b;* consonant *r;* consonant *h;* short *o;* consonant *d;* consonant *l;* short *e;* consonant *k;* short *u;* consonant *j;* /z/ spelled *s;* /s/ spelled *-ss;* verb ending *-ing;* *r* clusters; *l* clusters; *s* clusters; triple clusters; digraph *sh;* digraph *th;* digraph *ch;* long *a* (CVCe); /s/ spelled *c;* consonants *-nd;* consonants *-ng;* long *i* (CVCe); long *o* (CVCe); long *e* (CV); long *e* (CVCe); long *a* spelled *ay;* /o͞o/ spelled *oo;* base words + *-ing;* /ou/ spelled *ou;* /ou/ spelled *ow*

HIGH–FREQUENCY WORDS

and	he	is	playing	the
are	her	jumping	room	these
children	house	living	she	they
doing	in	now	table	what

HOUGHTON MIFFLIN   BOSTON

The Clapping, Tapping House

Mom said, "You cannot
wear a crown and gown
downtown, Rose."

Rose frowned. Rose scowled.

2

3

Mom said, "Now we can have fun downtown. When we get back, you can wear your crown and gown."

4

No Gown Downtown

Rose has a crown and a gown. Rose said, "I will wear my crown and gown downtown."

1

Grade 1

a	down	he	not	some	why
about	draw	hear	now	soon	world
afraid	eat	her	of	start	would
again	evening	here	old	table	write
all	every	hold	on	tall	you
also	fall	horse	once	teacher	your
and	family	house	one	the	
animal	far	how	or	their	
any	father	hungry	other	there	
are	find	hurt	our	these	
away	first	I	out	they	
bear	five	idea	over	three	
because	flower	in	own	through	
been	fly	is	paper	tiny	
bird	follow	jump	part	to	
blue	for	know	people	today	
both	forest	learn	picture	too	
brown	found	light	piece	try	
build	four	like	play	turn	
by	friend	little	pull	two	
call	full	live	read	under	
car	funny	long	right	upon	
children	girl	look	room	very	
climb	give	love	said	walk	
cold	go	many	see	wall	
color	goes	me	shall	want	
come	gone	more	she	was	
could	good	morning	shoe[s]	water	
cow	green	most	shout	we	
do	grow	mother	show	wear	
does	happy	my	sing	what	
door	hard	near	small	where	
	have	never	so	who	

Decoding skills taught to date: *m, s, c, t,* short *a;* consonant *n;* consonant *f;* consonant *p;* short *i;* consonant *b;* consonant *r;* consonant *h;* consonant *g;* short *o;* consonant *d;* consonant *w;* consonant *l;* consonant *x;* short *e;* consonant *y;* consonant *k;* consonant *v;* short *u;* /kw/ spelled *qu;* consonant *j;* consonant *z;* /z/ spelled *s;* consonants *-ck;* /l/ spelled *-ll;* /f/ spelled *-ff;* /s/ spelled *-ss;* /t/ spelled *-ed;* /d/ spelled *-ed;* verb ending *-ing;* *r* clusters; *l* clusters; *s* clusters; silent *k* in *kn;* silent *w* in *wr;* silent *g* in *gn;* triple clusters; digraph *sh;* digraph *th;* digraph *wh;* digraph *ch;* digraph *-tch;* long *a* (CVC*e*); /s/ spelled *c;* /j/ spelled *g;* consonants *-nd;* consonants *-ng;* consonants *-nk;* long *i* (CVC*e*); contractions; long *o* (CV); long *o* (CVC*e*); /o͞o/ spelled *u* (CVC*e*); /yo͞o/ spelled *u* (CVC*e*); consonants *-ft;* consonants *-lk;* consonants *-nt;* long *e* (CV); long *e* (CVC*e*); long *e* spelled *ee;* long *e* spelled *ea;* long *a* spelled *ai;* long *a* spelled *ay;* long *o* spelled *oa;* long *o* spelled *ow;* /o͞o/ spelled *oo;* /o͝o/ spelled *oo;* /o͞o/ spelled *ew;* /o͞o/ spelled *ue;* /o͞o/ spelled *ou;* long *i* spelled *igh;* long *i* spelled *ie;* /ĕd/ spelled *-ed;* base words + *-ing;* base words + *-s;* /ou/ spelled *ou;* /ou/ spelled *ow*

DECODABLE WORDS

Target Skill: /ou/ spelled *ow*

crown   gown
downtown   scowled
frowned

Previously Taught Skills

back	fun	Mom	when
can	get	no	will
cannot	has	Rose	

SKILLS APPLIED IN WORDS IN STORY: *m, s, c, t,* short *a;* consonant *n;* consonant *f;* short *i;* consonant *b;* consonant *r;* consonant *h;* consonant *g;* short *o;* consonant *d;* consonant *w;* consonant *l;* short *e;* consonant *y;* short *u;* /z/ spelled *s;* consonants *-ck;* /l/ spelled *-ll;* /d/ spelled *-ed;* *r* clusters; *s* clusters; digraph *wh;* consonants *-nd;* long *o* (CV); long *o* (CVCe); long *e* (CV); /o͞o/ spelled *ou*

HIGH–FREQUENCY WORDS

a	I	said	you
and	my	we	your
have	now	wear	

HOUGHTON MIFFLIN   BOSTON

No Gown Downtown

The mound is a house for
these mice. The mice come
out of the round mound.

The stout hound bounds.

2

3

The Stout Hound

The stout hound sniffs the ground. The stout hound found a round mound.

The hound is too stout to catch the mice. He lies on the ground.

Grade 1

a	down	he	not	some	why
about	draw	hear	now	soon	world
afraid	eat	her	of	start	would
again	evening	here	old	table	write
all	every	hold	on	tall	you
also	fall	horse	once	teacher	your
and	family	house	one	the	
animal	far	how	or	their	
any	father	hungry	other	there	
are	find	hurt	our	these	
away	first	I	out	they	
bear	five	idea	over	three	
because	flower	in	own	through	
been	fly	is	paper	tiny	
bird	follow	jump	part	to	
blue	for	know	people	today	
both	forest	learn	picture	too	
brown	found	light	piece	try	
build	four	like	play	turn	
by	friend	little	pull	two	
call	full	live	read	under	
car	funny	long	right	upon	
children	girl	look	room	very	
climb	give	love	said	walk	
cold	go	many	see	wall	
color	goes	me	shall	want	
come	gone	more	she	was	
could	good	morning	shoe[s]	water	
cow	green	most	shout	we	
do	grow	mother	show	wear	
does	happy	my	sing	what	
door	hard	near	small	where	
	have	never	so	who	

Decoding skills taught to date: m, s, c, t, short a; consonant n; consonant f; consonant p; short i; consonant b; consonant r; consonant h; consonant g; short o; consonant d; consonant w; consonant l; consonant x; short e; consonant y; consonant k; consonant v; short u; /kw/ spelled qu; consonant j; consonant z; /z/ spelled s; consonants -ck; /l/ spelled -ll; /f/ spelled -ff; /s/ spelled -ss; /t/ spelled -ed; /d/ spelled -ed; verb ending -ing; r clusters; l clusters; s clusters; silent k in kn; silent w in wr; silent g in gn; triple clusters; digraph sh; digraph th; digraph wh; digraph ch; digraph -tch; long a (CVCe); /s/ spelled c; /j/ spelled g; consonants -nd; consonants -ng; consonants -nk; long i (CVCe); contractions; long o (CV); long o (CVCe); /o͞o/ spelled u (CVCe); /yo͞o/ spelled u (CVCe); consonants -ft; consonants -lk; consonants -nt; long e (CV); long e (CVCe); long e spelled ee; long e spelled ea; long a spelled ai; long a spelled ay; long o spelled oa; long o spelled ow; /o͞o/ spelled oo; /o͝o/ spelled oo; /o͞o/ spelled ew; /o͞o/ spelled ue; /o͞o/ spelled ou; long i spelled igh; long i spelled ie; /ĕd/ spelled -ed; base words + -ing; base words + -s; /ou/ spelled ou; /ou/ spelled ow

The Stout Hound

DECODABLE WORDS

Target Skill: **/ou/ spelled *ou***

bounds   hound   round
ground   mound   stout

Previously Taught Skills

catch   mice
lies   sniffs

SKILLS APPLIED IN WORDS IN STORY: *m, s, c, t,* short *a*; consonant *n*; consonant *f*; short *i*; consonant *b*; consonant *r*; consonant *h*; consonant *g*; short *o*; consonant *d*; consonant *l*; /z/ spelled *s*; /f/ spelled *-ff*; *r* clusters; *s* clusters; digraph *th*; digraph *-tch*; /s/ spelled *c*; consonants *-nd*; long *i* (CVCe); long *e* (CV); long *e* (CVCe); /o͞o/ spelled *oo*; long *i* spelled *ie*; base words + *-s*

HIGH–FREQUENCY WORDS

a	found	is	out	to
come	he	of	the	too
for	house	on	these	

HOUGHTON MIFFLIN   BOSTON

The Stout Hound

These birds also fly. They
live in tree holes. These birds
can use their big beaks to
eat bugs and seeds.

Tree frogs can be green
or brown. This frog puffs up
when he calls out. He sleeps
all day and wakes up at night.

Look at these animals.
Which animals can fly? Which
one puffs up? Which one eats
bugs and seeds?

4

BOOK 75

Rain Forest Animals

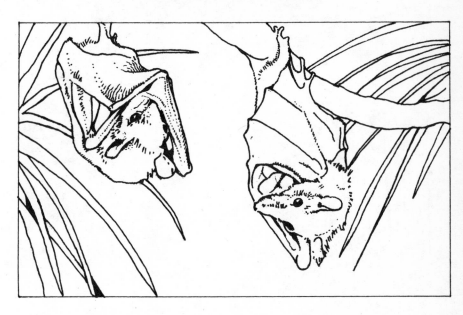

These bats live in groups.
Bat wings are like fans. Wings
keep bats cool on hot days.
Wings help bats to fly.

1

Grade 1

a	evening	hold	on	the
afraid	every	horse	once	their
again	fall	house	one	there
all	family	how	or	these
also	far	hungry	other	they
and	father	hurt	our	three
animal	find	I	out	through
any	first	idea	over	to
are	five	in	own	today
away	flower	is	paper	too
bear	fly	jump	people	try
been	follow	know	picture	turn
bird	for	learn	piece	two
blue	forest	light	play	under
both	found	like	pull	upon
brown	four	little	read	very
build	friend	live	right	walk
by	full	long	room	wall
call	funny	look	said	want
car	girl	love	see	was
children	give	many	shall	water
climb	go	me	she	we
cold	goes	more	shoe[s]	wear
color	gone	morning	shout	what
come	good	most	show	where
could	green	mother	sing	who
cow	grow	my	small	why
do	hard	near	so	world
does	have	never	some	would
door	he	not	soon	write
down	hear	now	start	you
eat	her	of	table	your
	here	old	tall	

Decoding skills taught to date: *m, s, c, t,* short *a;* consonant *n;* consonant *f;* consonant *p;* short *i;* consonant *b;* consonant *r;* consonant *h;* consonant *g;* short *o;* consonant *d;* consonant *w;* consonant *l;* consonant *x;* short *e;* consonant *y;* consonant *k;* consonant *v;* short *u;* /kw/ spelled *qu;* consonant *j;* consonant *z;* /z/ spelled *s;* consonants *-ck;* /l/ spelled *-ll;* /f/ spelled *-ff;* /s/ spelled *-ss;* /t/ spelled *-ed;* /d/ spelled *-ed;* verb ending *-ing;* *r* clusters; *l* clusters; *s* clusters; silent *k* in *kn;* silent *w* in *wr;* silent *g* in *gn;* triple clusters; digraph *sh;* digraph *th;* digraph *wh;* digraph *ch;* digraph *-tch;* long *a* (CVC*e*); /s/ spelled *c;* /j/ spelled *g;* consonants *-nd;* consonants *-ng;* consonants *-nk;* long *i* (CVC*e*); contractions; long *o* (CV); long *o* (CVC*e*); /o͞o/ spelled *u* (CVC*e*); /yo͞o/ spelled *u* (CVC*e*); consonants *-ft;* consonants *-lk;* consonants *-nt;* long *e* (CV); long *e* (CVC*e*); long *e* spelled *ee;* long *e* spelled *ea;* long *a* spelled *ai;* long *a* spelled *ay;* long *o* spelled *oa;* long *o* spelled *ow;* /o͞o/ spelled *oo;* /o͞o/ spelled *oo;* /o͞o/ spelled *ew;* /o͞o/ spelled *ue;* /o͞o/ spelled *ou;* long *i* spelled *igh;* long *i* spelled *ie;* /ĕd/ spelled *-ed;* base words + *-ing;* base words + *-s*

Rain Forest Animals

DECODABLE WORDS

Target Skill: base words + -s

bats	days	groups	seeds	wings
beaks	fans	holes	sleeps	
bugs	frogs	puffs	wakes	

Previously Taught Skills

at	cool	keep	up
bat	day	night	use
be	frog	rain	when
big	help	this	which
can	hot	tree	

SKILLS APPLIED IN WORDS IN STORY: *m, s, c, t,* short *a*; consonant *n*; consonant *f*; consonant *p*; short *i*; consonant *b*; consonant *r*; consonant *h*; consonant *g*; short *o*; consonant *d*; consonant *w*; consonant *l*; short *e*; consonant *k*; short *u*; /z/ spelled *s*; /f/ spelled *-ff*; *r* clusters; *l* clusters; *s* clusters; digraph *th*; digraph *wh*; digraph *ch*; long *a* (CVCe); consonants *-nd*; consonants *-ng*; long *i* (CVCe); long *o* (CVCe); /yo͞o/ spelled *u* (CVCe); long *e* (CV); long *e* (CVCe); long *e* spelled *ee*; long *e* spelled *ea*; long *a* spelled *ai*; long *a* spelled *ay*; /o͞o/ spelled *oo*; /o͝o/ spelled *oo*; /o͞o/ spelled *ou*; long *i* spelled *igh*

HIGH-FREQUENCY WORDS

all	brown	green	on	they
also	calls	he	one	to
and	eat	in	or	
animals	eats	like	out	
are	fly	live	their	
birds	forest	look	these	

HOUGHTON MIFFLIN   BOSTON

Rain Forest Animals

Bob's truck was steaming!
"I'll try watering it," said Bob.
Bob's truck went on huffing,
puffing, and steaming.

Bob's truck was hissing!
"I'll try cooling it," said Bob.
Bob's truck went on huffing,
puffing, steaming, and hissing.

Kids started calling, "Snacks and cones!" The huffing, puffing, steaming, and hissing went away!

4

The Huffing, Puffing, Truck

Bob's truck was huffing and puffing. "I'll try resting it," said Bob. Bob's truck went on huffing and puffing.

1

Grade 1

a	evening	hold	on	the
afraid	every	horse	once	their
again	fall	house	one	there
all	family	how	or	these
also	far	hungry	other	they
and	father	hurt	our	three
animal	find	I	out	through
any	first	idea	over	to
are	five	in	own	today
away	flower	is	paper	too
bear	fly	jump	people	try
been	follow	know	picture	turn
bird	for	learn	piece	two
blue	forest	light	play	under
both	found	like	pull	upon
brown	four	little	read	very
build	friend	live	right	walk
by	full	long	room	wall
call	funny	look	said	want
car	girl	love	see	was
children	give	many	shall	water
climb	go	me	she	we
cold	goes	more	shoe[s]	wear
color	gone	morning	shout	what
come	good	most	show	where
could	green	mother	sing	who
cow	grow	my	small	why
do	hard	near	so	world
does	have	never	some	would
door	he	not	soon	write
down	hear	now	start	you
eat	her	of	table	your
	here	old	tall	

Decoding skills taught to date: *m, s, c, t,* short *a;* consonant *n;* consonant *f;* consonant *p;* short *i;* consonant *b;* consonant *r;* consonant *h;* consonant *g;* short *o;* consonant *d;* consonant *w;* consonant *l;* consonant *x;* short *e;* consonant *y;* consonant *k;* consonant *v;* short *u;* /kw/ spelled *qu;* consonant *j;* consonant *z;* /z/ spelled *s;* consonants *-ck;* /l/ spelled *-ll;* /f/ spelled *-ff;* /s/ spelled *-ss;* /t/ spelled *-ed;* /d/ spelled *-ed;* verb ending *-ing;* *r* clusters; *l* clusters; *s* clusters; silent *k* in *kn;* silent *w* in *wr;* silent *g* in *gn;* triple clusters; digraph *sh;* digraph *th;* digraph *wh;* digraph *ch;* digraph *-tch;* long *a* (CVC*e*); /s/ spelled *c;* /j/ spelled *g;* consonants *-nd;* consonants *-ng;* consonants *-nk;* long *i* (CVC*e*); contractions; long *o* (CV); long *o* (CVC*e*); /o͞o/ spelled *u* (CVC*e*); /yo͞o/ spelled *u* (CVC*e*); consonants *-ft;* consonants *-lk;* consonants *-nt;* long *e* (CV); long *e* (CVC*e*); long *e* spelled *ee;* long *e* spelled *ea;* long *a* spelled *ai;* long *a* spelled *ay;* long *o* spelled *oa;* long *o* spelled *ow;* /o͞o/ spelled *oo;* /o͞o/ spelled *oo;* /o͞o/ spelled *ew;* /o͞o/ spelled *ue;* /o͞o/ spelled *ou;* long *i* spelled *igh;* long *i* spelled *ie;* /ĕd/ spelled *-ed;* base words + *-ing;* base words + *-s*

The Huffing, Puffing Truck

DECODABLE WORDS

Target Skill: base words + -ing

cooling	puffing
hissing	resting
huffing	steaming

Previously Taught Skills

Bob	it	truck
Bob's	kids	went
cones	snacks	

SKILLS APPLIED IN WORDS IN STORY: *m, s, c, t,* short *a;* consonant *n;* consonant *p;* short *i;* consonant *b;* consonant *r;* consonant *h;* short *o;* consonant *d;* consonant *w;* consonant *l;* short *e;* consonant *k;* short *u;* /z/ spelled *s;* consonants *-ck;* /l/ spelled *-ll;* /f/ spelled *-ff;* /s/ spelled *-ss;* verb ending *-ing;* *r* clusters; *s* clusters; digraph *th;* long *o* (CVCe); consonants *-nt;* consonants *-nd;* contractions; long *e* (CV); long *e* spelled *ea;* /o͞o/ spelled *oo*

HIGH-FREQUENCY WORDS

and	I'll	started	was
away	on	the	watering
calling	said	try	

HOUGHTON MIFFLIN   BOSTON

The Huffing, Puffing Truck

We mended the bench.
We sanded and painted it.

We tended the grass.
We cut it and weeded it.
We planted a tree, too!

We Mended
and
Tended

We are glad that we
mended and tended this
nice space!

This nice space needed
to be fixed.

4

1

HIGH-FREQUENCY WORDS TAUGHT TO DATE

Grade 1

a	evening	hold	on	the
afraid	every	horse	once	their
again	fall	house	one	there
all	family	how	or	these
also	far	hungry	other	they
and	father	hurt	our	three
animal	find	I	out	through
any	first	idea	over	to
are	five	in	own	today
away	flower	is	paper	too
bear	fly	jump	people	try
been	follow	know	picture	turn
bird	for	learn	piece	two
blue	forest	light	play	under
both	found	like	pull	upon
brown	four	little	read	very
build	friend	live	right	walk
by	full	long	room	wall
call	funny	look	said	want
car	girl	love	see	was
children	give	many	shall	water
climb	go	me	she	we
cold	goes	more	shoe[s]	wear
color	gone	morning	shout	what
come	good	most	show	where
could	green	mother	sing	who
cow	grow	my	small	why
do	hard	near	so	world
does	have	never	some	would
door	he	not	soon	write
down	hear	now	start	you
eat	her	of	table	your
	here	old	tall	

Decoding skills taught to date: *m, s, c, t,* short *a;* consonant *n;* consonant *f;* consonant *p;* short *i;* consonant *b;* consonant *r;* consonant *h;* consonant *g;* short *o;* consonant *d;* consonant *w;* consonant *l;* consonant *x;* short *e;* consonant *y;* consonant *k;* consonant *v;* short *u;* /kw/ spelled *qu;* consonant *j;* consonant *z;* /z/ spelled *s;* consonants *-ck;* /l/ spelled *-ll;* /f/ spelled *-ff;* /s/ spelled *-ss;* /t/ spelled *-ed;* /d/ spelled *-ed;* verb ending *-ing;* *r* clusters; *l* clusters; *s* clusters; silent *k* in *kn;* silent *w* in *wr;* silent *g* in *gn;* triple clusters; digraph *sh;* digraph *th;* digraph *wh;* digraph *ch;* digraph *-tch;* long *a* (CVC*e*); /s/ spelled *c;* /j/ spelled *g;* consonants *-nd;* consonants *-ng;* consonants *-nk;* long *i* (CVC*e*); contractions; long *o* (CV); long *o* (CVC*e*); /o͞o/ spelled *u* (CVC*e*); /yo͞o/ spelled *u* (CVC*e*); consonants *-ft;* consonants *-lk;* consonants *-nt;* long *e* (CV); long *e* (CVC*e*); long *e* spelled *ee;* long *e* spelled *ea;* long *a* spelled *ai;* long *a* spelled *ay;* long *o* spelled *oa;* long *o* spelled *ow;* /o͞o/ spelled *oo;* /o͝o/ spelled *oo;* /o͞o/ spelled *ew;* /o͞o/ spelled *ue;* /o͞o/ spelled *ou;* long *i* spelled *igh;* long *i* spelled *ie;* /ĕd/ spelled *-ed;* base words + *-ing;* base words + *-s*

We Mended and Tended

DECODABLE WORDS

Target Skill: /ĕd/ spelled -ed

mended	planted	weeded
needed	sanded	
painted	tended	

Previously Taught Skills

be	fixed	it	that
bench	glad	nice	this
cut	grass	space	tree

SKILLS APPLIED IN WORDS IN STORY: *m, s, c, t,* short *a*; consonant *n*; consonant *f*; consonant *p*; short *i*; consonant *b*; consonant *r*; consonant *g*; consonant *d*; consonant *w*; consonant *l*; consonant *x*; short *e*; short *u*; /s/ spelled *-ss*; /t/ spelled *-ed*; *r* clusters; *l* clusters; *s* clusters; digraph *th*; digraph *ch*; long *a* (CVCe); /s/ spelled *c*; consonants *-nd*; long *i* (CVCe); consonants *-nt*; long *e* (CV); long *e* spelled *ee*; long *a* spelled *ai*; /o͞o/ spelled *oo*

HIGH–FREQUENCY WORDS

a	the	we
and	to	
are	too	

HOUGHTON MIFFLIN   BOSTON

We Mended and Tended

I ♥ LOVE READING BOOKS

THEME 8
Our Earth

Who will win the prize pie?
Will Fran win the prize pie?
Will Brad win the prize pie?

Fran and Brad cross the line
at the same time. It is a tie!
Who will get the prize pie now?

Fran and Brad will each
have some prize pie.
  "Peach pie! Yum, yum,"
said Fran and Brad.

The Prize Pie

Fran and Brad will race.
The race prize is a big
peach pie.

HIGH-FREQUENCY WORDS TAUGHT TO DATE

Grade 1

a	every	horse	one	three
afraid	fall	house	or	through
again	family	how	other	to
all	far	hungry	our	today
also	father	hurt	out	too
and	find	I	over	try
animal	first	idea	own	turn
any	five	in	paper	two
are	flower	is	people	upon
away	fly	jump	picture	walk
bear	follow	know	play	wall
been	for	learn	pull	want
bird	forest	light	read	was
blue	found	like	right	water
both	four	little	room	we
brown	friend	live	said	what
by	full	long	see	where
call	funny	look	shall	who
car	girl	love	she	why
children	give	many	shout	world
climb	go	me	show	would
cold	goes	more	sing	write
color	gone	morning	small	you
come	good	most	so	your
could	green	mother	some	
cow	grow	my	soon	
do	hard	near	table	
does	have	never	tall	
door	he	not	the	
down	hear	now	their	
eat	her	of	there	
evening	here	on	these	
	hold	once	they	

Decoding skills taught to date: m, s, c, t, short a; consonant n; consonant f; consonant p; short i; consonant b; consonant r; consonant h; consonant g; short o; consonant d; consonant w; consonant l; consonant x; short e; consonant y; consonant k; consonant v; short u; /kw/ spelled qu; consonant j; consonant z; /z/ spelled s; consonants -ck; /l/ spelled -ll; /f/ spelled -ff; /s/ spelled -ss; /t/ spelled -ed; /d/ spelled -ed; verb ending -ing; r clusters; l clusters; s clusters; silent k in kn; silent w in wr; silent g in gn; triple clusters; digraph sh; digraph th; digraph wh; digraph ch; digraph -tch; long a (CVCe); /s/ spelled c; /j/ spelled g; consonants -nd; consonants -ng; consonants -nk; long i (CVCe); contractions; long o (CV); long o (CVCe); /o͞o/ spelled u (CVCe); /yo͞o/ spelled u (CVCe); consonants -ft; consonants -lk; consonants -nt; long e (CV); long e (CVCe); long e spelled ee; long e spelled ea; long a spelled ai; long a spelled ay; long o spelled oa; long o spelled ow; /o͞o/ spelled oo; /o͝o/ spelled oo; /o͞o/ spelled ew; /o͞o/ spelled ue; /o͞o/ spelled ou; long i spelled igh; long i spelled ie

The Prize Pie

DECODABLE WORDS

Target Skill: long *i* spelled *ie*

pie
tie

Previously Taught Skills

at	each	it	race	win
big	end	line	same	yum
Brad	Fran	peach	time	
cross	get	prize	will	

SKILLS APPLIED IN WORDS IN STORY: *m, s, c, t,* short *a*; consonant *n*; consonant *f*; consonant *p*; short *i*; consonant *b*; consonant *r*; consonant *g*; short *o*; consonant *d*; consonant *w*; consonant *l*; short *e*; consonant *y*; short *u*; consonant *z*; /z/ spelled *s*; /l/ spelled *-ll*; /s/ spelled *-ss*; *r* clusters; digraph *th*; digraph *ch*; long *a* (CVCe); /s/ spelled *c*; consonants *-nd*; long *i* (CVCe); long *e* (CV); long *e* spelled *ea*

HIGH–FREQUENCY WORDS

a	is	some
and	now	the
have	said	who

HOUGHTON MIFFLIN   BOSTON

The Prize Pie

Miss Moll was up high.
She called, "White Knight!
White Knight!"

White Knight climbed high
to get Miss Moll, but he did not
hang on tight. He fell on
his thigh.

Miss Moll came down
to White Knight. She said,
"You might like some pie."
White Knight just sighed.

4

White Knight

White Knight said, "I am
brave. I fight for what is right!"

1

Grade 1

a	every	horse	one	three
afraid	fall	house	or	through
again	family	how	other	to
all	far	hungry	our	today
also	father	hurt	out	too
and	find	I	over	try
animal	first	idea	own	turn
any	five	in	paper	two
are	flower	is	people	upon
away	fly	jump	picture	walk
bear	follow	know	play	wall
been	for	learn	pull	want
bird	forest	light	read	was
blue	found	like	right	water
both	four	little	room	we
brown	friend	live	said	what
by	full	long	see	where
call	funny	look	shall	who
car	girl	love	she	why
children	give	many	shout	world
climb	go	me	show	would
cold	goes	more	sing	write
color	gone	morning	small	you
come	good	most	so	your
could	green	mother	some	
cow	grow	my	soon	
do	hard	near	table	
does	have	never	tall	
door	he	not	the	
down	hear	now	their	
eat	her	of	there	
evening	here	on	these	
	hold	once	they	

Decoding skills taught to date: *m, s, c, t,* short *a;* consonant *n;* consonant *f;* consonant *p;* short *i;* consonant *b;* consonant *r;* consonant *h;* consonant *g;* short *o;* consonant *d;* consonant *w;* consonant *l;* consonant *x;* short *e;* consonant *y;* consonant *k;* consonant *v;* short *u;* /kw/ spelled *qu;* consonant *j;* consonant *z;* /z/ spelled *s;* consonants *-ck;* /l/ spelled *-ll;* /f/ spelled *-ff;* /s/ spelled *-ss;* /t/ spelled *-ed;* /d/ spelled *-ed;* verb ending *-ing;* *r* clusters; *l* clusters; *s* clusters; silent *k* in *kn;* silent *w* in *wr;* silent *g* in *gn;* triple clusters; digraph *sh;* digraph *th;* digraph *wh;* digraph *ch;* digraph *-tch;* long *a* (CVC*e*); /s/ spelled *c;* /j/ spelled *g;* consonants *-nd;* consonants *-ng;* consonants *-nk;* long *i* (CVC*e*); contractions; long *o* (CV); long *o* (CVC*e*); /o͞o/ spelled *u* (CVC*e*); /yo͞o/ spelled *u* (CVC*e*); consonants *-ft;* consonants *-lk;* consonants *-nt;* long *e* (CV); long *e* (CVC*e*); long *e* spelled *ee;* long *e* spelled *ea;* long *a* spelled *ai;* long *a* spelled *ay;* long *o* spelled *oa;* long *o* spelled *ow;* /o͞o/ spelled *oo;* /o͞o/ spelled *oo;* /o͞o/ spelled *ew;* /o͞o/ spelled *ue;* /o͞o/ spelled *ou;* long *i* spelled *igh;* long *i* spelled *ie*

BOOK 71

DECODABLE WORDS

Target Skill: long *i* spelled *igh*

fight	Knight	sighed	tight
high	might	thigh	

Previously Taught Skills

am	came	get	just	pie
brave	did	hang	Miss	up
but	fell	his	Moll	White

SKILLS APPLIED IN WORDS IN STORY: *m, s, c, t*, short *a*; consonant *n*; consonant *f*; consonant *p*; short *i*; consonant *b*; consonant *r*; consonant *h*; consonant *g*; short *o*; consonant *d*; consonant *l*; short *e*; consonant *y*; consonant *k*; consonant *v*; short *u*; consonant *j*; /z/ spelled *s*; /l/ spelled *-ll*; /s/ spelled *-ss*; /d/ spelled *-ed*; *r* clusters; *s* clusters; silent *k* in *kn*; digraph *sh*; digraph *th*; digraph *wh*; long *a* (CVCe); consonants *-ng*; long *i* (CVCe); long *e* (CV); /o͞o/ spelled *ou*; long *i* spelled *ie*

HIGH–FREQUENCY WORDS

called	he	not	she	what
climbed	I	on	some	you
down	is	right	to	
for	like	said	was	

White Knight

HOUGHTON MIFFLIN   BOSTON

STEP 2   You place the hen and one cup of rice into the big soup pot.

STEP 3   You fill the soup pot with water.   Cook the soup.

How to Make Rice Soup

STEP 4   Place some spice
that you like into the soup.
Soup is a good meal for you!

4

STEP 1   To make rice soup
you need rice, a hen, some
spice, and a big soup pot.

1

Grade 1

a	every	horse	one	three
afraid	fall	house	or	through
again	family	how	other	to
all	far	hungry	our	today
also	father	hurt	out	too
and	find	I	over	try
animal	first	idea	own	turn
any	five	in	paper	two
are	flower	is	people	upon
away	fly	jump	picture	walk
bear	follow	know	play	wall
been	for	learn	pull	want
bird	forest	light	read	was
blue	found	like	right	water
both	four	little	room	we
brown	friend	live	said	what
by	full	long	see	where
call	funny	look	shall	who
car	girl	love	she	why
children	give	many	shout	world
climb	go	me	show	would
cold	goes	more	sing	write
color	gone	morning	small	you
come	good	most	so	your
could	green	mother	some	
cow	grow	my	soon	
do	hard	near	table	
does	have	never	tall	
door	he	not	the	
down	hear	now	their	
eat	her	of	there	
evening	here	on	these	
	hold	once	they	

Decoding skills taught to date: *m, s, c, t,* short *a;* consonant *n;* consonant *f;* consonant *p;* short *i;* consonant *b;* consonant *r;* consonant *h;* consonant *g;* short *o;* consonant *d;* consonant *w;* consonant *l;* consonant *x;* short *e;* consonant *y;* consonant *k;* consonant *v;* short *u;* /kw/ spelled *qu;* consonant *j;* consonant *z;* /z/ spelled *s;* consonants *-ck;* /l/ spelled *-ll;* /f/ spelled *-ff;* /s/ spelled *-ss;* /t/ spelled *-ed;* /d/ spelled *-ed;* verb ending *-ing;* *r* clusters; *l* clusters; *s* clusters; silent *k* in *kn;* silent *w* in *wr;* silent *g* in *gn;* triple clusters; digraph *sh;* digraph *th;* digraph *wh;* digraph *ch;* digraph *-tch;* long *a* (CVC*e*); /s/ spelled *c;* /j/ spelled *g;* consonants *-nd;* consonants *-ng;* consonants *-nk;* long *i* (CVC*e*); contractions; long *o* (CV); long *o* (CVC*e*); /o͞o/ spelled *u* (CVC*e*); /yo͞o/ spelled *u* (CVC*e*); consonants *-ft;* consonants *-lk;* consonants *-nt;* long *e* (CV); long *e* (CVC*e*); long *e* spelled *ee;* long *e* spelled *ea;* long *a* spelled *ai;* long *a* spelled *ay;* long *o* spelled *oa;* long *o* spelled *ow;* /o͞o/ spelled *oo;* /o͞o/ spelled *oo;* /o͞o/ spelled *ew;* /o͞o/ spelled *ue;* /o͞o/ spelled *ou;* long *i* spelled *igh;* long *i* spelled *ie*

DECODABLE WORDS

Target Skill: /o͞o/ spelled *ou*

soup

Previously Taught Skills

big	fill	meal	pot	step
cook	hen	need	rice	that
cup	make	place	spice	with

SKILLS APPLIED IN WORDS IN STORY: *m, s, c, t,* short *a*; consonant *n*; consonant *f*; consonant *p*; short *i*; consonant *b*; consonant *r*; consonant *h*; consonant *g*; short *o*; consonant *d*; consonant *w*; consonant *l*; short *e*; consonant *y*; consonant *k*; short *u*; /z/ spelled *s*; /l/ spelled *-ll*; *l* clusters; *s* clusters; digraph *th*; long *a* (CVCe); /s/ spelled *c*; consonants *-nd*; long *i* (CVCe); long *e* (CV); long *e* spelled *ee*; long *e* spelled *ea*; /o͞o/ spelled *oo*

HIGH-FREQUENCY WORDS

a	good	is	one	to
and	how	like	some	water
for	into	of	the	you

HOUGHTON MIFFLIN   BOSTON

How to Make Rice Soup

"Look, a clue! I see a glue trail on the rug. I will find out where the glue trail goes."

The glue trail went to Sam's room.

"Sam, I have a clue," said Sue. "Is it true that you took my glue?"

"Sue, I took the glue,"
said Sam. "I made this gift
for you."

"Thank you!" said Sue.

4

BOOK 69

The Glue Clue

"I need glue," said Sue.
"Where is my glue? I need to
find a clue."

1

HIGH-FREQUENCY WORDS TAUGHT TO DATE

Grade 1

a	every	horse	one	three
afraid	fall	house	or	through
again	family	how	other	to
all	far	hungry	our	today
also	father	hurt	out	too
and	find	I	over	try
animal	first	idea	own	turn
any	five	in	paper	two
are	flower	is	people	upon
away	fly	jump	picture	walk
bear	follow	know	play	wall
been	for	learn	pull	want
bird	forest	light	read	was
blue	found	like	right	water
both	four	little	room	we
brown	friend	live	said	what
by	full	long	see	where
call	funny	look	shall	who
car	girl	love	she	why
children	give	many	shout	world
climb	go	me	show	would
cold	goes	more	sing	write
color	gone	morning	small	you
come	good	most	so	your
could	green	mother	some	
cow	grow	my	soon	
do	hard	near	table	
does	have	never	tall	
door	he	not	the	
down	hear	now	their	
eat	her	of	there	
evening	here	on	these	
	hold	once	they	

Decoding skills taught to date: *m, s, c, t,* short *a*; consonant *n*; consonant *f*; consonant *p*; short *i*; consonant *b*; consonant *r*; consonant *h*; consonant *g*; short *o*; consonant *d*; consonant *w*; consonant *l*; consonant *x*; short *e*; consonant *y*; consonant *k*; consonant *v*; short *u*; /kw/ spelled *qu*; consonant *j*; consonant *z*; /z/ spelled *s*; consonants *-ck*; /l/ spelled *-ll*; /f/ spelled *-ff*; /s/ spelled *-ss*; /t/ spelled *-ed*; /d/ spelled *-ed*; verb ending *-ing*; *r* clusters; *l* clusters; *s* clusters; silent *k* in *kn*; silent *w* in *wr*; silent *g* in *gn*; triple clusters; digraph *sh*; digraph *th*; digraph *wh*; digraph *ch*; digraph *-tch*; long *a* (CVC*e*); /s/ spelled *c*; /j/ spelled *g*; consonants *-nd*; consonants *-ng*; consonants *-nk*; long *i* (CVC*e*); contractions; long *o* (CV); long *o* (CVC*e*); /o͞o/ spelled *u* (CVC*e*); /yo͞o/ spelled *u* (CVC*e*); consonants *-ft*; consonants *-lk*; consonants *-nt*; long *e* (CV); long *e* (CVC*e*); long *e* spelled *ee*; long *e* spelled *ea*; long *a* spelled *ai*; long *a* spelled *ay*; long *o* spelled *oa*; long *o* spelled *ow*; /o͞o/ spelled *oo*; /o͞o/ spelled *oo*; /o͞o/ spelled *ew*; /o͞o/ spelled *ue*; /o͞o/ spelled *ou*; long *i* spelled *igh*; long *i* spelled *ie*

The Glue Clue

DECODABLE WORDS

Target Skill: /o͞o/ spelled *ue*

clue   true
glue
Sue

Previously Taught Skills

gift	need	Sam's	this	went
it	rug	thank	took	will
made	Sam	that	trail	

SKILLS APPLIED IN WORDS IN STORY: *m, s, c, t,* short *a;* consonant *n;* consonant *f;* short *i;* consonant *r;* consonant *g;* short *o;* consonant *d;* consonant *w;* consonant *l;* short *e;* consonant *y;* consonant *k;* short *u;* /z/ spelled *s;* /l/ spelled *-ll;* *r* clusters; *l* clusters; digraph *th;* long *a* (CVCe); consonants *-nk;* consonants *-ft;* consonants *-nt;* long *e* (CV); long *e* spelled *ee;* long *a* spelled *ai;* /o͞o/ spelled *oo;* /o͝o/ spelled *oo;* /o͞o/ spelled *ou*

HIGH–FREQUENCY WORDS

a	have	my	said	where
find	I	on	see	you
for	is	out	the	
goes	look	room	to	

The Glue Clue

Dew knew how to get up the yew tree, but he could not get down.

Dew was mewing. "Mew, mew, mew!"

What can May do?

"Hang on!" said May. She knew what to do.

"Mew, mew, mew!" said Dew.

Dew in the Yew Tree

Dan and his crew got Dew.
"Thank you," said May.
"Mew, mew," said Dew.

4

May had a new cat, Dew.
"Mew, mew, mew,"
said Dew.

1

Grade 1

a	every	horse	one	three
afraid	fall	house	or	through
again	family	how	other	to
all	far	hungry	our	today
also	father	hurt	out	too
and	find	I	over	try
animal	first	idea	own	turn
any	five	in	paper	two
are	flower	is	people	upon
away	fly	jump	picture	walk
bear	follow	know	play	wall
been	for	learn	pull	want
bird	forest	light	read	was
blue	found	like	right	water
both	four	little	room	we
brown	friend	live	said	what
by	full	long	see	where
call	funny	look	shall	who
car	girl	love	she	why
children	give	many	shout	world
climb	go	me	show	would
cold	goes	more	sing	write
color	gone	morning	small	you
come	good	most	so	your
could	green	mother	some	
cow	grow	my	soon	
do	hard	near	table	
does	have	never	tall	
door	he	not	the	
down	hear	now	their	
eat	her	of	there	
evening	here	on	these	
	hold	once	they	

Decoding skills taught to date: *m, s, c, t,* short *a;* consonant *n;* consonant *f;* consonant *p;* short *i;* consonant *b;* consonant *r;* consonant *h;* consonant *g;* short *o;* consonant *d;* consonant *w;* consonant *l;* consonant *x;* short *e;* consonant *y;* consonant *k;* consonant *v;* short *u;* /kw/ spelled *qu;* consonant *j;* consonant *z;* /z/ spelled *s;* consonants *-ck;* /l/ spelled *-ll;* /f/ spelled *-ff;* /s/ spelled *-ss;* /t/ spelled *-ed;* /d/ spelled *-ed;* verb ending *-ing;* *r* clusters; *l* clusters; *s* clusters; silent *k* in *kn;* silent *w* in *wr;* silent *g* in *gn;* triple clusters; digraph *sh;* digraph *th;* digraph *wh;* digraph *ch;* digraph *-tch;* long *a* (CVC*e*); /s/ spelled *c;* /j/ spelled *g;* consonants *-nd;* consonants *-ng;* consonants *-nk;* long *i* (CVC*e*); contractions; long *o* (CV); long *o* (CVC*e*); /o͞o/ spelled *u* (CVC*e*); /yo͞o/ spelled *u* (CVC*e*); consonants *-ft;* consonants *-lk;* consonants *-nt;* long *e* (CV); long *e* (CVC*e*); long *e* spelled *ee;* long *e* spelled *ea;* long *a* spelled *ai;* long *a* spelled *ay;* long *o* spelled *oa;* long *o* spelled *ow;* /o͞o/ spelled *oo;* /o͞o/ spelled *oo;* /o͞o/ spelled *ew;* /o͞o/ spelled *ue;* /o͞o/ spelled *ou;* long *i* spelled *igh;* long *i* spelled *ie*

DECODABLE WORDS

Target Skill: /o͞o/ spelled *ew*

crew	mew	yew
Dew	mewing	
knew	new	

Previously Taught Skills

but	Dan	had	May	up
can	get	hang	thank	
cat	got	his	tree	

SKILLS APPLIED IN WORDS IN STORY: *m, s, c, t,* short *a*; consonant *n*; consonant *p*; short *i*; consonant *b*; consonant *r*; consonant *h*; consonant *g*; short *o*; consonant *d*; short *e*; consonant *y*; consonant *k*; short *u*; /z/ spelled *s*; verb ending *-ing*; *r* clusters; silent *k* in *kn*; digraph *sh*; digraph *th*; consonants *-nd*; consonants *-ng*; consonants *-nk*; long *e* (CV); long *e* spelled *ee*; long *a* spelled *ay*; /o͞o/ spelled *ou*

HIGH–FREQUENCY WORDS

a	down	not	the	you
and	he	on	to	
could	how	said	was	
do	in	she	what	

BOOK 68

Dew in the Yew Tree

A loon dives into a
cool pool. Fish are food
for loons.

This hog digs for roots.
It likes to eat roots. Roots
are food for this hog.

BOOK 67

Animals Eat Food, Too!

We eat food. Animals eat food, too!

This raccoon is too little to get its own food. Its mom brings it food.

HIGH-FREQUENCY WORDS TAUGHT TO DATE

Grade 1

a	every	horse	one	three
afraid	fall	house	or	through
again	family	how	other	to
all	far	hungry	our	today
also	father	hurt	out	too
and	find	I	over	try
animal	first	idea	own	turn
any	five	in	paper	two
are	flower	is	people	upon
away	fly	jump	picture	walk
bear	follow	know	play	wall
been	for	learn	pull	want
bird	forest	light	read	was
blue	found	like	right	water
both	four	little	room	we
brown	friend	live	said	what
by	full	long	see	where
call	funny	look	shall	who
car	girl	love	she	why
children	give	many	shout	world
climb	go	me	show	would
cold	goes	more	sing	write
color	gone	morning	small	you
come	good	most	so	your
could	green	mother	some	
cow	grow	my	soon	
do	hard	near	table	
does	have	never	tall	
door	he	not	the	
down	hear	now	their	
eat	her	of	there	
evening	here	on	these	
	hold	once	they	

Decoding skills taught to date: *m, s, c, t,* short *a;* consonant *n;* consonant *f;* consonant *p;* short *i;* consonant *b;* consonant *r;* consonant *h;* consonant *g;* short *o;* consonant *d;* consonant *w;* consonant *l;* consonant *x;* short *e;* consonant *y;* consonant *k;* consonant *v;* short *u;* /kw/ spelled *qu;* consonant *j;* consonant *z;* /z/ spelled *s;* consonants *-ck;* /l/ spelled *-ll;* /f/ spelled *-ff;* /s/ spelled *-ss;* /t/ spelled *-ed;* /d/ spelled *-ed;* verb ending *-ing;* *r* clusters; *l* clusters; *s* clusters; silent *k* in *kn;* silent *w* in *wr;* silent *g* in *gn;* triple clusters; digraph *sh;* digraph *th;* digraph *wh;* digraph *ch;* digraph *-tch;* long *a* (CVC*e*); /s/ spelled *c;* /j/ spelled *g;* consonants *-nd;* consonants *-ng;* consonants *-nk;* long *i* (CVC*e*); contractions; long *o* (CV); long *o* (CVC*e*); /o͞o/ spelled *u* (CVC*e*); /yo͞o/ spelled *u* (CVC*e*); consonants *-ft;* consonants *-lk;* consonants *-nt;* long *e* (CV); long *e* (CVC*e*); long *e* spelled *ee;* long *e* spelled *ea;* long *a* spelled *ai;* long *a* spelled *ay;* long *o* spelled *oa;* long *o* spelled *ow;* /o͞o/ spelled *oo;* /o͞o/ spelled *oo;* /o͞o/ spelled *ew;* /o͞o/ spelled *ue;* /o͞o/ spelled *ou;* long *i* spelled *igh;* long *i* spelled *ie*

Animals Eat Food, Too!

DECODABLE WORDS

Target Skill: /o͞o/ spelled oo

cool	loons	roots
food	pool	
loon	raccoon	

Previously Taught Skills

brings	fish	it	this
digs	get	its	
dives	hog	mom	

SKILLS APPLIED IN WORDS IN STORY: *m, s, c, t,* short *a*; consonant *n*; consonant *f*; consonant *p*; short *i*; consonant *b*; consonant *r*; consonant *h*; consonant *g*; short *o*; consonant *d*; consonant *w*; consonant *l*; short *e*; consonant *k*; consonant *v*; /z/ spelled *s*; *r* clusters; digraph *sh*; digraph *th*; consonants *-ng*; long *i* (CVC*e*); long *e* (CV); long *e* spelled *ea*; long *o* spelled *ow*

HIGH-FREQUENCY WORDS

a	eat	is	own	we
animals	for	likes	to	
are	into	little	too	

HOUGHTON MIFFLIN   BOSTON

Animals Eat Food, Too!

The good cook slid
wood in the red hot nook.
Then she stood back.

The good cook slid a loaf
in the red hot nook. The loaf
took a long time to cook.

The Good Cook

The good cook took her hat from the hook.

1

The loaf is cooked. It looks and smells so good! The cook did a good job!

4

HIGH-FREQUENCY WORDS TAUGHT TO DATE

Grade 1

a	far	hurt	own	two
again	father	I	paper	upon
all	find	in	people	walk
also	first	is	picture	wall
and	five	jump	play	want
animal	flower	know	pull	was
are	fly	learn	read	we
away	for	light	right	what
been	forest	like	room	where
bird	found	little	said	who
blue	four	live	see	why
both	friend	long	shall	world
brown	full	look	she	would
by	funny	love	shout	write
call	girl	many	show	you
car	give	me	sing	your
children	go	more	small	
climb	goes	morning	so	
cold	gone	mother	some	
color	good	my	soon	
come	green	near	table	
could	grow	never	the	
cow	hard	not	their	
do	have	now	there	
does	he	of	these	
door	hear	on	they	
down	her	once	three	
eat	here	one	through	
evening	hold	or	to	
every	horse	other	today	
fall	house	our	too	
family	how	out	try	
	hungry	over	turn	

Decoding skills taught to date: m, s, c, t, short a; consonant n; consonant f; consonant p; short i; consonant b; consonant r; consonant h; consonant g; short o; consonant d; consonant w; consonant l; consonant x; short e; consonant y; consonant k; consonant v; short u; /kw/ spelled qu; consonant j; consonant z; /z/ spelled s; consonants -ck; /l/ spelled -ll; /f/ spelled -ff; /s/ spelled -ss; /t/ spelled -ed; /d/ spelled -ed; verb ending -ing; r clusters; l clusters; s clusters; silent k in kn; silent w in wr; silent g in gn; triple clusters; digraph sh; digraph th; digraph wh; digraph ch; digraph -tch; long a (CVCe); /s/ spelled c; /j/ spelled g; consonants -nd; consonants -ng; consonants -nk; long i (CVCe); contractions; long o (CV); long o (CVCe); /o͞o/ spelled u (CVCe); /yo͞o/ spelled u (CVCe); consonants -ft; consonants -lk; consonants -nt; long e (CV); long e (CVCe); long e spelled ee; long e spelled ea; long a spelled ai; long a spelled ay; long o spelled oa; long o spelled ow; /o͞o/ spelled oo

The Good Cook

DECODABLE WORDS

Target Skill: /ŏŏ/ spelled *oo*

cook	nook	wood
cooked	stood	
hook	took	

Previously Taught Skills

back	hat	job	slid	time
did	hot	loaf	smells	
from	it	red	then	

SKILLS APPLIED IN WORDS IN STORY: *m, s, c, t,* short *a;* consonant *n;* consonant *f;* short *i;* consonant *b;* consonant *r;* consonant *h;* consonant *g;* short *o;* consonant *d;* consonant *w;* consonant *l;* short *e;* consonant *k;* consonant *j;* /z/ spelled *s;* consonants *-ck;* /l/ spelled *-ll;* /t/ spelled *-ed;* *r* clusters; *l* clusters; *s* clusters; digraph *sh;* digraph *th;* consonants *-nd;* consonants *-ng;* long *i* (CVCe); long *o* (CV); long *e* (CV); long *o* spelled *oa*

HIGH–FREQUENCY WORDS

a	her	long	so
and	in	looks	the
good	is	she	to

HOUGHTON MIFFLIN   BOSTON

The Good Cook

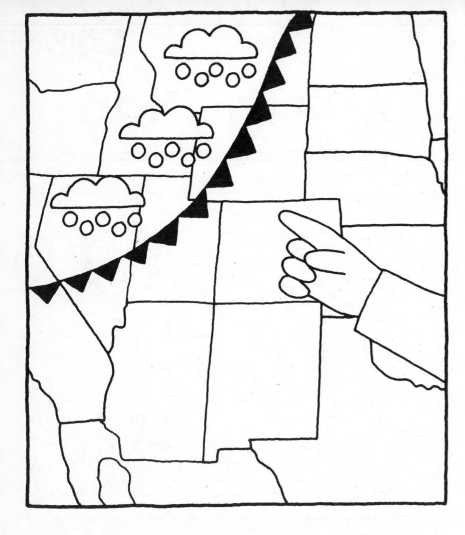

Lee Chen shows us that a slow wind will blow the snow over the hills.

2

Then, Lee Chen shows us that the wind will blow fast. Soon the snow will fall on our home.

3

Now we know when the
snow will fall. We love snow!
Let it snow, snow, snow!

4

A Snow Map

Lee Chen has a map that
shows where it will snow.

1

Grade 1

a	find	jump	pull	what
all	first	know	read	where
also	five	learn	right	who
and	flower	light	room	why
animal	fly	like	said	world
are	for	little	see	would
away	forest	live	shall	write
been	found	long	she	you
bird	four	look	shout	your
blue	friend	love	show	
brown	full	many	sing	
by	funny	me	small	
call	girl	more	so	
car	give	morning	some	
children	go	mother	soon	
climb	goes	my	table	
cold	good	near	the	
color	green	never	their	
come	grow	not	there	
could	have	now	these	
cow	he	of	they	
do	hear	on	three	
does	her	once	through	
door	here	one	to	
down	hold	other	today	
eat	horse	our	too	
evening	house	out	try	
every	how	over	two	
fall	hungry	own	upon	
family	hurt	paper	walk	
far	I	people	wall	
father	in	picture	was	
	is	play	we	

Decoding skills taught to date: *m, s, c, t,* short *a;* consonant *n;* consonant *f;* consonant *p;* short *i;* consonant *b;* consonant *r;* consonant *h;* consonant *g;* short *o;* consonant *d;* consonant *w;* consonant *l;* consonant *x;* short *e;* consonant *y;* consonant *k;* consonant *v;* short *u;* /kw/ spelled *qu;* consonant *j;* consonant *z;* /z/ spelled *s;* consonants *-ck;* /l/ spelled *-ll;* /f/ spelled *-ff;* /s/ spelled *-ss;* /t/ spelled *-ed;* /d/ spelled *-ed;* verb ending *-ing;* *r* clusters; *l* clusters; *s* clusters; silent *k* in *kn;* silent *w* in *wr;* silent *g* in *gn;* triple clusters; digraph *sh;* digraph *th;* digraph *wh;* digraph *ch;* digraph *-tch;* long *a* (CVC*e*); /s/ spelled *c;* /j/ spelled *g;* consonants *-nd;* consonants *-ng;* consonants *-nk;* long *i* (CVC*e*); contractions; long *o* (CV); long *o* (CVC*e*); /ōō/ spelled *u* (CVC*e*); /yōō/ spelled *u* (CVC*e*); consonants *-ft;* consonants *-lk;* consonants *-nt;* long *e* (CV); long *e* (CVC*e*); long *e* spelled *ee;* long *e* spelled *ea;* long *a* spelled *ai;* long *a* spelled *ay;* long *o* spelled *oa;* long *o* spelled *ow*

DECODABLE WORDS

Target Skill: long *o* spelled *ow*

blow snow
slow

Previously Taught Skills

Chen	hills	Lee	that	when
fast	home	let	then	will
has	it	map	us	wind

SKILLS APPLIED IN WORDS IN STORY: *m, s, c, t,* short *a;* consonant *n;* consonant *f;* consonant *p;* short *i;* consonant *b;* consonant *h;* short *o;* consonant *d;* consonant *w;* consonant *l;* short *e;* short *u;* /z/ spelled *s;* /l/ spelled *-ll;* *l* clusters; *s* clusters; silent *k* in *kn;* digraph *sh;* digraph *th;* digraph *wh;* digraph *ch;* consonants *-nd;* long *o* (CVCe); long *e* (CV); long *e* spelled *ee*

HIGH–FREQUENCY WORDS

a	love	our	soon	where
fall	now	over	the	
know	on	shows	we	

A Snow Map

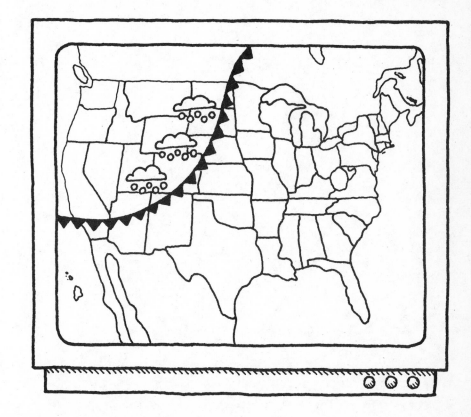

HOUGHTON MIFFLIN   BOSTON

We coach our goat every day. Our goat can run and leap. Our goat can do lots of fun tricks.

Our goat is in the tub of soap. We scrub our goat. Then we brush his coat.

2

3

BOOK 64

Our Goat

We have a goat. We feed
our goat lots of oats.

Our goat wins the big prize
in the goat show! "Our goat is
the best!" we boast.

Grade 1

a	find	jump	pull	what
all	first	know	read	where
also	five	learn	right	who
and	flower	light	room	why
animal	fly	like	said	world
are	for	little	see	would
away	forest	live	shall	write
been	found	long	she	you
bird	four	look	shout	your
blue	friend	love	show	
brown	full	many	sing	
by	funny	me	small	
call	girl	more	so	
car	give	morning	some	
children	go	mother	soon	
climb	goes	my	table	
cold	good	near	the	
color	green	never	their	
come	grow	not	there	
could	have	now	these	
cow	he	of	they	
do	hear	on	three	
does	her	once	through	
door	here	one	to	
down	hold	other	today	
eat	horse	our	too	
evening	house	out	try	
every	how	over	two	
fall	hungry	own	upon	
family	hurt	paper	walk	
far	I	people	wall	
father	in	picture	was	
	is	play	we	

Decoding skills taught to date: *m, s, c, t,* short *a;* consonant *n;* consonant *f;* consonant *p;* short *i;* consonant *b;* consonant *r;* consonant *h;* consonant *g;* short *o;* consonant *d;* consonant *w;* consonant *l;* consonant *x;* short *e;* consonant *y;* consonant *k;* consonant *v;* short *u;* /kw/ spelled *qu;* consonant *j;* consonant *z;* /z/ spelled *s;* consonants *-ck;* /l/ spelled *-ll;* /f/ spelled *-ff;* /s/ spelled *-ss;* /t/ spelled *-ed;* /d/ spelled *-ed;* verb ending *-ing;* *r* clusters; *l* clusters; *s* clusters; silent *k* in *kn;* silent *w* in *wr;* silent *g* in *gn;* triple clusters; digraph *sh;* digraph *th;* digraph *wh;* digraph *ch;* digraph *-tch;* long *a* (CVC*e*); /s/ spelled *c;* /j/ spelled *g;* consonants *-nd;* consonants *-ng;* consonants *-nk;* long *i* (CVC*e*); contractions; long *o* (CV); long *o* (CVC*e*); /o͞o/ spelled *u* (CVC*e*); /yo͞o/ spelled *u* (CVC*e*); consonants *-ft;* consonants *-lk;* consonants *-nt;* long *e* (CV); long *e* (CVC*e*); long *e* spelled *ee;* long *e* spelled *ea;* long *a* spelled *ai;* long *a* spelled *ay;* long *o* spelled *oa;* long *o* spelled *ow*

Our Goat

DECODABLE WORDS

Target Skill: **long *o* spelled *oa***

boast	goat
coach	oats
coat	soap

Previously Taught Skills

best	day	leap	scrub	wins
big	feed	lots	then	
brush	fun	prize	tricks	
can	his	run	tub	

SKILLS APPLIED IN WORDS IN STORY: *m, s, c, t,* short *a*; consonant *n*; consonant *f*; consonant *p*; short *i*; consonant *b*; consonant *r*; consonant *h*; consonant *g*; short *o*; consonant *d*; consonant *w*; consonant *l*; short *e*; short *u*; consonant *z*; /z/ spelled *s*; consonants *-ck*; *r* clusters; *s* clusters; triple clusters; digraph *sh*; digraph *th*; digraph *ch*; consonants *-nd*; long *i* (CVCe); long *e* (CV); long *e* spelled *ee*; long *e* spelled *ea*; long *a* spelled *ay*; long *o* spelled *ow*

HIGH–FREQUENCY WORDS

a	every	is	show
and	have	of	the
do	in	our	we

Our Goat

I ❤ LOVE READING BOOKS

THEME 7
We Can Work It Out

Ray lays clay on a wheel.
The clay sways and spins as it
takes shape. It is a pot!

Ray paints horses at play on
his clay pot. Ray paints all day.

Ray's Clay Pot

This is Ray. Ray makes clay pots.

At last Ray will bake his clay pot. Many people will pay for a clay pot made by Ray.

Grade 1

	flower	live	she	your
a	fly	long	shout	
all	for	look	show	
also	found	love	sing	
and	four	many	small	
animal	friend	me	so	
are	full	more	some	
away	funny	morning	table	
bird	girl	mother	the	
blue	give	my	their	
brown	go	never	there	
by	good	not	these	
call	green	now	they	
car	grow	of	three	
children	have	on	through	
climb	he	once	to	
cold	hear	one	today	
color	her	other	too	
come	here	our	try	
could	hold	out	two	
cow	horse	over	upon	
do	house	own	walk	
does	how	paper	wall	
door	hurt	people	was	
down	I	picture	we	
eat	in	play	what	
every	is	pull	where	
fall	jump	read	who	
family	know	right	why	
father	learn	room	world	
find	light	said	would	
first	like	see	write	
five	little	shall	you	

Decoding skills taught to date: *m, s, c, t,* short *a;* consonant *n;* consonant *f;* consonant *p;* short *i;* consonant *b;* consonant *r;* consonant *h;* consonant *g;* short *o;* consonant *d;* consonant *w;* consonant *l;* consonant *x;* short *e;* consonant *y;* consonant *k;* consonant *v;* short *u;* /kw/ spelled *qu;* consonant *j;* consonant *z;* /z/ spelled *s;* consonants *-ck;* /l/ spelled *-ll;* /f/ spelled *-ff;* /s/ spelled *-ss;* /t/ spelled *-ed;* /d/ spelled *-ed;* verb ending *-ing;* *r* clusters; *l* clusters; *s* clusters; silent *k* in *kn;* silent *w* in *wr;* silent *g* in *gn;* triple clusters; digraph *sh;* digraph *th;* digraph *wh;* digraph *ch;* digraph *-tch;* long *a* (CVC*e*); /s/ spelled *c;* /j/ spelled *g;* consonants *-nd;* consonants *-ng;* consonants *-nk;* long *i* (CVC*e*); contractions; long *o* (CV); long *o* (CVC*e*); /o͞o/ spelled *u* (CVC*e*); /yo͞o/ spelled *u* (CVC*e*); consonants *-ft;* consonants *-lk;* consonants *-nt;* long *e* (CV); long *e* (CVC*e*); long *e* spelled *ee;* long *e* spelled *ea;* long *a* spelled *ai;* long *a* spelled *ay*

Ray's Clay Pot

DECODABLE WORDS

Target Skill: long *a* spelled *ay*

clay	pay	sways
day	Ray	
lays	Ray's	

Previously Taught Skills

as	it	paints	spins	wheel
at	last	pot	takes	
bake	made	pots	this	
his	makes	shape	will	

SKILLS APPLIED IN WORDS IN STORY: *m, s, c, t,* short *a*; consonant *n*; consonant *p*; short *i*; consonant *b*; consonant *r*; consonant *h*; short *o*; consonant *d*; consonant *w*; consonant *l*; consonant *k*; /z/ spelled *s*; /l/ spelled *-ll*; *l* clusters; *s* clusters; digraph *sh*; digraph *th*; digraph *wh*; long *a* (CVCe); consonants *-nd*; consonants *-nt*; long *e* (CV); long *e* spelled *ee*; long *a* spelled *ai*

HIGH–FREQUENCY WORDS

a	by	is	people
all	for	many	play
and	horses	on	the

HOUGHTON MIFFLIN   BOSTON

Ray's Clay Pot

Snail went up the Mail
Trail. The Mail Trail was
long. Snail had to strain.

Rain fell on the Mail Trail.
"Rain, rain, rain!" wailed
Snail.

BOOK 62

Snail's Mail Trail

Snail did not fail. Snail got
the mail to Quail!

Snail had some mail
to take to Quail.

4

1

Grade 1

a	fly	look	sing
all	for	love	small
also	found	many	so
and	four	me	some
animal	friend	more	table
are	full	morning	the
away	funny	mother	their
bird	girl	my	there
blue	give	never	these
brown	go	not	they
by	good	now	three
call	green	of	through
car	grow	on	to
children	have	once	today
climb	he	one	too
cold	hear	other	try
color	her	our	two
come	here	out	upon
could	hold	over	walk
cow	horse	own	wall
do	house	paper	was
does	how	people	we
door	hurt	picture	what
down	I	play	where
eat	in	pull	who
every	is	read	why
fall	jump	right	world
family	know	room	would
father	learn	said	write
find	light	see	you
first	like	shall	your
five	little	she	
flower	live	shout	
	long	show	

Decoding skills taught to date: *m, s, c, t,* short *a;* consonant *n;* consonant *f;* consonant *p;* short *i;* consonant *b;* consonant *r;* consonant *h;* consonant *g;* short *o;* consonant *d;* consonant *w;* consonant *l;* consonant *x;* short *e;* consonant *y;* consonant *k;* consonant *v;* short *u;* /kw/ spelled *qu;* consonant *j;* consonant *z;* /z/ spelled *s;* consonants *-ck;* /l/ spelled *-ll;* /f/ spelled *-ff;* /s/ spelled *-ss;* /t/ spelled *-ed;* /d/ spelled *-ed;* verb ending *-ing;* *r* clusters; *l* clusters; *s* clusters; silent *k* in *kn;* silent *w* in *wr;* silent *g* in *gn;* triple clusters; digraph *sh;* digraph *th;* digraph *wh;* digraph *ch;* digraph *-tch;* long *a* (CVC*e*); /s/ spelled *c;* /j/ spelled *g;* consonants *-nd;* consonants *-ng;* consonants *-nk;* long *i* (CVC*e*); contractions; long *o* (CV); long *o* (CVC*e*); /o͞o/ spelled *u* (CVC*e*); /yo͞o/ spelled *u* (CVC*e*); consonants *-ft;* consonants *-lk;* consonants *-nt;* long *e* (CV); long *e* (CVC*e*); long *e* spelled *ee;* long *e* spelled *ea;* long *a* spelled *ai;* long *a* spelled *ay*

DECODABLE WORDS

Target Skill: **long *a* spelled *ai***

fail	Quail	Snail	strain	wailed
mail	rain	Snail's	Trail	

Previously Taught Skills

did	got	take	went
fell	had	up	

SKILLS APPLIED IN WORDS IN STORY: *m, s, c, t,* short *a*; consonant *n*; consonant *f*; consonant *p*; short *i*; consonant *r*; consonant *h*; consonant *g*; short *o*; consonant *d*; consonant *w*; consonant *l*; short *e*; consonant *k*; short *u*; /kw/ spelled *qu*; /z/ spelled *s*; /l/ spelled *-ll*; /d/ spelled *-ed*; *r* clusters; *s* clusters; triple clusters; digraph *th*; long *a* (CVCe); consonants *-ng*; consonants *-nt*; long *e* (CV)

HIGH–FREQUENCY WORDS

long	some	was
not	the	
on	to	

HOUGHTON MIFFLIN   BOSTON

Snail's Mail Trail

Clean and cut each peach.
Place it in a dish with cream.
What a treat!

These are peas. Peas grow
in pods that look like green
beans. How many pea pods do
you see?

You can steam peas for
a treat. A heap of peas!
What a feast!

4

A Peach and Some Peas

Reach for a big, ripe
peach. Each peach has a seed.
The seed is called a pit. Peach
trees grow from these seeds.

1

HIGH-FREQUENCY WORDS TAUGHT TO DATE

Grade 1

a	for	love	small
all	found	many	so
also	four	me	some
and	friend	more	the
animal	full	morning	their
are	funny	mother	these
away	girl	my	they
bird	give	never	three
blue	go	not	to
brown	good	of	today
by	green	on	too
call	grow	once	try
car	have	one	two
children	he	other	upon
climb	hear	our	walk
cold	her	out	was
color	here	over	we
come	hold	own	what
could	house	paper	where
do	how	people	who
does	hurt	picture	why
down	I	play	world
eat	in	pull	would
every	is	read	write
fall	jump	right	you
family	know	room	your
father	learn	said	
find	light	see	
first	like	shall	
five	little	she	
flower	live	shout	
fly	long	show	
	look	sing	

Decoding skills taught to date: *m, s, c, t,* short *a;* consonant *n;* consonant *f;* consonant *p;* short *i;* consonant *b;* consonant *r;* consonant *h;* consonant *g;* short *o;* consonant *d;* consonant *w;* consonant *l;* consonant *x;* short *e;* consonant *y;* consonant *k;* consonant *v;* short *u;* /kw/ spelled *qu;* consonant *j;* consonant *z;* /z/ spelled *s;* consonants *-ck;* /l/ spelled *-ll;* /f/ spelled *-ff;* /s/ spelled *-ss;* /t/ spelled *-ed;* /d/ spelled *-ed;* verb ending *-ing; r* clusters; *l* clusters; *s* clusters; silent *k* in *kn;* silent *w* in *wr;* silent *g* in *gn;* triple clusters; digraph *sh;* digraph *th;* digraph *wh;* digraph *ch;* digraph *-tch;* long *a* (CVC*e*); /s/ spelled *c;* /j/ spelled *g;* consonants *-nd;* consonants *-ng;* consonants *-nk;* long *i* (CVC*e*); contractions; long *o* (CV); long *o* (CVC*e*); /o͞o/ spelled *u* (CVC*e*); /yo͞o/ spelled *u* (CVC*e*); consonants *-ft;* consonants *-lk;* consonants *-nt;* long *e* (CV); long *e* (CVC*e*); long *e* spelled *ee;* long *e* spelled *ea*

A Peach and Some Peas

DECODABLE WORDS

Target Skill: long *e* spelled *ea*

beans	each	peach	reach
clean	feast	pea	steam
cream	heap	peas	treat

Previously Taught Skills

big	from	place	seeds
can	has	pods	that
cut	it	ripe	trees
dish	pit	seed	with

SKILLS APPLIED IN WORDS IN STORY: *m, s, c, t,* short *a*; consonant *n*; consonant *f*; consonant *p*; short *i*; consonant *b*; consonant *r*; consonant *h*; consonant *g*; short *o*; consonant *d*; consonant *w*; consonant *l*; consonant *k*; short *u*; /z/ spelled *s*; *r* clusters; *l* clusters; *s* clusters; digraph *sh*; digraph *th*; digraph *ch*; long *a* (CVCe); /s/ spelled *c*; consonants -*nd*; long *i* (CVCe); long *e* (CV); long *e* (CVCe); long *e* spelled *ee*

HIGH–FREQUENCY WORDS

a	for	is	see	you
and	green	like	some	
are	grow	look	the	
called	how	many	these	
do	in	of	what	

HOUGHTON MIFFLIN   BOSTON

A Peach and Some Peas

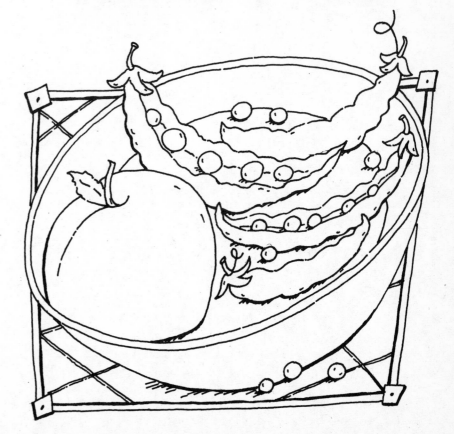

Three sheep graze by
a tree. Sheep feed on
green grass.

Pigs seem to like mud.
This pig's feet are deep in mud.
Mud keeps its feet cold.

Lee is sweeping. Sweep, sweep, sweep! Shh! The animals are sleeping.

BOOK 60

Meet the Animals

When chicks meet, they go, "cheep, cheep, cheep!" One chick has a seed.

Grade 1

a	for	love	small
all	found	many	so
also	four	me	some
and	friend	more	the
animal	full	morning	their
are	funny	mother	these
away	girl	my	they
bird	give	never	three
blue	go	not	to
brown	good	of	today
by	green	on	too
call	grow	once	try
car	have	one	two
children	he	other	upon
climb	hear	our	walk
cold	her	out	was
color	here	over	we
come	hold	own	what
could	house	paper	where
do	how	people	who
does	hurt	picture	why
down	I	play	world
eat	in	pull	would
every	is	read	write
fall	jump	right	you
family	know	room	your
father	learn	said	
find	light	see	
first	like	shall	
five	little	she	
flower	live	shout	
fly	long	show	
	look	sing	

Decoding skills taught to date: *m, s, c, t,* short *a;* consonant *n;* consonant *f;* consonant *p;* short *i;* consonant *b;* consonant *r;* consonant *h;* consonant *g;* short *o;* consonant *d;* consonant *w;* consonant *l;* consonant *x;* short *e;* consonant *y;* consonant *k;* consonant *v;* short *u;* /kw/ spelled *qu;* consonant *j;* consonant *z;* /z/ spelled *s;* consonants *-ck;* /l/ spelled *-ll;* /f/ spelled *-ff;* /s/ spelled *-ss;* /t/ spelled *-ed;* /d/ spelled *-ed;* verb ending *-ing;* *r* clusters; *l* clusters; *s* clusters; silent *k* in *kn;* silent *w* in *wr;* silent *g* in *gn;* triple clusters; digraph *sh;* digraph *th;* digraph *wh;* digraph *ch;* digraph *-tch;* long *a* (CVC*e*); /s/ spelled *c;* /j/ spelled *g;* consonants *-nd;* consonants *-ng;* consonants *-nk;* long *i* (CVC*e*); contractions; long *o* (CV); long *o* (CVC*e*); /ōō/ spelled *u* (CVC*e*); /yōō/ spelled *u* (CVC*e*); consonants *-ft;* consonants *-lk;* consonants *-nt;* long *e* (CV); long *e* (CVC*e*); long *e* spelled *ee;* long *e* spelled *ea*

Meet the Animals

DECODABLE WORDS

Target Skill: **long *e* spelled *ee***

cheep	feet	meet	sheep	sweeping
deep	keeps	seed	sleeping	tree
feed	Lee	seem	sweep	

Previously Taught Skills

chick	graze	mud	shh
chicks	has	pigs	this
grass	its	pig's	when

SKILLS APPLIED IN WORDS IN STORY: *m, s, c, t,* short *a*; consonant *n*; consonant *f*; consonant *p*; short *i*; consonant *r*; consonant *h*; consonant *g*; short *o*; consonant *d*; consonant *w*; consonant *l*; short *e*; consonant *k*; short *u*; consonant *z*; /z/ spelled *s*; consonants -*ck*; /s/ spelled -*ss*; verb ending -*ing*; *r* clusters; *l* clusters; *s* clusters; digraph *sh*; digraph *th*; digraph *wh*; digraph *ch*; long *a* (CVCe); /s/ spelled *c*; long *i* (CVCe); long *o* (CV); long *e* (CV)

HIGH–FREQUENCY WORDS

a	cold	is	the
animals	go	like	three
are	green	one	they
by	in	on	to

HOUGHTON MIFFLIN   BOSTON

Meet the Animals

These are homes on Crete where people live today.

2

This is where the king of Crete lived in the past.

3

Crete

Steve and Eve got these
pictures on Crete.

4

Steve and Eve went to Crete.
Crete is a Greek land in the sea.

1

HIGH-FREQUENCY WORDS TAUGHT TO DATE

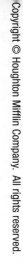

Grade 1

a	for	love	small
all	found	many	so
also	four	me	some
and	friend	more	the
animal	full	morning	their
are	funny	mother	these
away	girl	my	they
bird	give	never	three
blue	go	not	to
brown	good	of	today
by	green	on	too
call	grow	once	try
car	have	one	two
children	he	other	upon
climb	hear	our	walk
cold	her	out	was
color	here	over	we
come	hold	own	what
could	house	paper	where
do	how	people	who
does	hurt	picture	why
down	I	play	world
eat	in	pull	would
every	is	read	write
fall	jump	right	you
family	know	room	your
father	learn	said	
find	light	see	
first	like	shall	
five	little	she	
flower	live	shout	
fly	long	show	
	look	sing	

Decoding skills taught to date: *m, s, c, t,* short *a;* consonant *n;* consonant *f;* consonant *p;* short *i;* consonant *b;* consonant *r;* consonant *h;* consonant *g;* short *o;* consonant *d;* consonant *w;* consonant *l;* consonant *x;* short *e;* consonant *y;* consonant *k;* consonant *v;* short *u;* /kw/ spelled *qu;* consonant *j;* consonant *z;* /z/ spelled *s;* consonants *-ck;* /l/ spelled *-ll;* /f/ spelled *-ff;* /s/ spelled *-ss;* /t/ spelled *-ed;* /d/ spelled *-ed;* verb ending *-ing;* *r* clusters; *l* clusters; *s* clusters; silent *k* in *kn;* silent *w* in *wr;* silent *g* in *gn;* triple clusters; digraph *sh;* digraph *th;* digraph *wh;* digraph *ch;* digraph *-tch;* long *a* (CVC*e*); /s/ spelled *c;* /j/ spelled *g;* consonants *-nd;* consonants *-ng;* consonants *-nk;* long *i* (CVC*e*); contractions; long *o* (CV); long *o* (CVC*e*); /o͞o/ spelled *u* (CVC*e*); /yo͞o/ spelled *u* (CVC*e*); consonants *-ft;* consonants *-lk;* consonants *-nt;* long *e* (CV); long *e* (CVC*e*); long *e* spelled *ee;* long *e* spelled *ea*

Crete

DECODABLE WORDS

Target Skill: *long e* (CVC*e*)

Crete   Steve
Eve

Previously Taught Skills

got	homes	past	went
Greece	king	sea	
Greek	land	this	

SKILLS APPLIED IN WORDS IN STORY: *m, s, c, t,* short *a*; consonant *n*; consonant *p*; short *i*; consonant *r*; consonant *h*; consonant *g*; short *o*; consonant *d*; consonant *w*; consonant *l*; short *e*; consonant *k*; consonant *v*; /z/ spelled *s*; *r* clusters; *s* clusters; digraph *th*; /s/ spelled *c*; consonants *-nd*; consonants *-ng*; long *o* (CVC*e*); consonants *-nt*; long *e* (CV); long *e* spelled *ee*; long *e* spelled *ea*

HIGH–FREQUENCY WORDS

a	is	on	these
and	live	people	to
are	lived	pictures	today
in	of	the	where

HOUGHTON MIFFLIN   BOSTON

Crete

"Who will help me dust?"
asked Hen.

"It will not be I!"
said Pig.

"Who will help me eat
cake?" asked Hen.

"**ME! ME! ME!**" said Pig.

"Here is the mix, then!"
said Hen.

Who Will Help Me?

"Who will help me pick up
this mess?" asked Hen.
"It will not be I!" said Pig.

1

Pig made a cake.
"Who will eat cake?"
asked Pig.
"**WE** will!" said Hen.

4

HIGH-FREQUENCY WORDS TAUGHT TO DATE

Grade 1

a	for	love	small
all	found	many	so
also	four	me	some
and	friend	more	the
animal	full	morning	their
are	funny	mother	these
away	girl	my	they
bird	give	never	three
blue	go	not	to
brown	good	of	today
by	green	on	too
call	grow	once	try
car	have	one	two
children	he	other	upon
climb	hear	our	walk
cold	her	out	was
color	here	over	we
come	hold	own	what
could	house	paper	where
do	how	people	who
does	hurt	picture	why
down	I	play	world
eat	in	pull	would
every	is	read	write
fall	jump	right	you
family	know	room	your
father	learn	said	
find	light	see	
first	like	shall	
five	little	she	
flower	live	shout	
fly	long	show	
	look	sing	

Decoding skills taught to date: *m, s, c, t,* short *a;* consonant *n;* consonant *f;* consonant *p;* short *i;* consonant *b;* consonant *r;* consonant *h;* consonant *g;* short *o;* consonant *d;* consonant *w;* consonant *l;* consonant *x;* short *e;* consonant *y;* consonant *k;* consonant *v;* short *u;* /kw/ spelled *qu;* consonant *j;* consonant *z;* /z/ spelled *s;* consonants *-ck;* /l/ spelled *-ll;* /f/ spelled *-ff;* /s/ spelled *-ss;* /t/ spelled *-ed;* /d/ spelled *-ed;* verb ending *-ing;* *r* clusters; *l* clusters; *s* clusters; silent *k* in *kn;* silent *w* in *wr;* silent *g* in *gn;* triple clusters; digraph *sh;* digraph *th;* digraph *wh;* digraph *ch;* digraph *-tch;* long *a* (CVC*e*); /s/ spelled *c;* /j/ spelled *g;* consonants *-nd;* consonants *-ng;* consonants *-nk;* long *i* (CVC*e*); contractions; long *o* (CV); long *o* (CVC*e*); /o͞o/ spelled *u* (CVC*e*); /yo͞o/ spelled *u* (CVC*e*); consonants *-ft;* consonants *-lk;* consonants *-nt;* long *e* (CV); long *e* (CVC*e*); long *e* spelled *ee;* long *e* spelled *ea*

Who Will Help Me?

DECODABLE WORDS

Target Skill: long *e* (CV)

be

Previously Taught Skills

asked	help	made	pick	this
cake	Hen	mess	Pig	up
dust	it	mix	then	will

SKILLS APPLIED IN WORDS IN STORY: *m, s, c, t,* short *a*; consonant *n*; consonant *p*; short *i*; consonant *b*; consonant *h*; consonant *g*; short *o*; consonant *d*; consonant *w*; consonant *l*; consonant *x*; short *e*; consonant *k*; short *u*; /z/ spelled *s*; consonants *-ck*; /l/ spelled *-ll*; /s/ spelled *-ss*; /t/ spelled *-ed*; *s* clusters; digraph *th*; long *a* (CVCe); long *e* spelled *ea*

HIGH–FREQUENCY WORDS

a	I	not	we
eat	is	said	who
here	me	the	

HOUGHTON MIFFLIN   BOSTON

Who Will Help Me?

Kent went home with his tent. The tent pole was bent. It had a dent.

Kent went back to Rent-a-Tent. "This tent pole is bent. It has a dent," said Kent. Then Kent got a good tent pole.

2

3

Rent a Tent, Kent

Kent went to get a tent.
He went to the shop Rent-a-Tent.

Kent went home with his
good tent pole. He pitched his
tent and went in!

Grade 1

a	friend	more	three
all	full	mother	to
also	funny	my	today
and	girl	never	too
animal	give	not	try
are	go	of	two
away	good	on	upon
bird	green	once	walk
blue	grow	one	was
brown	have	other	we
call	he	our	what
car	hear	over	where
children	her	own	who
cold	here	paper	why
color	hold	people	world
come	house	picture	would
could	how	play	write
do	hurt	pull	you
does	I	read	your
down	in	right	
eat	is	room	
every	jump	said	
fall	know	see	
family	learn	shall	
father	light	she	
find	like	sing	
first	little	small	
five	live	so	
flower	long	some	
fly	look	the	
for	love	their	
four	many	these	
	me	they	

Decoding skills taught to date: *m, s, c, t,* short *a;* consonant *n;* consonant *f;* consonant *p;* short *i;* consonant *b;* consonant *r;* consonant *h;* consonant *g;* short *o;* consonant *d;* consonant *w;* consonant *l;* consonant *x;* short *e;* consonant *y;* consonant *k;* consonant *v;* short *u;* /kw/ spelled *qu;* consonant *j;* consonant *z;* /z/ spelled *s;* consonants *-ck;* /l/ spelled *-ll;* /f/ spelled *-ff;* /s/ spelled *-ss;* /t/ spelled *-ed;* /d/ spelled *-ed;* verb ending *-ing;* *r* clusters; *l* clusters; *s* clusters; silent *k* in *kn;* silent *w* in *wr;* silent *g* in *gn;* triple clusters; digraph *sh;* digraph *th;* digraph *wh;* digraph *ch;* digraph *-tch;* long *a* (CVC*e*); /s/ spelled *c;* /j/ spelled *g;* consonants *-nd;* consonants *-ng;* consonants *-nk;* long *i* (CVC*e*); contractions; long *o* (CV); long *o* (CVC*e*); /oo/ spelled *u* (CVC*e*); /yoo/ spelled *u* (CVC*e*); consonants *-ft;* consonants *-lk;* consonants *-nt*

DECODABLE WORDS

Target Skill: consonants -*nt*

bent	rent	went
dent	Rent-a-Tent	
Kent	tent	

Previously Taught Skills

back	had	home	pole	this
get	has	it	shop	with
got	his	pitched	then	

SKILLS APPLIED IN WORDS IN STORY: *m, s, c, t,* short *a*; consonant *n*; consonant *p*; short *i*; consonant *b*; consonant *r*; consonant *h*; consonant *g*; short *o*; consonant *d*; consonant *w*; consonant *l*; short *e*; consonant *k*; /z/ spelled *s*; consonants -*ck*; /t/ spelled -*ed*; digraph *sh*; digraph *th*; digraph -*tch*; consonants -*nd*; long *o* (CVCe)

HIGH–FREQUENCY WORDS

a	he	said	was
and	in	the	
good	is	to	

HOUGHTON MIFFLIN   BOSTON

Rent a Tent, Kent

Lin drank some milk.
She spilled the milk on the
silk cloth!

"What a mess!" said Lin.
"I can not give this silk cloth
to Mom."

Lin was sad. She sulked
and sulked.

"Why are you sulking, Lin?"
asked Mom.

"I spilled milk on your gift,"
said Lin.

2

3

The Silk Cloth

"Do not sulk, Lin," said Mom.
"This silk cloth is a nice gift.
We can get rid of the milk spot."

4

Lin had a silk cloth. The silk
cloth was a gift for Mom.

1

HIGH-FREQUENCY WORDS TAUGHT TO DATE

Grade 1

a	friend	more	three
all	full	mother	to
also	funny	my	today
and	girl	never	too
animal	give	not	try
are	go	of	two
away	good	on	upon
bird	green	once	walk
blue	grow	one	was
brown	have	other	we
call	he	our	what
car	hear	over	where
children	her	own	who
cold	here	paper	why
color	hold	people	world
come	house	picture	would
could	how	play	write
do	hurt	pull	you
does	I	read	your
down	in	right	
eat	is	room	
every	jump	said	
fall	know	see	
family	learn	shall	
father	light	she	
find	like	sing	
first	little	small	
five	live	so	
flower	long	some	
fly	look	the	
for	love	their	
four	many	these	
	me	they	

Decoding skills taught to date: *m, s, c, t,* short *a;* consonant *n;* consonant *f;* consonant *p;* short *i;* consonant *b;* consonant *r;* consonant *h;* consonant *g;* short *o;* consonant *d;* consonant *w;* consonant *l;* consonant *x;* short *e;* consonant *y;* consonant *k;* consonant *v;* short *u;* /kw/ spelled *qu;* consonant *j;* consonant *z;* /z/ spelled *s;* consonants *-ck;* /l/ spelled *-ll;* /f/ spelled *-ff;* /s/ spelled *-ss;* /t/ spelled *-ed;* /d/ spelled *-ed;* verb ending *-ing; r* clusters; *l* clusters; *s* clusters; silent *k* in *kn;* silent *w* in *wr;* silent *g* in *gn;* triple clusters; digraph *sh;* digraph *th;* digraph *wh;* digraph *ch;* digraph *-tch;* long *a* (CVC*e*); /s/ spelled *c;* /j/ spelled *g;* consonants *-nd;* consonants *-ng;* consonants *-nk;* long *i* (CVC*e*); contractions; long *o* (CV); long *o* (CVC*e*); /o͞o/ spelled *u* (CVC*e*); /yo͞o/ spelled *u* (CVC*e*); consonants *-ft;* consonants *-lk;* consonants *-nt*

The Silk Cloth

DECODABLE WORDS

Target Skill: consonants -lk

milk	sulked
silk	sulking
sulk	

Previously Taught Skills

asked	get	mess	sad
can	gift	Mom	spilled
cloth	had	nice	spot
drank	Lin	rid	this

SKILLS APPLIED IN WORDS IN STORY: *m, s, c, t,* short *a*; consonant *n*; consonant *f*; consonant *p*; short *i*; consonant *r*; consonant *h*; consonant *g*; short *o*; consonant *d*; consonant *l*; short *e*; consonant *k*; short *u*; /z/ spelled *s*; /l/ spelled *-ll*; /s/ spelled *-ss*; /t/ spelled *-ed*; /d/ spelled *-ed*; verb ending *–ing*; *r* clusters; *l* clusters; *s* clusters; digraph *th*; /s/ spelled *c*; consonants *-nd*; consonants *-nk*; long *i* (CVCe); consonants *-ft*

HIGH–FREQUENCY WORDS

a	I	said	was	your
are	is	she	we	
do	not	some	what	
for	of	the	why	
give	on	to	you	

HOUGHTON MIFFLIN   BOSTON

The Silk Cloth

This is a soft wind. Let's drift in the raft. **Drift, drift, drift!**

See the raft drift right? Shift the raft to the left. **Left, left, left!**

Did the wind shift?
This raft is swift. **Swift,
swift, swift!**

4

A Swift Raft

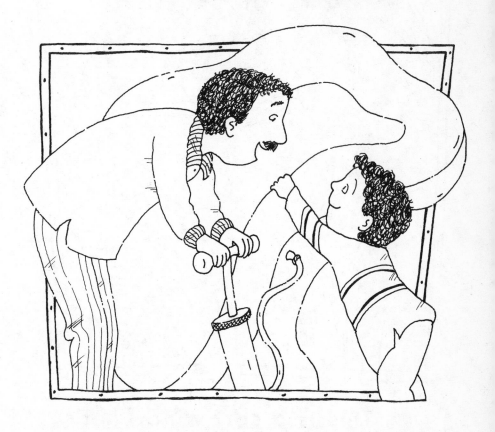

We pump up a raft. Lift
the raft. **Lift, lift, lift!**

1

HIGH-FREQUENCY WORDS TAUGHT TO DATE

Grade 1

a	friend	more	three
all	full	mother	to
also	funny	my	today
and	girl	never	too
animal	give	not	try
are	go	of	two
away	good	on	upon
bird	green	once	walk
blue	grow	one	was
brown	have	other	we
call	he	our	what
car	hear	over	where
children	her	own	who
cold	here	paper	why
color	hold	people	world
come	house	picture	would
could	how	play	write
do	hurt	pull	you
does	I	read	your
down	in	right	
eat	is	room	
every	jump	said	
fall	know	see	
family	learn	shall	
father	light	she	
find	like	sing	
first	little	small	
five	live	so	
flower	long	some	
fly	look	the	
for	love	their	
four	many	these	
	me	they	

Decoding skills taught to date: m, s, c, t, short a; consonant n; consonant f; consonant p; short i; consonant b; consonant r; consonant h; consonant g; short o; consonant d; consonant w; consonant l; consonant x; short e; consonant y; consonant k; consonant v; short u; /kw/ spelled qu; consonant j; consonant z; /z/ spelled s; consonants -ck; /l/ spelled -ll; /f/ spelled -ff; /s/ spelled -ss; /t/ spelled -ed; /d/ spelled -ed; verb ending -ing; r clusters; l clusters; s clusters; silent k in kn; silent w in wr; silent g in gn; triple clusters; digraph sh; digraph th; digraph wh; digraph ch; digraph -tch; long a (CVCe); /s/ spelled c; /j/ spelled g; consonants -nd; consonants -ng; consonants -nk; long i (CVCe); contractions; long o (CV); long o (CVCe); /ōō/ spelled u (CVCe); /yōō/ spelled u (CVCe); consonants -ft; consonants -lk; consonants -nt

A Swift Raft

DECODABLE WORDS

Target Skill: consonants -ft

drift	lift	shift	swift
left	raft	soft	

Previously Taught Skills

did	pump	up
let's	this	wind

SKILLS APPLIED IN WORDS IN STORY: *m, s, c, t,* short *a*; consonant *n*; consonant *f*; consonant *p*; short *i*; consonant *r*; short *o*; consonant *d*; consonant *w*; consonant *l*; short *e*; short *u*; /z/ spelled *s*; *r* clusters; *s* clusters; digraph *sh*; digraph *th*; consonants -*nd*; contractions

HIGH–FREQUENCY WORDS

a	is	see	to
in	right	the	we

HOUGHTON MIFFLIN   BOSTON

A Swift Raft

I can use my cubes to make
a huge, huge cube stack! How
huge can I make my cube stack?

I made my cube stack **too huge!**

I Use Cubes

This is my huge cube pile.

How can I use my cubes?

My huge cube stack fell!

How can I use my cubes, next?

Grade 1

a	friend	more	three
all	full	mother	to
also	funny	my	today
and	girl	never	too
animal	give	not	try
are	go	of	two
away	good	on	upon
bird	green	once	walk
blue	grow	one	was
brown	have	other	we
call	he	our	what
car	hear	over	where
children	her	own	who
cold	here	paper	why
color	hold	people	world
come	house	picture	would
could	how	play	write
do	hurt	pull	you
does	I	read	your
down	in	right	
eat	is	room	
every	jump	said	
fall	know	see	
family	learn	shall	
father	light	she	
find	like	sing	
first	little	small	
five	live	so	
flower	long	some	
fly	look	the	
for	love	their	
four	many	these	
	me	they	

Decoding Skills Taught to Date: *m, s, c, t,* short *a;* consonant *n;* consonant *f;* consonant *p;* short *i;* consonant *b;* consonant *r;* consonant *h;* consonant *g;* short *o;* consonant *d;* consonant *w;* consonant *l;* consonant *x;* short *e;* consonant *y;* consonant *k;* consonant *v;* short *u;* /kw/ spelled *qu;* consonant *j;* consonant *z;* /z/ spelled *s;* consonants *-ck;* /l/ spelled *-ll;* /f/ spelled *-ff;* /s/ spelled *-ss;* /t/ spelled *-ed;* /d/ spelled *-ed;* verb ending *–ing;* *r* clusters; *l* clusters; *s* clusters; silent *k* in *kn;* silent *w* in *wr;* silent *g* in *gn;* triple clusters; digraph *sh;* digraph *th;* digraph *wh;* digraph *ch;* digraph *-tch;* long *a* (CVC*e*); /s/ spelled *c;* /j/ spelled *g;* consonants *-nd;* consonants *-ng;* consonants *-nk;* long *i* (CVC*e*); contractions; long *o* (CV); long *o* (CVC*e*); /o͞o/ spelled *u* (CVC*e*); /yo͞o/ spelled *u* (CVC*e*); consonants *-ft;* consonants *-lk;* consonants *-nt*

I Use Cubes

DECODABLE WORDS

Target Skill: */yōo/* spelled *u* (CVCe)

cube   huge
cubes   use

Previously Taught Skills

can   make   stack
fell   next   this
made   pile

SKILLS APPLIED IN WORDS IN STORY: *m, s, c, t,* short *a*; consonant *n*; consonant *f*; consonant *p*; short *i*; consonant *b*; consonant *h*; consonant *d*; consonant *l*; consonant *x*; short *e*; consonant *k*; /z/ spelled *s*; consonants *-ck*; /l/ spelled *-ll*; *s* clusters; digraph *th*; long *a* (CVCe); /j/ spelled *g*; long *i* (CVCe)

HIGH–FREQUENCY WORDS

a   is   too
how   my
I   to

HOUGHTON MIFFLIN   BOSTON

I Use Cubes

"I will prune this spruce,"
said Bruce. "As I prune, I will
sing a tune!"

Luke picked up his tube
game. Luke's pup, Duke,
helped, too!

"Let's do this every June!"
said Mom.

4

It Is June!

"Bruce! Luke!" called Mom.
"It is June first! Can you help
me to spruce up the house?"

1

Grade 1

a	friend	more	three
all	full	mother	to
also	funny	my	today
and	girl	never	too
animal	give	not	try
are	go	of	two
away	good	on	upon
bird	green	once	walk
blue	grow	one	was
brown	have	other	we
call	he	our	what
car	hear	over	where
children	her	own	who
cold	here	paper	why
color	hold	people	world
come	house	picture	would
could	how	play	write
do	hurt	pull	you
does	I	read	your
down	in	right	
eat	is	room	
every	jump	said	
fall	know	see	
family	learn	shall	
father	light	she	
find	like	sing	
first	little	small	
five	live	so	
flower	long	some	
fly	look	the	
for	love	their	
four	many	these	
	me	they	

Decoding skills taught to date: *m, s, c, t,* short *a;* consonant *n;* consonant *f;* consonant *p;* short *i;* consonant *b;* consonant *r;* consonant *h;* consonant *g;* short *o;* consonant *d;* consonant *w;* consonant *l;* consonant *x;* short *e;* consonant *y;* consonant *k;* consonant *v;* short *u;* /kw/ spelled *qu;* consonant *j;* consonant *z;* /z/ spelled *s;* consonants *-ck;* /l/ spelled *-ll;* /f/ spelled *-ff;* /s/ spelled *-ss;* /t/ spelled *-ed;* /d/ spelled *-ed;* verb ending *-ing;* *r* clusters; *l* clusters; *s* clusters; silent *k* in *kn;* silent *w* in *wr;* silent *g* in *gn;* triple clusters; digraph *sh;* digraph *th;* digraph *wh;* digraph *ch;* digraph *-tch;* long *a* (CVC*e*); /s/ spelled *c;* /j/ spelled *g;* consonants *-nd;* consonants *-ng;* consonants *-nk;* long *i* (CVC*e*); contractions; long *o* (CV); long *o* (CVC*e*); /o͞o/ spelled *u* (CVC*e*); /yo͞o/ spelled *u* (CVC*e*); consonants *-ft;* consonants *-lk;* consonants *-nt*

It Is June!

DECODABLE WORDS

Target Skill: /ōō/ spelled *u* (CVC*e*)

Bruce	Luke	spruce	tune
Duke	Luke's	tube	
June	prune	tubes	

Previously Taught Skills

as	help	it	picked	up
can	helped	let's	pup	will
game	his	Mom	this	

SKILLS APPLIED IN WORDS IN STORY: *m, s, c, t,* short *a*; consonant *n*; consonant *p*; short *i*; consonant *b*; consonant *r*; consonant *h*; consonant *g*; short *o*; consonant *d*; consonant *w*; consonant *l*; short *e*; consonant *k*; short *u*; consonant *j*; /z/ spelled *s*; consonants *-ck*; /l/ spelled *-ll*; /t/ spelled *-ed*; *r* clusters; triple clusters; digraph *th*; long *a* (CVC*e*); /s/ spelled *c*; consonants *-ng*; contractions

HIGH–FREQUENCY WORDS

a	first	me	to
called	house	said	too
do	I	sing	you
every	is	the	

It Is June!

This is a dome home.
Can you see those dome
shapes on it?

This home is made of stone.
Can you see those cone shapes
on top?

Copyright © Houghton Mifflin Company. All rights reserved.

Can you find domes, stones, and cones on these homes?

4

Homes Have Shapes

Homes are made with lots of shapes. What shapes are on this home?

1

HIGH-FREQUENCY WORDS TAUGHT TO DATE

Grade 1

a	friend	more	three
all	full	mother	to
also	funny	my	today
and	girl	never	too
animal	give	not	try
are	go	of	two
away	good	on	upon
bird	green	once	walk
blue	grow	one	was
brown	have	other	we
call	he	our	what
car	hear	over	where
children	her	own	who
cold	here	paper	why
color	hold	people	world
come	house	picture	would
could	how	play	write
do	hurt	pull	you
does	I	read	your
down	in	right	
eat	is	room	
every	jump	said	
fall	know	see	
family	learn	shall	
father	light	she	
find	like	sing	
first	little	small	
five	live	so	
flower	long	some	
fly	look	the	
for	love	their	
four	many	these	
	me	they	

Decoding skills taught to date: *m, s, c, t,* short *a;* consonant *n;* consonant *f;* consonant *p;* short *i;* consonant *b;* consonant *r;* consonant *h;* consonant *g;* short *o;* consonant *d;* consonant *w;* consonant *l;* consonant *x;* short *e;* consonant *y;* consonant *k;* consonant *v;* short *u;* /kw/ spelled *qu;* consonant *j;* consonant *z;* /z/ spelled *s;* consonants *-ck;* /l/ spelled *-ll;* /f/ spelled *-ff;* /s/ spelled *-ss;* /t/ spelled *-ed;* /d/ spelled *-ed;* verb ending *-ing;* *r* clusters; *l* clusters; *s* clusters; silent *k* in *kn;* silent *w* in *wr;* silent *g* in *gn;* triple clusters; digraph *sh;* digraph *th;* digraph *wh;* digraph *ch;* digraph *-tch;* long *a* (CVC*e*); /s/ spelled *c;* /j/ spelled *g;* consonants *-nd;* consonants *-ng;* consonants *-nk;* long *i* (CVC*e*); contractions; long *o* (CV); long *o* (CVC*e*); /ōō/ spelled *u* (CVC*e*); /yōō/ spelled *u* (CVC*e*); consonants *-ft;* consonants *-lk;* consonants *-nt*

Homes Have Shapes

DECODABLE WORDS

Target Skill: long *o* (CVC*e*)

cone	dome	home	stone	those
cones	domes	homes	stones	

Previously Taught Skills

can	lots	shapes	top
it	made	this	with

SKILLS APPLIED IN WORDS IN STORY: *m, s, c, t,* short *a*; consonant *n*; consonant *p*; short *i*; consonant *h*; short *o*; consonant *d*; consonant *w*; consonant *l*; /z/ spelled *s*; *s* clusters; digraph *sh*; digraph *th*; long *a* (CVC*e*); consonants *-nd*

HIGH–FREQUENCY WORDS

a	find	of	these
and	have	on	what
are	is	see	you

HOUGHTON MIFFLIN   BOSTON

Homes Have Shapes

Bo said, "Jo, go to the rink with me."

"No!" said Jo. "It is so cold."

Bo said, "Jo, go in the lake with me."

"No!" said Jo. "It is so wet."

Bo said, "Jo, go jumping
with me." Jo **did** go!

4

Go, Jo!

Bo said, "Jo, go to the top
with me."
"No!" said Jo. "It is so big."

1

Grade 1

a	friend	more	three
all	full	mother	to
also	funny	my	today
and	girl	never	too
animal	give	not	try
are	go	of	two
away	good	on	upon
bird	green	once	walk
blue	grow	one	was
brown	have	other	we
call	he	our	what
car	hear	over	where
children	her	own	who
cold	here	paper	why
color	hold	people	world
come	house	picture	would
could	how	play	write
do	hurt	pull	you
does	I	read	your
down	in	right	
eat	is	room	
every	jump	said	
fall	know	see	
family	learn	shall	
father	light	she	
find	like	sing	
first	little	small	
five	live	so	
flower	long	some	
fly	look	the	
for	love	their	
four	many	these	
	me	they	

Decoding skills taught to date: *m, s, c, t,* short *a;* consonant *n;* consonant *f;* consonant *p;* short *i;* consonant *b;* consonant *r;* consonant *h;* consonant *g;* short *o;* consonant *d;* consonant *w;* consonant *l;* consonant *x;* short *e;* consonant *y;* consonant *k;* consonant *v;* short *u;* /kw/ spelled *qu;* consonant *j;* consonant *z;* /z/ spelled *s;* consonants *-ck;* /l/ spelled *-ll;* /f/ spelled *-ff;* /s/ spelled *-ss;* /t/ spelled *-ed;* /d/ spelled *-ed;* verb ending *-ing;* *r* clusters; *l* clusters; *s* clusters; silent *k* in *kn;* silent *w* in *wr;* silent *g* in *gn;* triple clusters; digraph *sh;* digraph *th;* digraph *wh;* digraph *ch;* digraph *-tch;* long *a* (CVC*e*); /s/ spelled *c;* /j/ spelled *g;* consonants *-nd;* consonants *-ng;* consonants *-nk;* long *i* (CVC*e*); contractions; long *o* (CV); long *o* (CVC*e*); /o͞o/ spelled *u* (CVC*e*); /yo͞o/ spelled *u* (CVC*e*); consonants *-ft;* consonants *-lk;* consonants *-nt*

Go, Jo!

DECODABLE WORDS

Target Skill: *long o* **(CV)**

Bo	no
Jo	

Previously Taught Skills

big	it	rink	wet
did	lake	top	with

SKILLS APPLIED IN WORDS IN STORY: *m, s, c, t,* short *a*; consonant *n*; consonant *p*; short *i*; consonant *b*; consonant *r*; consonant *g*; short *o*; consonant *d*; consonant *w*; consonant *l*; short *e*; consonant *k*; short *u*; consonant *j*; /z/ spelled *s*; verb ending *-ing*; digraph *th*; long *a* (CVC*e*); consonants *-nk*

HIGH–FREQUENCY WORDS

cold	is	said	to
go	jumping	so	
in	me	the	

HOUGHTON MIFFLIN   BOSTON

Go, Jo!

I ♥ LOVE READING BOOKS

THEME 6
Animal Adventures

BOOK 51	Go, Jo!	BOOK 58	Who Will Help Me?
BOOK 52	Homes Have Shapes	BOOK 59	Crete
BOOK 53	It Is June!	BOOK 60	Meet the Animals
BOOK 54	I Use Cubes	BOOK 61	A Peach and Some Peas
BOOK 55	A Swift Raft	BOOK 62	Snail's Mail Trail
BOOK 56	The Silk Cloth	BOOK 63	Ray's Clay Pot
BOOK 57	Rent a Tent, Kent		

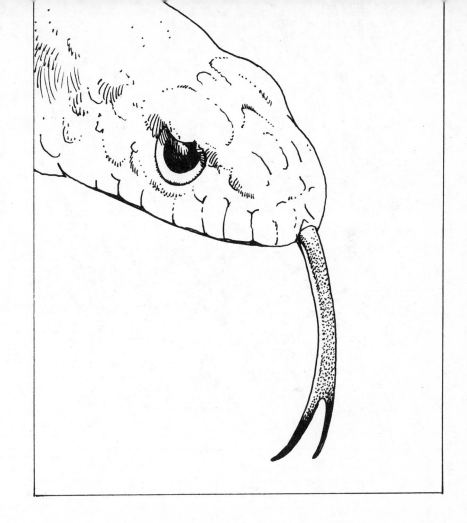

Snake skin can't stretch. When a snake gets big, it'll shed its skin.

A snake can't see well, but it can smell well. It can smell people.

2

3

It's a Snake!

Snakes can't run. Snakes slide. If a snake smells you, it'll slide away.

4

Let's look at a snake.
It's in a den.

1

Grade 1

a	full	of	walk
all	funny	on	we
also	girl	once	what
and	go	one	where
animal	green	other	who
are	grow	over	why
away	have	own	world
bird	he	paper	would
blue	hear	people	write
brown	here	picture	you
call	hold	play	your
car	house	pull	
children	how	read	
cold	hurt	right	
color	I	room	
come	in	said	
could	is	see	
do	jump	shall	
does	know	she	
down	learn	sing	
eat	light	small	
every	like	so	
fall	live	some	
family	long	the	
father	look	their	
find	love	these	
first	many	they	
five	me	three	
flower	more	to	
for	mother	today	
four	my	too	
friend	never	two	
	not	upon	

Decoding skills taught to date: *m, s, c, t,* short *a;* consonant *n;* consonant *f;* consonant *p;* short *i;* consonant *b;* consonant *r;* consonant *h;* consonant *g;* short *o;* consonant *d;* consonant *w;* consonant *l;* consonant *x;* short *e;* consonant *y;* consonant *k;* consonant *v;* short *u;* /kw/ spelled *qu;* consonant *j;* consonant *z;* /z/ spelled *s;* consonants *-ck;* /l/ spelled *-ll;* /f/ spelled *-ff;* /s/ spelled *-ss;* /t/ spelled *-ed;* /d/ spelled *-ed;* verb ending *-ing;* *r* clusters; *l* clusters; *s* clusters; silent *k* in *kn;* silent *w* in *wr;* silent *g* in *gn;* triple clusters; digraph *sh;* digraph *th;* digraph *wh;* digraph *ch;* digraph *-tch;* long *a* (CVC*e*); /s/ spelled *c;* /j/ spelled *g;* consonants *-nd;* consonants *-ng;* consonants *-nk;* long *i* (CVC*e*); contractions

DECODABLE WORDS

Target Skill: contractions

can't	it's
it'll	let's

Previously Taught Skills

at	den	its	slide	snakes
big	gets	run	smell	stretch
but	if	shed	smells	well
can	it	skin	snake	when

SKILLS APPLIED IN WORDS IN STORY: *m, s, c, t,* short *a*; consonant *n*; consonant *f*; short *i*; consonant *b*; consonant *r*; consonant *g*; consonant *d*; consonant *w*; consonant *l*; short *e*; consonant *k*; short *u*; /z/ spelled *s*; /l/ spelled *-ll*; *l* clusters; *s* clusters; triple clusters; digraph *sh*; digraph *wh*; digraph *-tch*; long *a* (CVCe); long *i* (CVCe)

HIGH–FREQUENCY WORDS

a	in	people	you
away	look	see	

HOUGHTON MIFFLIN   BOSTON

It's a Snake!

The white mice slide on ice. Slide, mice, slide!

The white mice take a drive. Drive, mice, drive!

White Mice

The white mice had
a nice time!

The white mice ride bikes.
Ride, mice, ride!

4

1

Grade 1

a	full	of	walk
all	funny	on	we
also	girl	once	what
and	go	one	where
animal	green	other	who
are	grow	over	why
away	have	own	world
bird	he	paper	would
blue	hear	people	write
brown	here	picture	you
call	hold	play	your
car	house	pull	
children	how	read	
cold	hurt	right	
color	I	room	
come	in	said	
could	is	see	
do	jump	shall	
does	know	she	
down	learn	sing	
eat	light	small	
every	like	so	
fall	live	some	
family	long	the	
father	look	their	
find	love	these	
first	many	they	
five	me	three	
flower	more	to	
for	mother	today	
four	my	too	
friend	never	two	
	not	upon	

Decoding skills taught to date: *m, s, c, t*, short *a*; consonant *n*; consonant *f*; consonant *p*; short *i*; consonant *b*; consonant *r*; consonant *h*; consonant *g*; short *o*; consonant *d*; consonant *w*; consonant *l*; consonant *x*; short *e*; consonant *y*; consonant *k*; consonant *v*; short *u*; /kw/ spelled *qu*; consonant *j*; consonant *z*; /z/ spelled *s*; consonants *-ck*; /l/ spelled *-ll*; /f/ spelled *-ff*; /s/ spelled *-ss*; /t/ spelled *-ed*; /d/ spelled *-ed*; verb ending *-ing*; *r* clusters; *l* clusters; *s* clusters; silent *k* in *kn*; silent *w* in *wr*; silent *g* in *gn*; triple clusters; digraph *sh*; digraph *th*; digraph *wh*; digraph *ch*; digraph *-tch*; long *a* (CVC*e*); /s/ spelled *c*; /j/ spelled *g*; consonants *-nd*; consonants *-ng*; consonants *-nk*; long *i* (CVC*e*); contractions

DECODABLE WORDS

Target Skill: **long *i* (CVC*e*)**

bikes	ice	nice	slide	white
drive	mice	ride	time	

Previously Taught Skills

had

take

SKILLS APPLIED IN WORDS IN STORY: *m, s, c, t,* short *a*; consonant *n*; consonant *b*; consonant *r*; consonant *h*; short *o*; consonant *d*; consonant *l*; consonant *k*; consonant *v*; *r* clusters; *l* clusters; *s* clusters; digraph *wh*; long *a* (CVC*e*); /s/ spelled *c*

HIGH–FREQUENCY WORDS

a

on

the

HOUGHTON MIFFLIN   BOSTON

White Mice

Frank gave Hank a trunk.
"Thank you, Frank!"
said Hank.

Then Frank left. Hank got
some ink and blank paper.
"I will thank Frank,"
said Hank.

2

3

Thanks, Frank!

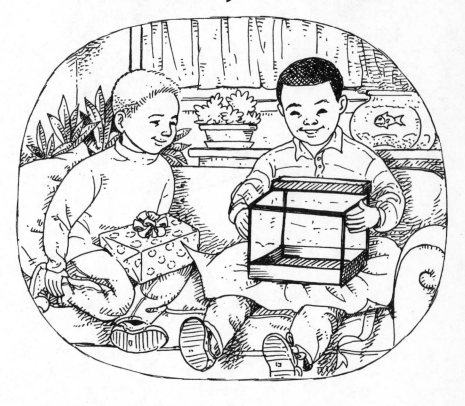

Frank gave Hank a fish tank.
"Thank you, Frank!"
said Hank.

1

Frank,
Thank you
for the tank
and the trunk!
Your friend,
Hank

Hank gave this page
to Frank!

4

HIGH-FREQUENCY WORDS TAUGHT TO DATE

Grade 1

a	funny	one	world
all	girl	other	write
also	go	paper	you
and	green	people	your
animal	grow	picture	
are	have	play	
away	he	pull	
bird	hear	read	
blue	here	right	
brown	hold	room	
call	hurt	said	
car	I	see	
children	in	shall	
color	is	she	
come	jump	sing	
could	know	small	
do	learn	some	
does	light	the	
down	like	their	
eat	live	these	
every	long	they	
fall	look	three	
family	love	to	
father	many	today	
find	me	too	
first	more	two	
five	mother	upon	
flower	my	walk	
for	never	we	
four	not	what	
friend	of	where	
full	on	who	
	once	why	

Decoding skills taught to date: *m, s, c, t,* short *a;* consonant *n;* consonant *f;* consonant *p;* short *i;* consonant *b;* consonant *r;* consonant *h;* consonant *g;* short *o;* consonant *d;* consonant *w;* consonant *l;* consonant *x;* short *e;* consonant *y;* consonant *k;* consonant *v;* short *u;* /kw/ spelled *qu;* consonant *j;* consonant *z;* /z/ spelled *s;* consonants *-ck;* /l/ spelled *-ll;* /f/ spelled *-ff;* /s/ spelled *-ss;* /t/ spelled *-ed;* /d/ spelled *-ed;* verb ending *-ing;* *r* clusters; *l* clusters; *s* clusters; silent *k* in *kn;* silent *w* in *wr;* silent *g* in *gn;* triple clusters; digraph *sh;* digraph *th;* digraph *wh;* digraph *ch;* digraph *-tch;* long *a* (CVC*e*); /s/ spelled *c;* /j/ spelled *g;* consonants *-nd;* consonants *-ng;* consonants *-nk*

Thanks, Frank!

DECODABLE WORDS

Target Skill: consonants -nk

blank	ink	thanks
Frank	tank	trunk
Hank	thank	

Previously Taught Skills

fish	left	this
gave	page	will
got	then	

SKILLS APPLIED IN WORDS IN STORY: *m, s, c, t,* short *a*; consonant *n*; consonant *f*; consonant *p*; short *i*; consonant *b*; consonant *r*; consonant *h*; consonant *g*; short *o*; consonant *w*; consonant *l*; short *e*; consonant *v*; short *u*; /l/ spelled *-ll*; *r* clusters; *l* clusters; digraph *sh*; digraph *th*; long *a* (CVCe); /j/ spelled *g*; consonants *-nd*

HIGH–FREQUENCY WORDS

a	friend	said	to
and	I	some	you
for	paper	the	your

HOUGHTON MIFFLIN   BOSTON

Thanks, Frank!

"Ring bells! Sing songs!"
said King Bing. Meg did not
wake up.

"That is it!" said King Bing.
"Bring me the big, big gong!"

2

3

BONG! BONG! BONG!

"I am up! I am up, Dad!"

said Meg.

4

A Big Gong

"Wake up!" said King

Bing. Meg did not wake up.

1

HIGH-FREQUENCY WORDS TAUGHT TO DATE

Grade 1

a	funny	one	would
all	girl	other	write
also	go	paper	you
and	green	people	your
animal	grow	picture	
are	have	play	
away	he	pull	
bird	hear	read	
blue	here	right	
brown	hold	room	
call	hurt	said	
car	I	see	
children	in	shall	
cold	is	she	
color	jump	sing	
come	know	small	
do	learn	some	
does	light	the	
down	like	their	
eat	live	these	
every	long	they	
fall	look	three	
family	love	to	
father	many	today	
find	me	too	
first	more	two	
five	mother	upon	
flower	my	walk	
for	never	we	
four	not	what	
friend	of	where	
full	on	who	
	once	why	

Decoding skills taught to date: *m, s, c, t,* short *a;* consonant *n;* consonant *f;* consonant *p;* short *i;* consonant *b;* consonant *r;* consonant *h;* consonant *g;* short *o;* consonant *d;* consonant *w;* consonant *l;* consonant *x;* short *e;* consonant *y;* consonant *k;* consonant *v;* short *u;* /kw/ spelled *qu;* consonant *j;* consonant *z;* /z/ spelled *s;* consonants *-ck;* /l/ spelled *-ll;* /f/ spelled *-ff;* /s/ spelled *-ss;* /t/ spelled *-ed;* /d/ spelled *-ed;* verb ending *-ing;* *r* clusters; *l* clusters; *s* clusters; silent *k* in *kn;* silent *w* in *wr;* silent *g* in *gn;* triple clusters; digraph *sh;* digraph *th;* digraph *wh;* digraph *ch;* digraph *-tch;* long *a* (CVC*e*); /s/ spelled *c;* /j/ spelled *g;* consonants *-nd;* consonants *-ng;* consonants *-nk*

A Big Gong

DECODABLE WORDS

Target Skill: consonants -ng

Bing	gong	songs
bring	King	
bong	ring	

Previously Taught Skills

am	dad	Meg	wake
bells	did	that	
big	it	up	

SKILLS APPLIED IN WORDS IN STORY: *m, s, c, t,* short *a;* consonant *n;* consonant *p;* short *i;* consonant *b;* consonant *r;* consonant *g;* short *o;* consonant *d;* consonant *w;* short *e;* consonant *k;* short *u;* /z/ spelled *s;* /l/ spelled *-ll;* *r* clusters; digraph *th;* long *a* (CVCe)

HIGH–FREQUENCY WORDS

a	me	sing
I	not	the
is	said	

HOUGHTON MIFFLIN   BOSTON

A Big Gong

BONG!

BONG!

BONG!

BONG!

Nets are strands of string.
Men must mend and mend
the strands with their hands.

2

A gust of wind whips the net.
"Lend a hand, if you can!"
calls the blond man.

3

Stand and Mend

The men get the net and
find a rock.

Then the men can stand
and mend in the wind.

Ships land.

Men stand in the sand
and mend the fishing nets.

4

1

Grade 1

a	funny	one	would
all	girl	other	write
also	go	paper	you
and	green	people	your
animal	grow	picture	
are	have	play	
away	he	pull	
bird	hear	read	
blue	here	right	
brown	hold	room	
call	hurt	said	
car	I	see	
children	in	shall	
cold	is	she	
color	jump	sing	
come	know	small	
do	learn	some	
does	light	the	
down	like	their	
eat	live	these	
every	long	they	
fall	look	three	
family	love	to	
father	many	today	
find	me	too	
first	more	two	
five	mother	upon	
flower	my	walk	
for	never	we	
four	not	what	
friend	of	where	
full	on	who	
	once	why	

Decoding skills taught to date: *m, s, c, t,* short *a;* consonant *n;* consonant *f;* consonant *p;* short *i;* consonant *b;* consonant *r;* consonant *h;* consonant *g;* short *o;* consonant *d;* consonant *w;* consonant *l;* consonant *x;* short *e;* consonant *y;* consonant *k;* consonant *v;* short *u;* /kw/ spelled *qu;* consonant *j;* consonant *z;* /z/ spelled *s;* consonants *-ck;* /l/ spelled *-ll;* /f/ spelled *-ff;* /s/ spelled *-ss;* /t/ spelled *-ed;* /d/ spelled *-ed;* verb ending *-ing;* *r* clusters; *l* clusters; *s* clusters; silent *k* in *kn;* silent *w* in *wr;* silent *g* in *gn;* triple clusters; digraph *sh;* digraph *th;* digraph *wh;* digraph *ch;* digraph *-tch;* long *a* (CVC*e*); /s/ spelled *c;* /j/ spelled *g;* consonants *-nd;* consonants *-ng;* consonants *-nk*

Stand and Mend

DECODABLE WORDS

Target Skill: consonants -nd

blond	hands	lend	sand	strands
hand	land	mend	stand	wind

Previously Taught Skills

can	if	net	string
fishing	man	nets	then
get	men	rock	whips
gust	must	ships	with

SKILLS APPLIED IN WORDS IN STORY: *m, s, c, t,* short *a*; consonant *n*; consonant *f*; consonant *p*; short *i*; consonant *b*; consonant *r*; consonant *h*; consonant *g*; short *o*; consonant *d*; consonant *w*; consonant *l*; short *e*; short *u*; /z/ spelled *s*; consonants -*ck*; verb ending –*ing*; *l* clusters; *s* clusters; triple clusters; digraph *sh*; digraph *th*; digraph *wh*; consonants -*ng*

HIGH–FREQUENCY WORDS

a	calls	of	you
and	find	the	
are	in	their	

HOUGHTON MIFFLIN   BOSTON

Stand and Mend

The king said, "This cage
is not big. I must have a
big cage."

Jed got the king a big cage,
but the king said, "This cage is not
big. I must have a big, big cage."

Jed got the king a big, big cage.

"Jed, you are the best page!" said the king.

4

The Page and the Cage

Jed is a page. A page takes things to the king.

1

HIGH-FREQUENCY WORDS TAUGHT TO DATE

Grade 1

a	funny	one	would
all	girl	other	write
also	go	paper	you
and	green	people	your
animal	grow	picture	
are	have	play	
away	he	pull	
bird	hear	read	
blue	here	right	
brown	hold	room	
call	hurt	said	
car	I	see	
children	in	shall	
cold	is	she	
color	jump	sing	
come	know	small	
do	learn	some	
does	light	the	
down	like	their	
eat	live	these	
every	long	they	
fall	look	three	
family	love	to	
father	many	today	
find	me	too	
first	more	two	
five	mother	upon	
flower	my	walk	
for	never	we	
four	not	what	
friend	of	where	
full	on	who	
	once	why	

Decoding skills taught to date: *m, s, c, t,* short *a;* consonant *n;* consonant *f;* consonant *p;* short *i;* consonant *b;* consonant *r;* consonant *h;* consonant *g;* short *o;* consonant *d;* consonant *w;* consonant *l;* consonant *x;* short *e;* consonant *y;* consonant *k;* consonant *v;* short *u;* /kw/ spelled *qu;* consonant *j;* consonant *z;* /z/ spelled *s;* consonants -*ck;* /l/ spelled -*ll;* /f/ spelled -*ff;* /s/ spelled -*ss;* /t/ spelled -*ed;* /d/ spelled -*ed;* verb ending -*ing;* *r* clusters; *l* clusters; *s* clusters; silent *k* in *kn;* silent *w* in *wr;* silent *g* in *gn;* triple clusters; digraph *sh;* digraph *th;* digraph *wh;* digraph *ch;* digraph -*tch;* long *a* (CVC*e*); /s/ spelled *c;* /j/ spelled *g;* consonants -*nd;* consonants -*ng;* consonants -*nk*

The Page and the Cage

DECODABLE WORDS

Target Skill: /j/ spelled g

cage
page

Previously Taught Skills

best	got	must	this
big	Jed	takes	
but	king	things	

SKILLS APPLIED IN WORDS IN STORY: *m, s, c, t,* short *a*; consonant *n*; consonant *p*; short *i*; consonant *b*; consonant *g*; short *o*; consonant *d*; short *e*; consonant *k*; short *u*; consonant *j*; /z/ spelled *s*; *s* clusters; digraph *th*; long *a* (CVCe); consonants *-nd*; consonants *-ng*

HIGH–FREQUENCY WORDS

a	have	not	to
and	I	said	you
are	is	the	

HOUGHTON MIFFLIN   BOSTON

The Page and the Cage

Bang! The race is on!
Go, Vince! Vince is fast.
Vince is in first place.

Here comes Vance. Go,
Vance! Vance runs with such
grace. Vance is in first place.

A Race

Vince and Vance will race.

Vance wins the race!

Vince calls to Vance,

"What a race!"

HIGH-FREQUENCY WORDS TAUGHT TO DATE

Grade 1

a	funny	one	would
all	girl	other	write
also	go	paper	you
and	green	people	your
animal	grow	picture	
are	have	play	
away	he	pull	
bird	hear	read	
blue	here	right	
brown	hold	room	
call	hurt	said	
car	I	see	
children	in	shall	
cold	is	she	
color	jump	sing	
come	know	small	
do	learn	some	
does	light	the	
down	like	their	
eat	live	these	
every	long	they	
fall	look	three	
family	love	to	
father	many	today	
find	me	too	
first	more	two	
five	mother	upon	
flower	my	walk	
for	never	we	
four	not	what	
friend	of	where	
full	on	who	
	once	why	

Decoding skills taught to date: m, s, c, t, short a; consonant n; consonant f; consonant p; short i; consonant b; consonant r; consonant h; consonant g; short o; consonant d; consonant w; consonant l; consonant x; short e; consonant y; consonant k; consonant v; short u; /kw/ spelled qu; consonant j; consonant z; /z/ spelled s; consonants -ck; /l/ spelled -ll; /f/ spelled -ff; /s/ spelled -ss; /t/ spelled -ed; /d/ spelled -ed; verb ending -ing; r clusters; l clusters; s clusters; silent k in kn; silent w in wr; silent g in gn; triple clusters; digraph sh; digraph th; digraph wh; digraph ch; digraph -tch; long a (CVCe); /s/ spelled c; /j/ spelled g; consonants -nd; consonants -ng; consonants -nk

A Race

DECODABLE WORDS

Target Skill: /s/ spelled *c*

grace	race	Vince
place	Vance	

Previously Taught Skills

bang	runs	will	with
fast	such	wins	

SKILLS APPLIED IN WORDS IN STORY: *m, s, c, t,* short *a*; consonant *n*; consonant *f*; consonant *p*; short *i*; consonant *b*; consonant *r*; consonant *g*; short *o*; consonant *w*; consonant *l*; consonant *v*; short *u*; /z/ spelled *s*; /l/ spelled *-ll*; *r* clusters; *l* clusters; *s* clusters; digraph *th*; digraph *ch*; long *a* (CVCe); consonants *-nd*; consonants *-ng*

HIGH–FREQUENCY WORDS

a	comes	here	on	what
and	first	in	the	
calls	go	is	to	

A Race

Nate writes his name and
the date on the page.
Kate makes shapes and
plays a math game.

Nate and Kate made a
picture of a lake. Miss Bates
will tape it.

Nate and Kate wave at
the gate.

"See you, Nate," said Kate.

"See you, Kate," said Nate.

4

BOOK 43

Nate and Kate

Nate and Kate are in first
grade. Nate and Kate are in
the same class.

1

HIGH-FREQUENCY WORDS TAUGHT TO DATE

Grade 1

a	funny	one	would
all	girl	other	write
also	go	paper	you
and	green	people	your
animal	grow	picture	
are	have	play	
away	he	pull	
bird	hear	read	
blue	here	right	
brown	hold	room	
call	hurt	said	
car	I	see	
children	in	shall	
cold	is	she	
color	jump	sing	
come	know	small	
do	learn	some	
does	light	the	
down	like	their	
eat	live	these	
every	long	they	
fall	look	three	
family	love	to	
father	many	today	
find	me	too	
first	more	two	
five	mother	upon	
flower	my	walk	
for	never	we	
four	not	what	
friend	of	where	
full	on	who	
	once	why	

Decoding skills taught to date: *m, s, c, t,* short *a;* consonant *n;* consonant *f;* consonant *p;* short *i;* consonant *b;* consonant *r;* consonant *h;* consonant *g;* short *o;* consonant *d;* consonant *w;* consonant *l;* consonant *x;* short *e;* consonant *y;* consonant *k;* consonant *v;* short *u;* /kw/ spelled *qu;* consonant *j;* consonant *z;* /z/ spelled *s;* consonants *-ck;* /l/ spelled *-ll;* /f/ spelled *-ff;* /s/ spelled *-ss;* /t/ spelled *-ed;* /d/ spelled *-ed;* verb ending *-ing;* *r* clusters; *l* clusters; *s* clusters; silent *k* in *kn;* silent *w* in *wr;* silent *g* in *gn;* triple clusters; digraph *sh;* digraph *th;* digraph *wh;* digraph *ch;* digraph *-tch;* long *a* (CVC*e*); /s/ spelled *c;* /j/ spelled *g;* consonants *-nd;* consonants *-ng;* consonants *-nk*

Nate and Kate

DECODABLE WORDS

Target Skill: long *a* (CVC*e*)

Bates	grade	makes	same
date	Kate	name	shapes
game	lake	Nate	tape
gate	make	page	wave

Previously Taught Skills

at	math
class	Miss
his	will
it	

SKILLS APPLIED IN WORDS IN STORY: *m, s, c, t,* short *a*; consonant *n*; consonant *p*; short *i*; consonant *b*; consonant *r*; consonant *h*; consonant *g*; short *o*; consonant *d*; consonant *w*; consonant *l*; consonant *k*; consonant *v*; /z/ spelled *s*; /l/ spelled *-ll*; /s/ spelled *-ss*; *r* clusters; *l* clusters; digraph *sh*; digraph *th*; /j/ spelled *g*; consonants *-nd*

HIGH–FREQUENCY WORDS

a	in	plays	writes
and	of	said	you
are	on	see	
first	picture	the	

HOUGHTON MIFFLIN   BOSTON

Nate and Kate

Mitch said, "I will call Patch. Patch has a big truck."

Patch got the hitch. Then, Patch got in the truck. Patch pulled the car up.

Mitch Is Stuck!

Mitch got stuck in a ditch.

"I am glad that Patch
pitched in!" said Mitch.

4

1

Grade 1

a	funny	play
all	girl	pull
also	go	read
and	green	said
animal	have	see
are	he	shall
away	hear	she
bird	here	sing
blue	hold	some
brown	hurt	the
call	I	their
car	in	they
children	is	three
cold	jump	to
color	know	today
come	learn	too
do	like	two
does	live	upon
down	look	walk
eat	love	we
every	many	what
fall	me	where
family	mother	who
father	my	why
find	never	would
first	not	write
five	of	you
flower	on	your
for	once	
four	one	
friend	paper	
full	people	
	picture	

Decoding skills taught to date: *m, s, c, t*, short *a*; consonant *n*; consonant *f*; consonant *p*; short *i*; consonant *b*; consonant *r*; consonant *h*; consonant *g*; short *o*; consonant *d*; consonant *w*; consonant *l*; consonant *x*; short *e*; consonant *y*; consonant *k*; consonant *v*; short *u*; /kw/ spelled *qu*; consonant *j*; consonant *z*; /z/ spelled *s*; consonants *-ck*; /l/ spelled *-ll*; /f/ spelled *-ff*; /s/ spelled *-ss*; /t/ spelled *-ed*; /d/ spelled *-ed*; verb ending *-ing*; *r* clusters; *l* clusters; *s* clusters; silent *k* in *kn*; silent *w* in *wr*; silent *g* in *gn*; triple clusters; digraph *sh*; digraph *th*; digraph *wh*; digraph *ch*; digraph *-tch*

Mitch is Stuck!

DECODABLE WORDS

Target Skill: digraph *-tch*

ditch	Mitch	pitched
hitch	Patch	

Previously Taught Skills

am	got	that	up
big	has	then	will
glad	stuck	truck	

SKILLS APPLIED IN WORDS IN STORY: *m, s, c, t,* short *a;* consonant *n;* consonant *p;* short *i;* consonant *b;* consonant *r;* consonant *h;* consonant *g;* short *o;* consonant *d;* consonant *w;* consonant *l;* short *e;* short *u;* /z/ spelled *s;* consonants *-ck;* /l/ spelled *-ll;* /t/ spelled *-ed;* *r* clusters; *l* clusters; *s* clusters; digraph *th*

HIGH–FREQUENCY WORDS

a	car	in	pulled	the
call	I	is	said	

Mitch Is Stuck!

Chuck chats as he chips.

Chuck chats with Chick.

Chat, chat, chat, Chuck!

Chuck chops as he chips.

Chuck chops with an ax.

Chop, chop, chop, Chuck!

Chuck Chips

Chuck chips away at a log.
Chuck has chips on his chin.
Chip, chip, chip, Chuck!

1

Chuck chips too much.
Chuck quits! Chuck naps.
Nap, nap, nap, Chuck.

4

Grade 1

a	funny	play
all	girl	pull
also	go	read
and	green	said
animal	have	see
are	he	shall
away	hear	she
bird	here	sing
blue	hold	some
brown	hurt	the
call	I	their
car	in	they
children	is	three
cold	jump	to
color	know	today
come	learn	too
do	like	two
does	live	upon
down	look	walk
eat	love	we
every	many	what
fall	me	where
family	mother	who
father	my	why
find	never	would
first	not	write
five	of	you
flower	on	your
for	once	
four	one	
friend	paper	
full	people	
	picture	

Decoding skills taught to date: *m, s, c, t,* short *a;* consonant *n;* consonant *f;* consonant *p;* short *i;* consonant *b;* consonant *r;* consonant *h;* consonant *g;* short *o;* consonant *d;* consonant *w;* consonant *l;* consonant *x;* short *e;* consonant *y;* consonant *k;* consonant *v;* short *u;* /kw/ spelled *qu;* consonant *j;* consonant *z;* /z/ spelled *s;* consonants *-ck;* /l/ spelled *-ll;* /f/ spelled *-ff;* /s/ spelled *-ss;* /t/ spelled *-ed;* /d/ spelled *-ed;* verb ending *-ing;* *r* clusters; *l* clusters; *s* clusters; silent *k* in *kn;* silent *w* in *wr;* silent *g* in *gn;* triple clusters; digraph *sh;* digraph *th;* digraph *wh;* digraph *ch;* digraph *-tch*

Chuck Chips

DECODABLE WORDS

Target Skill: digraph *ch*

chat	Chick	chip	chop	Chuck
chats	chin	chips	chops	much

Previously Taught Skills

an	ax	log	quits
as	has	nap	with
at	his	naps	

SKILLS APPLIED IN WORDS IN STORY: *m, s, c, t,* short *a;* consonant *n;* consonant *p;* short *i;* consonant *h;* consonant *g;* short *o;* consonant *w;* consonant *l;* consonant *x;* short *u;* /kw/ spelled *qu;* /z/ spelled *s;* consonants *-ck;* digraph *th*

HIGH–FREQUENCY WORDS

a	he	too
away	on	

HOUGHTON MIFFLIN   BOSTON

Chuck Chips

Bob whips, whips, whips the mix. The mix looks like fluff!

Jill gets a whiff.
"When can we eat?" asks Jill. "When, when, when?"

Whip the Mix

The fluff mix is in two cups.
Which cup will Jill pick?

4

Bob has a whisk. Bob can
whip the mix with his whisk.

1

Grade 1

a	funny	play
all	girl	pull
also	go	read
and	green	said
animal	have	see
are	he	shall
away	hear	she
bird	here	sing
blue	hold	some
brown	hurt	the
call	I	their
car	in	they
children	is	three
cold	jump	to
color	know	today
come	learn	too
do	like	two
does	live	upon
down	look	walk
eat	love	we
every	many	what
fall	me	where
family	mother	who
father	my	why
find	never	would
first	not	write
five	of	you
flower	on	your
for	once	
four	one	
friend	paper	
full	picture	

Decoding skills taught to date: *m, s, c, t*, short *a;* consonant *n;* consonant *f;* consonant *p;* short *i;* consonant *b;* consonant *r;* consonant *h;* consonant *g;* short *o;* consonant *d;* consonant *w;* consonant *l;* consonant *x;* short *e;* consonant *y;* consonant *k;* consonant *v;* short *u;* /kw/ spelled *qu;* consonant *j;* consonant *z;* /z/ spelled *s;* consonants -*ck;* /l/ spelled -*ll;* /f/ spelled -*ff;* /s/ spelled -*ss;* /t/ spelled -*ed;* /d/ spelled -*ed;* verb ending -*ing;* *r* clusters; *l* clusters; *s* clusters; silent *k* in *kn;* silent *w* in *wr;* silent *g* in *gn;* triple clusters; digraph *sh;* digraph *th;* digraph *wh;* digraph *ch;* digraph -*tch*

Whip the Mix

DECODABLE WORDS

Target Skill: digraph *wh*

when	whiff	whips
which	whip	whisk

Previously Taught Skills

asks	cup	gets	Jill	will
Bob	cups	has	mix	with
can	fluff	his	pick	

SKILLS APPLIED IN WORDS IN STORY: *m, s, c, t,* short *a*; consonant *n*; consonant *f*; consonant *p*; short *i*; consonant *b*; consonant *h*; consonant *g*; short *o*; consonant *w*; consonant *l*; consonant *x*; short *e*; consonant *k*; short *u*; consonant *j*; /z/ spelled *s*; consonants *-ck*; /l/ spelled *-ll*; /f/ spelled *-ff*; *l* clusters; *s* clusters; digraph *th*; digraph *ch*

HIGH–FREQUENCY WORDS

a	is	the
eat	like	two
in	looks	we

Whip the Mix

The cloth of this top
is thin, thin, thin.

The cloth of this top is best.

A moth is on the cloth!
"Yum, yum, yum," said
the moth.

4

Moth on the Cloth

The cloth of this top
is thick, thick, thick.

1

HIGH-FREQUENCY WORDS TAUGHT TO DATE

Grade 1

a	funny	play
all	girl	pull
also	go	read
and	green	said
animal	have	see
are	he	shall
away	hear	she
bird	here	sing
blue	hold	some
brown	hurt	the
call	I	their
car	in	they
children	is	three
cold	jump	to
color	know	today
come	learn	too
do	like	two
does	live	upon
down	look	walk
eat	love	we
every	many	what
fall	me	where
family	mother	who
father	my	why
find	never	would
first	not	write
five	of	you
flower	on	your
for	once	
four	one	
friend	paper	
full	people	
	picture	

Decoding skills taught to date: *m, s, c, t,* short *a;* consonant *n;* consonant *f;* consonant *p;* short *i;* consonant *b;* consonant *r;* consonant *h;* consonant *g;* short *o;* consonant *d;* consonant *w;* consonant *l;* consonant *x;* short *e;* consonant *y;* consonant *k;* consonant *v;* short *u;* /kw/ spelled *qu;* consonant *j;* consonant *z;* /z/ spelled *s;* consonants *-ck;* /l/ spelled *-ll;* /f/ spelled *-ff;* /s/ spelled *-ss;* /t/ spelled *-ed;* /d/ spelled *-ed;* verb ending *-ing;* *r* clusters; *l* clusters; *s* clusters; silent *k* in *kn;* silent *w* in *wr;* silent *g* in *gn;* triple clusters; digraph *sh;* digraph *th;* digraph *wh;* digraph *ch;* digraph *-tch*

Moth on the Cloth

DECODABLE WORDS

Target Skill: digraph *th*

cloth	thick	this
moth	thin	

Previously Taught Skills

best	yum
top	

SKILLS APPLIED IN WORDS IN STORY: *m, s, c, t,* short *a;* consonant *n;* consonant *p;* short *i;* consonant *b;* short *o;* consonant *l;* short *e;* consonant *y;* short *u;* /z/ spelled *s;* consonants *-ck; l* clusters; *s* clusters

HIGH–FREQUENCY WORDS

a	of	said
is	on	the

HOUGHTON MIFFLIN   BOSTON

Moth on the Cloth

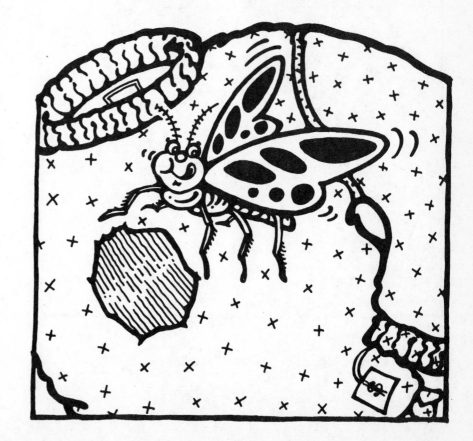

Shag gets a bath. Splish, splash! Splish, splash!

2

I brush Shag. Brush, brush, brush.

3

Shag Sheds

Shag sheds. Shag
sheds a lot.

1

Shag does not shed.
Shag looks fresh.

4

HIGH-FREQUENCY WORDS TAUGHT TO DATE

Grade 1

a	funny	play
all	girl	pull
also	go	read
and	green	said
animal	have	see
are	he	shall
away	hear	she
bird	here	sing
blue	hold	some
brown	hurt	the
call	I	their
car	in	they
children	is	three
cold	jump	to
color	know	today
come	learn	too
do	like	two
does	live	upon
down	look	walk
eat	love	we
every	many	what
fall	me	where
family	mother	who
father	my	why
find	never	would
first	not	write
five	of	you
flower	on	your
for	once	
four	one	
friend	paper	
full	people	
	picture	

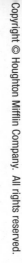

Decoding skills taught to date: m, s, c, t, short a; consonant n; consonant f; consonant p; short i; consonant b; consonant r; consonant h; consonant g; short o; consonant d; consonant w; consonant l; consonant x; short e; consonant y; consonant k; consonant v; short u; /kw/ spelled qu; consonant j; consonant z; /z/ spelled s; consonants -ck; /l/ spelled -ll; /f/ spelled -ff; /s/ spelled -ss; /t/ spelled -ed; /d/ spelled -ed; verb ending -ing; r clusters; l clusters; s clusters; silent k in kn; silent w in wr; silent g in gn; triple clusters; digraph sh; digraph th; digraph wh; digraph ch; digraph -tch

Shag Sheds

DECODABLE WORDS

Target Skill: digraph *sh*

brush	Shag	sheds	splish
fresh	shed	splash	

Previously Taught Skills

bath	lot
gets	

SKILLS APPLIED IN WORDS IN STORY: *m, s, c, t,* short *a*; consonant *n*; consonant *f*; consonant *p*; short *i*; consonant *b*; consonant *r*; consonant *g*; short *o*; consonant *d*; consonant *l*; short *e*; short *u*; /z/ spelled *s*; *r* clusters; triple clusters; digraph *th*

HIGH–FREQUENCY WORDS

a	looks
does	not
I	

HOUGHTON MIFFLIN   BOSTON

Shag Sheds

I ♥ LOVE READING BOOKS

THEME 5
Home Sweet Home